PROJECT LEARNING TREE ®

PROJECT LEARNING TREE is an environmental education project jointly sponsored by the Western Regional Environmental Education Council and the American Forest Institute.

Supplementary Activity Guide
For Grades 7 through 12

PREFACE

PROJECT LEARNING TREE offers an opportunity for educators and students to step into the forest, thereby developing awarenesses, knowledge, and skills related to understanding of renewable and nonrenewable resources on a finite planet.

Everyone on the earth today knows and can relate to trees in some form — so we begin with trees to provide a familiar base from which to explore the interrelationships between all living and non-living things. Initial activities in these materials involve the students in engaging their primary senses — feeling the sun, hearing the sounds of nature and culture, seeing the diversity of natural resources even within our immediate environments, such as in school classrooms and on campus grounds.

Further activities provide students the opportunity to experience the spectrum of ways in which their lives are nourished and changed each day, affected by the existence of renewable and nonrenewable natural resources . . . and human dependence on them.

People are products of their culture, as well as of nature. Thus a number of the PROJECT LEARNING TREE activities place use of natural resources in a cultural context, providing opportunities to explore the historical and present day effects of these resources on people — and people's effects on them. Tools for understanding these interrelationships are stressed, including techniques for analysis of human communication.

People have characteristically differed about the appropriate uses of natural resources. Rather than ignore these differences and the difficult issues frequently involved, students can explore opportunities to hone their basic skills, developing their capacities for creative and critical thinking, and in the process address issues fundamental to the continued use of natural resources.

Addressing of substantive issues requires a breadth of information and experience, as well as skills of intuition and logic. PROJECT LEARNING TREE has been designed to provide such experience and skills. These materials are presented in the form of learning activities for use by educators with students in the elementary and secondary grades. The activities may be used as the basis for a course of study, but are more likely to be used to supplement existing curricula. The activities are based on a conceptual framework for environmental education designed to engage students in interdisciplinary exploration of concepts underlying all of the major academic disciplines — from the social sciences, humanities, communication arts, natural sciences, mathematics, and physical sciences; at the same time making use of the basic skills of information acquisition, analysis, evaluation, and inventiveness necessary to the development of creative and thoughtful minds . . . minds ready to meet the challenges of today, and for the future.

ACKNOWLEDGMENTS

PROJECT LEARNING TREE is a program of the Western Regional Environmental Education Council and the American Forest Foundation, administered for the Foundation by the American Forest Institute.

Project Learning Tree Planning and Advisory Council

John A. Ball, Champion International Corporation, co-chairperson
Rudolph J. H. Schafer, California Department of Education, co-chairperson

Charles W. Eddington, Potlatch Corporation
Gerard R. Griffin, Louisiana-Pacific Corporation
William F. Hammond, Lee County (Florida) Schools
William R. Hernbrode, Oracle Wildlife Refuge
Louis A. Iozzi, Rutgers University
David A. Kennedy, Washington State Office of the Superintendent of Public
    Instruction
James L. Leary, Adrian (Michigan) Public Schools
Joseph L. Leitzinger, Simpson Timber Company
Clarence Streetman, Bowater Southern Paper Company
Edward J. Wren, Southwest Forest Industries

June McSwain, Director, Education, American Forest Institute
Cheryl Charles, Director, PLT Staff
Jan Rensel, Implementation Coordinator, PLT Staff
Judy Dawson, Administrative Assistant, PLT Staff

Mary Hawkins, Technical Editor, *PLT Guides*

Supplementary Activity Guides originally developed and produced by Education/Research Systems, Inc.; Thomas L. Eckman, Project Supervisor; Thomas F. Ris, President.

Photographs and artwork by Bob Samples, Cheryl Charles, and Olina Gilbert.

Design by Bob Samples, Cheryl Charles, Olina Gilbert, Dick Gilbert, and Jan Rensel, of *Essentia*.

Typesetting by Pacific Sun under the supervision of Kathy Parker. Thanks to Gail Bartholomew, Stephen Leiper, Valerie Leland, Karen Michel and Patricia Waters.

INTRODUCTION

To paraphrase Mark Twain's famous observation on the weather, everyone talks about interdisciplinary environmental education programs which involve a wide community of interests, but hardly anyone ever produces them. Project Learning Tree represents an honest effort to transform this elusive ideal into reality.

The project began with a deceptively simple charge. The American Forest Institute commissioned the Western Regional Environmental Education Council, an association of state department of education and resource management personnel from 13 western states, to develop a project which elementary and secondary teachers could use in helping students understand their interdependence with the total forest community and develop the knowledge, skills and commitment all citizens need if society is to use these resource lands wisely for the long-term benefit of all.

The completed project represents the philosophy, expertise, and hard work of a great many people from widely diverse backgrounds. Among those having a part in the development and revision of these materials were elementary and secondary classroom teachers, state and federal resource management personnel, state department of education consultants, professional foresters, representatives of the wood products industry, school administrators, representatives of private conservation organizations, college professors, and others.

It would be comforting to say that there was complete unanimity and accord in all phases of the project. This was not the case. Everyone tends to see things from a particular vantage point. People in the industry and the various management agencies quite naturally place a high value on the forest as a producer of usable products. The phrase "tree farm" is often used to describe lands upon which a valuable crop is grown differing from wheat, corn, barley and other useful plants only in terms of size and growing time. Industry people are proud of a technology which has made it nearly possible to halve the growing time of Douglas Fir and other commercially desirable species, harvest trees efficiently, and utilize nearly every scrap of material produced in their operations, while maintaining, in their view, the long term ecological health of the forest lands.

A differing emphasis is advocated by many citizens active in the environmental movement. In a position statement solicited from a group of people active in citizen conservation organizations after they had participated in a review of the materials, these observations were made:

> "As a group, we feel that material presented as environmental education should reflect the realization that both resources and energy are limited, that we must develop new attitudes toward how we use them, and that we need more effective ways of conserving them. The forest is an important resource, one to be managed with greater wisdom, for it has many values to humans and to the health of the planet earth. We have taken the abundance of forest products for granted for too long. Hopefully, our society will begin to decrease its impact on the forest through reuse, recycling, the design of longer-lived, energy-efficient products, and the use of forest practices which minimize environmental damage.

"Environmental education is an important tool for helping reform society's values. We feel that Project Learning Tree materials should inspire teachers to help their students develop a concern for the diversity of values found in and obtained from the forest. If ultimately students develop a new ethic based on our dependence upon a healthy ecosystem, these materials will have been successful — if not . . ."

Applying the above perspective, this group provided suggestions regarding the general emphasis and objectivity of PLT activities. In response to their criticisms, and those received from many others, revisions were made in the final draft ensuring a balanced presentation. Neither industry nor the environmental groups' representatives believe their own point-of-view has been exclusively represented.

Following completion of the first phase of the project, an extensive field test was carried out in the eleven western states. Over 3,000 teachers and school administrators participated in 150 one-day workshops prior to using the materials with their students. These workshops were conducted by the PLT Staff and members of the Western Regional Environmental Education Council. An independent testing organization was employed to conduct a formal evaluation of the program in terms of student accomplishment, and those who participated in the workshops were encouraged to write in comments as to their experience with the materials in classroom situations. On the basis of the field test experience, and suggestions from other experienced educators and resource management personnel, the materials were revised, deletions made, and new materials added as needed. The final result is a selection of effective learning experiences of proven worth.

What is important is for educators to recognize that in forest conservation as well as in most human activities there are no right and wrong answers — only wise and intelligent choices. Therefore, the goal of the teacher should be to help students develop skills in evaluating information and in making careful decisions rather than to indoctrinate them with "correct" opinions.

Making wise decisions involves skills and knowledge in a great many areas, for as Barry Commoner advises us: "Everything is connected to everything else." Social, political, economic, and aesthetic factors must be considered along with the scientific and technological aspects of all environmental questions. For this reason, a major consideration in developing these materials was that they involve the widest possible array of discipline and skill areas.

The most effective environmental education programs emphasize student interaction with the natural and social environment. Using the out of doors as a learning laboratory whenever possible is emphasized throughout the materials at all grade levels. The social processes through which people make and implement environmental decisions — government, law, economics, communications and others — are also best studied in the community where they operate, and educators are urged to make full use of such local learning resources.

Of those of us who participated in the development of the Project Learning Tree materials, it may be said that we worked hard and tried to do a fair and honest job. To those of you who will use these materials, we hope that you will find the results of our labor useful in your work with our most precious asset — the children and young people in our schools.

Rudolph J. H. Schafer
Western Regional Environmental
Education Council

HOW TO USE THESE MATERIALS

The PROJECT LEARNING TREE (PLT) activities, although intended to supplement existing curricula, are arranged in this *Guide* according to an overall conceptual framework. This Curriculum Framework (See Appendices, pages 192-199) is based upon seven key principles:

The first principle speaks to the concern reflected throughout the PROJECT LEARNING TREE materials for **ENVIRONMENTAL AWARENESS,** beginning with simple experiences in sharpening senses and appreciating nature.

The second principle, **DIVERSITY OF FOREST ROLES**, relates to the development of an awareness of the importance of forest resources in the many ways they relate to the environmental, economic, and sociological health of the region . . . the country . . . and the planet.

The third principle places our explorations within **CULTURAL CONTEXTS** with the development of understanding of the impact of our forest environments in shaping political, economic, and sociological events of the past, present, and future.

SOCIETAL PERSPECTIVES ON ISSUES, the fourth principle, pertains to the viewpoints from which various interest groups judge contemporary forest and environmental issues. It also refers to the communication processes by which these issues are resolved, and ways in which the outcomes may be influenced.

The fifth principle, **MANAGEMENT AND INTERDEPENDENCE OF NATURAL RESOURCES**, focuses on the development of knowledge and skills for the intelligent prediction and evaluation of the impact of specific management policies on the forest and its interrelated communities.

The sixth principle emphasizes the interwoven nature of the **LIFE SUPPORT SYSTEMS** of our planet, with a close look at the short-term and, more importantly, long-range effects of manipulating various segments of these systems.

Having acquired the understanding, knowledge, and skills reflected in the first six principles, each of us can choose to evaluate and modify our own **LIFESTYLES.**

Most of the PLT activities touch upon ideas contained in more than one of the principles; however, each activity appears in the *PLT Guide* according to the principle most emphasized. Thus if you as an educator have an interest that focuses particularly on any one of the principles, you could begin using this *Guide* by turning to the activities in the section of the book devoted dominantly to that principle. It should also be noted that each subsequent principle builds on and extends the learnings emphasized in previous principles. Thus it is possible to select one or two activities from each section of the book, developing attitudes, knowledge, and skills from *awareness* to *lifestyles.*

Each of the PLT activities is presented in a similar format. The body of each activity usually consists of these components:

Subject Area   PLT is an interdisciplinary program. Thus, this designation is offered only to assist educators in finding activities which correspond with a particular subject. It is not meant to suggest that an activity is appropriate solely in the subject area designated.

Grade Level   This is an approximation of the maturity level likely to be appropriate for a particular activity. Most activities can be adapted for use at higher or lower levels than are listed.

PLT Principle   This is a statement of the *long-range goal* of the activity. Each number listed refers to one of the seven principles listed in the PLT Curriculum Framework.

Concepts   These are more detailed statements of the main ideas underlying the PLT principles in the Curriculum Framework. When an activity deals with more than one concept, these concepts are usually listed according to the specificity with which the activity deals with them. The numbers refer to the concepts as they appear in the Curriculum Framework. The key words merely suggest the content of the concept.

Skills   These are the intellectual *processes* which the activity attempts to develop and/or refine. When an activity deals with more than one skill, the skills are listed according to how specifically the activity deals with them. The Roman numerals and key words refer to the skills as they appear in the Curriculum Framework.

Objective   This is a statement of the specific learning outcome to be anticipated through use of the activity.

Activity   This is an explanation of the instructional procedure.

Variation   This is an alternative activity, offered as another means to accomplish the stated objective. Although the same in purpose, each activity and variation is different enough that teachers may frequently want to do both with their students.

Extensions   These are suggestions for additional projects, based upon the activity and designed to provide an opportunity for more depth and breadth.

The Appendices at the back of the *Guide* include a Glossary; Curriculum Framework; Intellectual and Valuing Skills; Resources, listed for each activity and referenced to the Bibliography; Bibliography, not intended to be comprehensive, but as a useful source of information; Metric Table, to be used in making approximate conversions; and Topic Index. Note that *approximate* conversions to metric measure have been used in activities throughout this *Guide*.

TABLE OF CONTENTS

1 ENVIRONMENTAL AWARENESS

2 DIVERSITY OF FOREST ROLES

3 CULTURAL CONTEXTS

4 SOCIETAL PERSPECTIVES ON ISSUES

5 MANAGEMENT AND INTERDEPENDENCE OF NATURAL RESOURCES

6 LIFE SUPPORT SYSTEMS

7 LIFESTYLES

ENVIRONMENTAL AWARENESS

Sylvan Serenade

OBJECTIVE

Students will be able to describe emotions evoked in them by a musical composition.

ACTIVITY

Suggest that your students present a band, orchestra, or choral concert using music which shows how different composers have interpreted the natural environment. If the students are not able to present such a concert by playing or singing the music, they might present the concert in the form of recordings.

Examples of music which could be on the program are "The Falling Leaves" by Benson; "Tall Cedars" by Osterling; and "Green Leaves of Summer" by Tiomkin. The concert might be devoted entirely to classical selections or to contemporary selections — or it might include both.

Examples of other works might include:

Pastoral Symphony by Beethoven
Woodland Sketches by MacDowell
Pines and Fountains of Rome by Respighi
Peter and the Wolf by Prokofiev
Finlandia by Sibelius
Appalachian Spring by Copland
My Fatherland by Smetana
Forest Murmurs by Wagner

Preludes:

Steps on the Snow, What the Westwind Saw, and *Dead Leaves* by Debussy
Carnival of the Animals by Saint-Saëns
To Spring, To Morning, and other compositions by Grieg
William Tell Overture by Rossini

Examples of popular works might include:
El Condor Pasa by Paul Simon
Seasons Suite and *Rocky Mountain Suite* by John Denver

SUBJECTS
Fine Arts
Language Arts and
Humanities
GRADES
7-12
PLT PRINCIPLES
1. Environmental
Awareness
3. Cultural Contexts
7. Lifestyles
CONCEPTS
1.1 Variety and
Aesthetics Essential to
Life Support
1.13 Psychological
Benefits from Nature
3.4111 Forest Model for
Creative Expression
3.4121 Cultural Artifacts
7.4 Creative Expression
and the Environment
SKILLS
II. Communication
I. Gaining Information

(Continued)

Ask your students to research the music selected and to write program notes. The notes could be in several forms. Students may choose to write short poems or paragraphs describing the environment which inspired the composition and the composer's attitude toward it as interpreted through his music. They might write short descriptions of the emotions which the music evoked in them. And they might accompany these notes with line drawings, water colors, natural collages, photographs, or other visual interpretations of such things as the emotions evoked.

After the concert, invite the students to describe any emotions the musical selections evoked in them while they listened.

VARIATION

Substitute natural sounds heard in the forest at appropriate places in the compositions chosen. Ask students to create new arrangements for the music selected or to compose a new piece using natural sounds instead of traditional musical instruments.

EXTENSIONS

1. Invite local musicians to class, musicians knowledgeable about varying musical and cultural traditions. Ask them to talk about the feelings they have when they play and hear music.

2. Create musical instruments from natural materials. Compose your own music.

Tree Verse

OBJECTIVE

Students will be able to express attitudes and feelings about trees and/or forests in a poetic form.

ACTIVITY

This activity should be conducted outdoors, if possible.

Ask each student to brainstorm a list of 15 adjectives which could describe a tree or a forest. Repeat the exercise using verbs. Ask the students to arrange words from these lists into poems in the form of free verse, haiku, or cinquain. Rather than brainstorming the lists individually, the entire group of students can generate extensive lists of words. Then each student might work independently to write one or more poems.

Haiku, originated by the Japanese, consists of three lines of five, seven, and five syllables each. The emphasis is syllabic, not rhyming. Example:

> The snow covered tree
> Sparkles in the soft moonlight
> The wind rushes by

Cinquain is derived from the French and Spanish words for five. This form of poetry also is based on syllables, but there are five lines. Each line has a mandatory purpose and number of syllables. These are (1) the title in two syllables, (2) a description of the title in four syllables, (3) a description of action in six syllables, (4) a description of a feeling in eight syllables, and (5) another word for the title in two syllables. Example:

> Forests
>
> Graceful, growing
> Climb among the clouds
> Joyfully stalking the sunset
> Alive

SUBJECT
Language Arts and Humanities

GRADES
7-12

PLT PRINCIPLES
1. Environmental Awareness
3. Cultural Contexts
7. Lifestyles

CONCEPTS
1.1 Variety in Aesthetics Essential
3.4 People and Biosphere
7.4 Creative Expression and the Environment

SKILLS
I. Gaining Information
II. Communication
VI. Valuing

After the students have completed their poems, you and they might discuss these questions, encouraging the students to investigate some ideas they feel they have insufficient information to discuss:

Does your poem convey your view of humankind's place in nature? How? Does it include any effects humankind may have on nature? That nature has on humankind? Discuss some of these interactions.

In the past what has been Western culture's view of nature? Do you believe this view is changing? On what evidence is your answer based?

Has Eastern culture, such as in Japan where haiku began, viewed nature and humankind's place in nature differently than Western culture? Are traditional Eastern views changing? In what ways? What is the evidence to support your answer?

Have Native American cultures viewed nature the same or differently than the dominant Eastern and Western philosophies? In what ways?

Do Third World nations appear to view nature differently than the dominant cultures in the rest of the world? Give evidence to support your reasons.

Does the poetry produced by the people of these cultures provide any indications of their views of nature?

Have these cultures' views of nature influenced their behavior toward it? If so, how? What implications for future generations do you see as a result of each of these cultures' view of nature and behavior toward living and nonliving things?

Shades of Meaning

OBJECTIVE

Students will be able to use a poetic form to explore a spectrum of ideas related to natural resources.

ACTIVITY

Ask the students to write a diamante (a poem shaped in the form of a diamond) having something to do with natural resources and that demonstrates that words are related through shades of meaning from one extreme to the opposite extreme. For example, "birth" and "death" are two words which can serve to represent opposites. Any words the students choose will have either literal or metaphoric meanings related to natural resources, or both.

birth
green   bright
shining   growing   blooming
heat   motion   sun   food
fading   slowing   dimming
brown   old
death

The words chosen should match the following pattern of parts of speech:

noun
adjective   adjective
participle   participle   participle
noun   noun   noun   noun
participle   participle   participle
adjective   adjective
noun

Suggested pairs of words with opposite meaning might include:

Exploitation — Preservation
Freedom — Regulation
Harvest — Planting
Harmony — Discord
Materialism — Asceticism
Diversity — Uniformity
Use — Misuse

Wilderness — Megalopolis
Cost — Benefit
Fertility — Barrenness
Abundance — Scarcity
Rain — Drought
Whole — Fragment
Beginning — End

SUBJECT
  Language Arts and
  Humanities
GRADES
  7-9
PLT PRINCIPLES
  1. Environmental
     Awareness
  3. Cultural Contexts
  4. Societal Perspectives
     on Issues
CONCEPTS
  1.7 Variety and
      Aesthetics Essential to
      Life Support
  3.421 Cultural
        Perceptions
  4.14 Consideration of
       Reality
  4.13 Value-Loaded
       Language
SKILL
  II. Communication

4

Natural Materials Art

OBJECTIVE

Students will be able to list ways in which their art activities have an impact on the environment.

ACTIVITY

While in an outdoor setting, ask your students to work alone or in small groups in order to create collages using only the materials they can obtain from this natural environment. If they are gathering these materials, remind the students to take care to do no permanent harm to the environment. The students might also use drawing paper to create a picture using only those colors they can obtain from natural sources. They might use charcoal from burned wood to produce black; soil or rocks for brown, gray, or red; leaves for green; berries for purple.

You may wish to "fix" the completed collages or pictures with lacquer, approved-propellant hair spray, or plastic wrap but, first, ask students if they consider adding the preservative "natural."

While still in the outdoor setting, help students analyze the impact of their activity on the environment. Questions could include:

What impact, if any, has the creation of your art work had on the environment?

If all students used the same outdoor site, how quickly would it lose its naturalness?

How could you have created your art with even less impact on the environment?

How much did your project change the environment?

Was the change for better or for worse? What criteria are you using to judge the impact as good or bad?

Will this environment recover from the changes you made? Could the recovery process be speeded up, slowed down, or stopped? How?

Do you think your art work was a fair trade-off for the natural elements you used up? Would someone else feel the same as you?

Ask students to list ways in which their art activities, in indoor settings as well as outdoor settings, may have an impact on the environment. Suggest they create a list of recommended practices involving art and the environment.

(Continued)

4

VARIATIONS

1. Ask your students to think of and list materials which can be used in some form of art or craft. Second, ask them to classify these materials into those derived from trees and those from other sources. Some materials obtained from trees are paper, charcoal, and turpentine (see Resources) and some from other sources are plaster of paris, clay, and stone.

   Make a third list of materials whose origins the students do not know. Invite individual students to research each of these and report to the class on the sources of the materials. As a class, determine the importance of the forest as a source of art and craft materials. Do the students think the forest is important both as a source of materials and as a source of inspiration for art?

2. Suggest that your students create a "returnable" piece of art from natural materials, materials derived without having done significant harm to the environment. The art work must be returned to the place from which its raw materials came. Challenge students to create a piece which is aesthetically pleasing in its natural surroundings and in a human-made environment. All designs should be completely biodegradable.

EXTENSION

Don't stop with art materials. Look at other natural resources used in the classroom to enhance instruction and learning. Weigh the environmental impact of these materials against the potential for instruction they afford.

A Cassette Tour
of Neighborhood Trees

OBJECTIVE

Students will demonstrate their understanding of values of trees by identifying those values for younger students.

ACTIVITY

Ask students, as individuals or in small groups, to write scripts to be tape-recorded for use on a tour of neighborhood trees by younger students or another class. The neighborhood might be local residential, in the business community, at a park or arboretum, or simply on the school grounds. The general objective is to help others become more aware of the community's trees, their growth, their needs, and their contribution to life and people's enjoyment of life.

The students might begin their script-writing by brainstorming the information they may wish to share about the trees on the tour. The list might include:

1. Each tree's location.
2. Each tree's name; the real name or a descriptive name or both.
3. Each tree's growing cycle (be sure a variety of species are included on the tour).
4. Some details about leaves, flowers, and seeds.
5. The interrelationship of each tree with other organisms, including people.
6. Whether a tree was planted and, if so, when and by whom.
7. Who takes care of each tree.
8. Interesting details of each tree's history.
9. Each tree's animal, bird, and insect inhabitants and visitors.
10. Each tree's general health. (Is there any disease or visual damage?)
11. Each tree's future. Are there any plans to trim or remove it? Will another tree be planted in its place?
12. The values of trees of this type, including commercial, aesthetic, habitat and other values.

(Continued)

As students plan their tour, remind them to be conscious of the safety and the attention spans of younger students. Encourage them to try to think about the ways people learn, trying to make the tour as interesting and informing as possible to the younger students. Once on the tour, they are likely to discover quickly the length of the younger students' attention spans!

The students might test their scripts and the tour on a few young friends or members of another class before they record the final version. They may wish to make changes in response to questions or comments they receive during the trial run.

These cassette tours are likely to be of interest to others in the community. You and the students could announce their availability. Such tours could well provide a needed community service and might also serve as a fund-raising mechanism for other student projects.

DIVERSITY OF FOREST ROLES

6

Johnny Appleseed on Mars

OBJECTIVE

Students will be able to discuss the role trees play as producers of oxygen and to value healthy trees as one means for positively affecting air quality in their community.

ACTIVITY

One way to reduce air pollution is to avoid losing trees which filter the air and produce oxygen, especially in urban areas. Ask your students to read the short story "The Green Morning" in the *Martian Chronicles* by Ray Bradbury (see Resources). The story tells of an earthman on Mars and of the "fruit" his trees produce. Interesting any time, the story's impact can be profound if read and discussed on a smoggy day!

You and the students might then investigate and discuss these questions and others:

How much oxygen can a tree produce in one day? Do healthy trees produce more than unhealthy ones? Does a tree's age affect the amount of oxygen it produces? Do some species produce more oxygen than others? What other factors might influence the amount produced?

What about houseplants? How much oxygen do some species of houseplants produce in one day?

How much oxygen does one person consume in respiration in one day?

Are trees and other plants damaged by smog? Are some species more tolerant of smog than others? Identify some of these. Which, if any, of these species are being planted in your community?

What is the real cause of the pollution problem? Does planting pollution-tolerant trees solve it?

If there is an air-pollution problem in your community, as there is in most, are plans being made to solve it? If there are ordinances, who is responsible for seeing that they are enforced? How effective are efforts at enforcement? Have levels of air pollution in your community risen, dropped, or remained about the same in recent years?

(Continued)

Go outside and find evidence of effects of automobile emissions on trees and other plants. For example, you might look for damage on trees and other plants near heavily traveled thoroughfares. Check the plants' foliage for damage such as yellowing and blotching. Try to use scientific procedures to gather your data and localize the apparent causes of the plant damage you observe. You might try to determine what:

Species of trees are more sensitive to air pollution than others.

Species of trees appear to function more effectively than others as oxygen producers in your community.

Steps are being taken in your community or state to reduce the production of air pollution.

Problems, if any, are involved; for example, enforcement, economic implications, trade-offs.

Value trees have as a means for positively affecting air quality in your community.

RESOURCES

For procedures related to students' conducting of air pollution experiments in controlled settings, see:

Air Pollution Experiments for Junior and Senior High School Classes, available from Air Pollution Control Association

and "Exercises About Pollution" in *Pollution*, published by the National Association of Biology Teachers. Both of these are listed in the Resources section of the PLT materials.

7

Nature's Air Conditioners

OBJECTIVE

Students will be able to calculate the amount of moisture evaporated by plants through the process of transpiration.

ACTIVITY

Direct each of your students to tie a plastic bag around a leaf on a tree. Including a small, clean pebble weights the bag so it hangs down, and the water collects rather than runs out of the bag. The bag should be secured tightly on the stem of the twig to which the leaf is attached and left for 24 hours.

Ask your students to observe the condensation of moisture on the interior of the plastic bag as a result of what is called *transpiration*. Students should remove the bags carefully so that none of the water is spilled and measure the water by volume and by weight. Then they might discuss and answer these questions:

How much water did the leaf transpire in 24 hours?
Count the number of leaves on a small tree. How much water do you estimate was evaporated by the entire tree?
How might trees' transpiration affect the temperatures and humidity in a forest?
If possible, measure the temperature and humidity in a forest area and see if you are right. Compare with data gathered from a nonforested area.
What effect, if any, might trees have on weather and atmosphere in a populated urban area? In an irrigated desert region?
What other implications are there related to tree transpiration?

EXTENSIONS

1. Conduct the leaf experiment again using two different leaves. Wash both leaves gently. Then dust flour on one leaf; keep the other leaf clean. Wrap each leaf with a plastic bag as before. Taste the water collected in each bag. Discuss the differences and their implications; for example, related to pollution.

   Caution: If a spray has been used on the tree, *don't* taste the water!

2. Check the difference, if any, in transpiration rates in daylight hours and hours of darkness, and on cloudy days as contrasted with cloudless, sunshine-bright days. Try to explain any differences.

Green Mufflers

OBJECTIVE

Students will be able to describe the noise-abating qualities of roadside vegetation.

ACTIVITY

Ask students to devise a procedure to compare the relative volume of noise along heavily traveled roads where (1) there is little or no roadside vegetation and (2) there is a row of trees or shrubs along the roadside. One method would be to use tape recorders set at the same volume at different locations.

Discuss with your class some of the variables which should be controlled or considered in analysis of results of the experiment. Among these variables are type of traffic, distance from road edge, wind direction and speed, and type of vegetation.

Through investigation and discussion, encourage your students to:

Find out how different species (kinds) of trees or shrubs affect the level of noise.

Determine which species appear to be the most effective in abating noise. Are these broadleaf or coniferous? How does this vary during all seasons of the year?

Identify locations in your community where vegetation has resulted in effective noise abatement.

Identify trees more sensitive to air pollution from vehicles than others? Can you find evidence for this sensitivity? If so, does this have a bearing on the choice of species to be planted for noise abatement? What about the distance the trees are planted from the road edge? The number of vehicles and their emission controls using the roadway?

Help your students identify a location suffering from a noise pollution that would be improved by the addition of a vegetational noise screen. Let the class take whatever action it can to get the screen planted. Their action may include a report to local officials, including a presentation of the data they have accumulated in their study of the noise-abatement qualities of the vegetation they are recommending be planted, and a clear statement of the value of such vegetation to the community.

SUBJECTS
  Science
  Driver Education
  Social Studies
  Mathematics
GRADES
  9-12
PLT PRINCIPLES
  2. Diversity of Forest Roles
  7. Lifestyles
CONCEPTS
  2.1214 Plants as Screens and Windbreaks
  7.21111 Auto Pollution Effects on Forests
SKILLS
  I. Gaining Information
  VI. Valuing

9

Forest Products All Around Us

OBJECTIVE

Students will be able to identify ways in which forest products are an integral part of contemporary lifestyles in their country.

ACTIVITY

The forest industry, like every other industry based on a major natural resource, provides goods which are integral parts of our country's economy and lifestyle. In turn, the continuing supply of those integral parts depends upon the intelligent management of the forest resource. Management options and policies ultimately are influenced by consumer demand for products and services.

Ask students to list at least ten distinctly different products they know of which are made from wood. Invite them to move around the classroom and carefully observe everything as they look for wood products. After allowing sufficient time for them to discover and think of other wood products — and to verify the derivation of some products (There are often surprises with this activity!) — create with them a master list. Item by item, discuss, investigating further where necessary:

What would happen if suddenly this product were unavailable.

Whether this product's disappearance would affect any of the essentials necessary for survival as, for example, food or shelter. What things are truly *necessary* for survival? Decide.

Whether the product's current use is wasteful. How? If it is, whether the use might be eliminated. Determine the possible impacts if it were.

Suggest a substitute for this forest product. Is the substitute made from a renewable or nonrenewable raw material? What would be the environmental impact of the substitute?

EXTENSIONS

1. Conduct this activity including a walking tour of the school area.
2. Invite students to add inputs to the list from home, family members, and other people.

(Continued)

VARIATIONS

1. Allow 15 minutes for each student to list ways he or she uses paper and other forest products within a specified time period, such as a year. Ask students then to draw a line through items on their lists they believe are least important to them and to circle three items they consider essential or most important.

   Next to each of the three top priority items, ask students to write down a product or material which could be substituted for it. For example, instead of using paper to record thoughts, cassette tapes could be substituted.

   After time for investigation by the students, lead a class discussion on the comparative merits of the alternatives proposed:

   The environmental and economic factors involved.

   Whether the substitute serves the same purpose as efficiently and as cheaply.

   Whether the substitute is made from a renewable or nonrenewable raw material.

   Whether the substitute will require more or less energy to produce than the original forest product.

   Whether there are any long-term implications for continued use of the priority items and/or substitutes for them.

2. Ask your students to brainstorm a list of environmental factors affected by the forests. The list might include such things as water quality, air quality, and landscape aesthetics. Invite each student to choose one item from the list and create a poster advertising its value to people, other organisms, and/or the biosphere. Posters can be displayed, shared with other classes, and discussed.

3. Organize a wood-finding tour of the retail marketplace. To accomplish this, you may get permission from a store manager and make a class visit to a local department store, *or* you might even use a mail-order catalog in the classroom. As a preliminary step, ask students to make up a survey sheet for recording information. Divide the class into teams of three or four students each and ask each team to name one of its members as "recorder." The recorder can log team observations on its survey sheet.

   Each team can pick a different department in the store or a different section of the catalog. Ask students to identify and record as many items as they can which use wood or other forest products. Additional information such as unit cost and place of origin also may be gathered.

(Continued)

After data have been collected and tabulated, discuss:

How your lifestyle might be altered if forest products suddenly become unavailable.

How many items listed represent basic survival needs. Determine how you decide which are needs and which are only wants.

Using existing technology, what substitute you might find for any of the items listed. Identify the environmental and economic tradeoffs involved.

What factors (lifestyles, population growth, management, increased demands of the Third World) might affect the supply and price of forest products.

4. Ask your students to brainstorm a list of forest products used in these areas of home living:
   - Kitchen (cutting board, knife handles, and ?)
   - Interior (furniture, shutters, coat hangers, and ?)
   - Maintenance (broom handle, vacuum cleaner bags, and ?)
   - Food (vanilla, nuts, wild game, and ?)
   - Exterior (fence posts, picnic table, and ?)

Which of the items listed are necessary for human survival?

Which of the items are wasteful and which reflect sound conservation practices? Specify what criteria you used to make this judgment.

Which of the wasteful products are you willing to eliminate or find a substitute for? Determine what the environmental and economic impact on our society would be if everyone avoided the wasteful products.

Look at the items you decided were essential. Find out whether there are materials available, using existing technology, that could be substituted for the forest products used. Determine what environmental and economic trade-offs would be involved in the substitution. Compare the efficiency of the substitute material with that of the forest product.

The Three Little Pigs – Revisited

SUBJECTS
Social Studies
Home Economics
Industrial Arts

GRADES
9-12

PLT PRINCIPLES
2. Diversity of Forest Roles
7. Lifestyles
5. Management and Interdependence of Natural Resources

CONCEPTS
2.111 Resource Needs for Human Dwellings
7.2 Cultural Effects on Resources
7.21 Cultural Changes and Resources
5.5 Trade-offs

SKILLS
I. Gaining Information
IV. Critical Thinking
VI. Valuing

OBJECTIVE

Students will be able to compare the environmental and social costs and benefits related to use of various materials in home construction.

ACTIVITY

Ask students to survey their immediate community or neighborhood to find out, through observation and some research, which materials are most commonly used to construct homes. After the class has compiled a list of the most-used materials, ask students to contact building supply retailers, contractors, and architects to ask why these materials are the most popular. They might also ask about new trends in materials and use. Factors such as availability, cost, cultural preference, energy consumption, and climate should be considered.

Using the information they have gathered, the students might:

Identify which materials are derived from renewable resources and which from nonrenewable resources.

Compare the environmental impact of extracting and manufacturing each of the materials used.

Find out how frequently the material which has the least effect on the environment is used in your community.

Find out whether the kinds of building materials used most have changed in recent years.

VARIATIONS

1. Before beginning the preceding activity, ask students to name the type of materials they would choose to build a house and the reasons for their choices. Repeat this process at the end of the activity. Discuss: Have the students' opinions changed? Why or why not? Can we reconcile the American dream of a separate house for every family, built of whatever material desired, with the goal of preserving a quality environment?

2. Ask your students to brainstorm a list of the building materials used in your community, such as wood, brick, aluminum, stone, cement, stucco. Divide the class into groups, one for each material mentioned. Ask each team to locate at least one building constructed predominantly from one or more of these materials. Get a small sample of the materials and find out (1) the local source of the materials, (2) the extent to which the materials were used, (3) the approximate quantity of each material used in the building, (4) the date the building was constructed, and (5) the degree the structure has weathered.

(Continued)

Discuss these questions:

How do the materials compare as to initial cost, degree of difficulty in construction use, maintenance cost, and environmental cost?

How much energy is consumed in extracting and/or manufacturing each of the materials?

How much of each material is required to achieve the same degree of insulation in a structure?

Does the material used in a home's construction relate to the time period in which it was built? (For example, brick may be more popular when wood prices are high.)

What are the effects of climate and cultural preferences on the choice of materials?

If we keep the initial cost of a house low by choosing the least expensive building material, what might we sacrifice, or gain, in addition to the lower cost?

From the information they have gathered as a basis for their decision, what do your students believe are the most appropriate materials for use in what kinds of buildings in your community?

EXTENSION

Divide your class into four groups. Ask each group to read the classified advertising section of a local newspaper and select a home that is advertised. Ask one group to choose a house for rent, the second a mobile home for rent, the third a house for sale, and the fourth a mobile home for sale.

Ask each group to gather information in order to compute the annual total cost of living in the type of shelter assigned. Costs should include such items as taxes, insurance, mortgage interest, lot or house rent, utility deposits and bills, and heating and cooling costs.

Encourage your students to interview their parents and neighbors, realtors, mobile home dealers, home mortgage institutions, and other individuals and agencies to obtain the most accurate cost estimates available. Students might also ask people their reasons for choosing their residences.

After the data have been gathered and compiled, ask students to compare the different types of shelters. Which appear to be the least expensive both initially and in the long run? What is the basis for their conclusion? Which type of shelter and which construction material would the students choose? What are their reasons?

Talk about the minimum housing standards set by local, state, and national governments. Are any of these standards dictated by cultural expectations? Would the students be willing to do without any of these cultural standards? If so, what would they accept?

How Paper Is Made

OBJECTIVE

Students will be able to create a flow chart depicting the process and resources used to manufacture drafting paper.

ACTIVITY

Provide your students with a list of the types of paper used in drafting. Ask your students working individually or in small groups to research (using the references listed) the processes necessary to make one of these commonly used drafting papers. From the information for the paper they have researched, ask each student or group of students to plan and draw a flow chart depicting the steps in the process from raw wood fiber to finished product. The students also could indicate points along this chain where there is a potential for environmental contamination and indicate the pollution abatement procedures used to avoid such contamination.

Once the flow charts are completed, discuss questions such as the following with the students:

How might the paper used in drafting become a source of pollution? Which stages in the life cycle of paper can cause pollution? What, if any, pollution control devices and procedures are used to reduce or alleviate pollution?

How might we as consumers help to minimize pollution and more effectively use resources through our own actions when drafting?

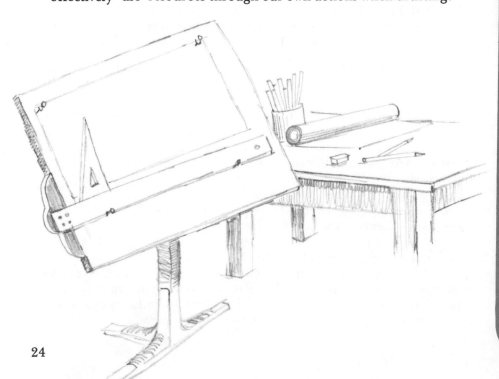

12

Local Recreation Preferences

OBJECTIVE

Students will be able to generalize about recreational experiences and preferences, based on their use of a survey instrument.

ACTIVITY

Suggest that students brainstorm a list of questions that could be used in surveying people concerning the use of local recreation facilities. Questions might include:

1. Have you ever been to any local recreation areas? If so, which one(s)?
2. Have you been to (*name a local area*)?
3. If yes, have you been there within the last year?
4. How often have you visited any outdoor recreation areas in the last year?
5. Do you go to any *forest* recreation areas?
6. If yes, which ones?
7. Is it difficult for you and/or your family to get transportation to recreation areas you enjoy?
8. What kinds of outdoor recreation activities do you enjoy?
9. Which outdoor recreation area that you have visited do you most enjoy?
10. Is it difficult for you to find a recreation area where you can participate in the kinds of outdoor activities you enjoy?
11. What do you like most about outdoor recreation?
12. What do you like least about outdoor recreation?
13. Are you willing to pay fees for the use of recreation areas?

From the list of questions you and the students generate, ask the students to prepare and distribute a questionnaire on the use of the forest and other outdoor areas for recreation. The students might include a space on each questionnaire to indicate information such as the age of the person being interviewed (under 15 years of age, 16-18 years of age, 18-25 years of age, etc.). It is often helpful to construct a questionnaire so that information falls into categories and can be quickly checked. For example, you could specify in question No. 4 above: 0 visits, 1-5 visits, 6-10 visits, more than 10 visits, leaving space for the interviewer to check the respondent's answer. Once the data have been collected, the students can put the data into a table which compares the differences in the responses to questions by age group and whatever other descriptions they have established.

The following table could be used for those questions which can be answered by "yes" or "no." Similar tables could be made up to tabulate other data, such as number of visits to an area, popularity of features of recreational areas, or fees charged by different areas.

(Continued)

USE OF RECREATIONAL AREAS

QUESTION	AGE IN YEARS												RESPONSE (number)
	Under 15				16-49				Over 50				
	Yes		No		Yes		No		Yes		No		
	No.	%	No.	%	No.	%	No.	%	No.	%	No.	%	Total
No. 1													
No. 2													
Etc.													

Using data from the table they construct, ask each student to write a generalization (a summary statement and/or tentative conclusion) reflecting the experiences and preferences of the different age groups surveyed. Discuss these questions:

Do all age groups appear to prefer the same types of outdoor recreation areas or activities?

What might cause differences in preferences?

What type of recreational areas appear to be in the greatest demand? Are these areas adequately supplied?

How important does outdoor recreation appear to be to your community's economy?

What do most people in the community appear to need in order to have a good time in the outdoors?

EXTENSIONS

1. With a mail-order catalog as a reference, ask students to calculate the cost of camping for a family of four by means of backpacking; car camping with a tent; and car camping with a trailer or motor home.

2. Select a recreational area in your state, preferably near your school. A city park would be adequate.

   Ask students to visit the area and photograph, write down, or tape-record the variety of uses made of the park. Uses would include such things as picnicking, boating, sports, meeting rooms, museums, camping, and bike riding.

   In class, ask students to prepare a report, booklet, bulletin board, mural, or other project that depicts the diversity of uses they have found. Each student then should select one use and do a report (in any medium) on what would happen if this use were eliminated.

13

A Guide to Local Recreation

OBJECTIVE

Students will be able to describe local, outdoor recreation sites.

ACTIVITY

Your students can conduct a survey of the recreation areas in your state, including publicly and privately owned parks and forests. Invite the class to select one area they would like to know more about.

Divide the students into study groups, each to collect data on one topic. Topics might include the area's history, size, geography, animals, plants, human constituency, activities, administration and major purposes (such as wilderness, recreation, water sports, camping).

Suggest that the students try to find people among their relatives, friends and acquaintances who have visited the area and interview them to determine what the visitors enjoyed most; what time of year they think is best there; unusual activities, facilities, or sites available; best route to the area; and if there are any problems related to the area.

VARIATIONS

1. As a class project, create a brochure describing recreation areas available either locally or throughout your region. The brochure may include photographs or drawings of the area; maps; dos and don'ts for visitors; and other information similar to that gathered in the preceding activity for a specific site. The brochure could be duplicated and distributed to other classes, to parents, or throughout the community. Students could also prepare a slide show on local recreational areas, making it available to other interested community members.

   These projects might also be initiated on an individual basis, with each student designing a promotional brochure or media presentation describing a favorite recreational site; its facilities, features, and location.

2. Arrange a class field trip to a nearby recreation area and make an appointment to talk to one of the staff who works at the site. Before the trip, students could prepare a list of questions to ask the staff person. Sample questions are:

   1) What government agency, private individual, or company maintains and manages this area?

   2) What is the annual maintenance cost?

3) Who pays for maintenance? Where does the money come from — taxes, timber sales, user fees?

4) How heavily is the site used? Is it used too much or not enough?

5) Does the area serve purposes other than recreation?

6) If the primary purpose of the area is not recreation, what is the purpose?

The students may want to submit their questions in advance to the staff person so that he or she may have the responses ready.

EXTENSION

Explore urban and alternative recreation sites. For example, create a "Walker's Guide to the Neighborhood," including such points of interest as street murals, craft shops, weekend garage sales, and interesting front-yard gardens.

RESOURCES

Check your community's phone book for addresses of private organizations, individuals, or companies who operate recreation sites or provide areas open to recreation on the land.

See also: "Zone Management: Key to Controlling Recreational Impact in Developed Campsites," by Douglas McEwen and S. Ross Tocher, *Journal of Forestry*, February 1976.

The Retreat from Riches: Affluence and Its Enemies by Peter Passell and Leonard Ross, Viking, New York, 1973.

14

Community Land Use

OBJECTIVE

Students will be able to describe changes which have occurred in a specific locality as a result of people's activities, distinguishing between what appear to be (1) planned and unplanned and (2) helpful and harmful changes.

ACTIVITY

Divide the class into five groups. Ask each group to study their community's land use in one of five time periods: the present; 25 years ago; 50 years ago; 100 years ago; and 200 years ago.

Ask each group to collect data from community records, including old maps and photographs, and make a map illustrating the land-use pattern during the period being investigated. All five maps should be made to the same scale. It is helpful in comparing the data on the maps if the students agree in advance to a key, and all use the key in making their maps.

After the maps are completed, the students can compare the land-use patterns reflected by the maps, applying categories of analysis. For example:

Has the community's size changed? If so, how?

Have the land-use patterns changed? What uses have increased?

What uses are decreasing? Have any of the original uses disappeared?

How have uses such as schools, housing, industry and open space changed?

Ask the students, either individually or in small groups, to show the completed maps to residents who have lived in the community for from 25 to 50 years, asking these people about their perceptions of the changes in their community. If possible, the interviews should be recorded on tape.

From those interviewed, the students can determine:

1. The ratio of the people surveyed who believed the land-use changes were harmful as compared to those who believed they were helpful.
2. Reasons the residents gave for their opinions on the changes.
3. Whether any residents who believed a change would be helpful at the time it took place now think it was detrimental to the community. Whether any of them believe a change they originally thought was harmful has turned out to be beneficial.
4. Whether the changes made appear to have been planned or unplanned.
5. A general sense of the attitudes of these older people to life within their community.

The students might then look for any trends, discussing what land-use changes appear to be coming in the future. Do the students think these will be helpful or harmful? Ask them to state reasons and criteria to support their opinions. Ask the students to suggest mechanisms that could be used to ensure that most changes will be beneficial.

VARIATION

Ask your students to make or look at a map of their community which identifies current uses of the land (such as shopping areas, parks, streets, industrial sites).

Using the map, students can compile a table showing the amount of land devoted to each type of use. Small groups of students might calculate the land areas devoted to a specific use.

After the table is finished, you and the students could discuss some of these questions:

What kind of use occupies the greatest amount of land.

What portion of the land is devoted to green or open space. Is it enough? How do you decide?

Is there a pattern to the land use or does it appear to have developed by chance?

Whether the use of land appears to be well-suited to the needs, interests, and long-term health of the community.

Does your community have a land-use plan? If so, what are the goals of the plan and how is it put into effect? If there is no plan, are any steps being taken to develop one?

What do you see as advantages or disadvantages of a land-use plan for your community?

CULTURAL
3
CONTEXTS

15

Where Are the Cedars of Lebanon?

SUBJECT
Social Studies

GRADES
11-12

PLT PRINCIPLE
3. Cultural Contexts

CONCEPT
3.32 Historical Effects
of Forest Use or Misuse

SKILLS
I. Gaining Information
IV. Critical Thinking

OBJECTIVE

Students will be able to describe how one civilization's development was affected by its treatment of natural resources.

ACTIVITY

Divide the class into two groups to prepare for and then hold a debate. The students might agree to choose only one of these civilizations for the debate; to discuss them in a series of separate debates; or to consider them all together: ancient China, ancient Persia, ancient Greece, ancient Rome, and ancient Egypt.

Here is the statement for debate:

The rise and/or fall of _____ (one or all of the civilizations) was *primarily* the result of its use or abuse of natural resources, especially its land.

One debate team is to argue that land use or abuse was the *major factor* in the rise and/or fall of the civilization(s). The other should take the position that land use or abuse played only a *minor* role.

EXTENSION

Research and discuss present-day problems related to land use and specifically soil. Include in your research an "update" on the land areas that were involved during the time of each of the ancient civilizations above.

RESOURCES

References cited in the Resources section of the PLT materials are suitable for most upper level high school students and generally relate to the *misuse* of the land. Most social studies textbooks detail the rise of these ancient civilizations with regard to development of their agriculture through *use* of the land.

The Influence of Forests on Your Region's History

OBJECTIVE

Students will be able to compare uses of the forest by early Indians, by the immigrant pioneers, and by contemporary society.

ACTIVITY

Divide your class into three research teams, one for each of these three time periods: the time of the early Indians, before immigrant settlers arrived; the immigrant pioneer era; and the time we are living in today.

Ask each team to prepare a multi-media presentation (using such media as pictures, filmstrips, taped interviews, and cartoons) that communicates what the students have found out about human use of the forest (or other major natural resources) in their region during the time period assigned.

For each time period, ask the students to consider:

Whether the humans live in the forests.

What, if any, forest products they use.

Whether the forest plays a part in their religion.

How these humans harvest the forest products.

Whether they appear to be careless in their harvest and wasteful of their resources. Does their technology encourage, allow, or deter their wastefulness?

Whether they behave as though they believe conservation of the forest is important.

What other major natural resources the people depend upon or use, and how they tend to treat these resources.

For the immigrant pioneers, the students might also ask:

If they lived in the forest, what were the first things these settlers did when they moved into the forest area? Cleared land for a cabin? Planted crops?

Did they use the same forest products as those the early Indians used? What did they learn from the Indians? Did the Indians learn anything from them?

Were all the forest products harvested for their own use or did they sell or trade some? If so, which?

And in considering present-day society:

What forest products do we use that the pioneers or the early Indians did not? What did the early Indians and pioneers use that we do not use today?

SUBJECTS
   Social Studies
   Language Arts and
     Humanities
GRADES
   7-9
PLT PRINCIPLE
   3. Cultural Contexts
CONCEPTS
   3.33 Forest Influence on
     U.S. History
   3.412 Cultural Concept
     of Forests
SKILLS
   I. Gaining Information
   II. Communication
   V. Problem Solving

How do some present-day Indians use forest products and forest resources differently from the rest of contemporary society?

What people today seem to play a role in conserving the forest for the future, and in what ways? Officials of the government? Private citizens? Activists in environmental fields? Members of forest-related industries? Native-American foresters? Others?

When the presentations are ready, ask the students to share them in class. Through discussion and — where necessary — further investigation, ask the students to compare the roles the forests have played in the history of their region:

Compare the uses of the forest and/or other major natural resources during all time periods.

Compare the apparent exploitation of resources in all time periods.

Compare the concern shown for resource conservation in all time periods.

Describe how time and circumstances might have affected people's uses of the forest and other natural resources.

Describe events happening outside the region that might have influenced the behavior of its population toward the forest.

Determine how the use of forest products has increased or decreased in the region, and whether the kinds of products used have changed.

Discuss how technology has changed humans' abilities to affect their environment.

RESOURCES

Visit logging and saw mill museums as well as tree farms. Many museums are listed in *Forestry Products Industry Museums,* cited in the Resources Section of the PLT materials.

Turn also to the Resources section for additional suggestions.

Artisans in Wood

OBJECTIVE

Students will be able to state how power hand tools have influenced the work of local artisans or craftspeople.

ACTIVITY

Suggest that students interview older, local, skilled artisans who have wood-related jobs — such as furniture makers, carpenters, and wood carvers. Remind the students of the importance of showing consideration and respect for any people they interview. Before conducting the interviews, the students could develop a list of questions, such as:

1. How did you learn your trade?
2. Who got you interested in it?
3. How long have you worked at (whatever they do)?
4. Has your job changed much over the years?
5. How have new styles of tools and power tools changed your work?
6. Do you feel that your products are better made and more durable than factory-made or mass-produced products? If yes, in what ways? If no, in what ways are the other products better?
7. How, if at all, have power tools and new methods of doing your job affected your satisfaction with your work?

After the interviews ask the students to report on the work of the artisans and any changing techniques and influences in their crafts. Also encourage the students to describe the feelings conveyed by these artisans during the interviews, reflecting any enthusiasm and pride they feel for their craft.

EXTENSION

Some students may wish to project the discussion of power tools to a discussion of technology and modern industrial methods in general. This would be a good time to introduce the "appropriate technology" concept. The April 1977 issue of *The Futurist,* the journal of the World Future Society (see Resources section) is devoted to an explanation and discussions of appropriate technology. Students can find other articles relating to technology listed in the *Readers' Guide to Periodical Literature*.

SUBJECTS
Industrial Arts
Social Studies
Language Arts and
  Humanities
GRADES
7-12
PLT PRINCIPLE
3. Cultural Contexts
CONCEPT
3.4121 Cultural Artifacts
SKILLS
II. Communication
 I. Gaining Information

18

Native Americans and the Forest

OBJECTIVE

Students will be able to describe how the cultures and economies of Native American Indian tribes have been and continue to be influenced by the forest and other natural resources.

ACTIVITY

First, find out which Native American tribes have been and are active in your state, province, or region. Then, divide the class into groups of three to five students each. Ask each group to obtain information on one of the indigenous Indian tribes. If possible, they might research changes in the tribe's culture and lifestyle that may have taken place to the present.

While they are gathering data about any given period of time, students can consider the following:

How the tribe's culture and religion relate to the forest and to other natural resources. (For example, Chief Colorow of the Utes used a "council tree" which was sacred to his tribe. Annually his braves visited this tree, located on what is now the Rooney Ranch southwest of Denver, to meet and to bathe in a deposit of red mud on the site.)

How the tribe's economy depends upon the forest and its products, including wildlife. (Has the tribe, for instance, used tree bark or fruit for food or medicine?) If there is no forest in the region, where does this tribe live and on what natural resources does the tribe's economy depend?

Ask the students to share the information they have collected and to discuss these questions, engaging in additional research to provide information necessary to the discussion:

To what degree have the tribes — past and present — been dependent upon the forest environment for survival? On other natural resources?

If a tribe does not live in the forest, has it used any forest products? If so, how has it gotten these products?

How much has the forest contributed to the religious beliefs of the tribes? How might this have affected the behavior of Native Americans toward the forest?

How did each tribe's attitudes toward and relationship with the forest during the period of the region's early history differ from those of early migrating settlers?

Do the Native American tribes studied still view the forest and other natural resources as they did in early historical periods?

Do the descendents of the early immigrant settlers still view the forest and other natural resources as they did in early historical periods?

What have been the trends in the use of natural resources by the early immigrant settlers to the present day, by each of the Native American tribes to the present day? Compare these.

VARIATION

Proceed as described in the first exercise, except assign half the groups to investigate the lifestyles of Indians who lived or presently live in a different environment than is found locally. For example, if local Indian tribes lived or live in the forest, half the class might investigate tribes who lived or live on the prairies or deserts. Then, as a class, compare and discuss the different ways of life:

Describe each tribe's environment and its influence on religious beliefs and other cultural characteristics.

Determine whether Indians living in one type of environment use materials or products from another. If so, how have they acquired them?

Offer your opinions as to which tribes lead or have led easier lives. Describe the bases for your feelings.

Describe each tribe's treatment of its native environment.

Identify each tribe's major source of food. Hunting? Farming? Fishing?

Describe those elements or aspects of the tribe's culture which have remained to the present.

EXTENSION

Suggest that your students read *Light in the Forest* by Conrad Richter. Lead a class discussion on True Son's attitude toward the white society's civilization. How are his attitudes as an adopted Indian different from his brother Gordy's attitudes toward the environment and toward other living things, including humans? Ask your students (alone or in small groups) to write a dialog between Gordy and True Son as they discuss their choices for a way of life.

19

Native American Web of Life

OBJECTIVE

Students will be able to identify differences and similarities in different Native American Indian tribes' uses of and attitudes toward natural resources.

ACTIVITY

Ask your students to pick a Native American tribe, and, individually or in small groups, research the lifestyle and habitat of members of this Indian tribe during a specific period of time they choose. Ask them to determine the things these tribal members need in order to survive, including such things as food, water, shelter, space, and territory. Students can create a visual "web of life" for the group of Native Americans they've researched. If possible, ask them to create such a web for one Native American surviving alone. In discussion, include consideration and comparison of various Native American uses of and attitudes toward natural resources.

VARIATIONS

1. Students can pick different tribes all living during the same historical period, and as a result be able to see more clearly the differences or similarities in lifestyle and habitat among various Native American tribes. Look for differences and similarities in the various tribes' uses of and attitudes toward the same resources.

2. Students can create webs of life for the same Native American tribes during different historical periods; for example: 200 years ago, 100 years ago, 50 years ago, 15 years ago, the present. Look for differences or similarities over time in Native American attitudes toward and uses of natural resources and means of meeting survival needs.

EXTENSIONS

1. Research different cultures' uses of and relationships to natural resources throughout the world.
2. Create similar webs of life for various immigrant groups, during different historical periods.
3. Create a web of life representing your community and its members today.
4. Create a web of life for yourself.

Indian Summer, Winter, Spring, and Fall

OBJECTIVE

Students will be able to describe specific relationships with the environment expressed in Native American culture.

ACTIVITY

"What is life? It is the flash of a firefly in the night. It is the breath of a buffalo in the winter time. It is the shadow which runs across the grass and loses itself in the Sunset."

— Crowfoot, April 1890

In his dying hours, his last words were of life.

(From *Touch the Earth, A Self Portrait of Indian Existence*, by T. C. McLuhan. See the Resources section of the PLT materials.)

Through research and discussion with your students, explore the significance of the seasons to the religious, economic, and social existence of various Native American tribes. Discuss the many and varied ways relationships with natural resources are expressed in Native American culture.

VARIATION

Suggest that your students create a cultural fair, including examples of Native American relationships to natural resources as expressed through their culture; for example, in legends, art work, costumes, and artifacts.

SUBJECT
Social Studies
GRADES
7-12
PLT PRINCIPLES
3. Cultural Contexts
6. Life-Support Systems
CONCEPTS
3.421 Cultural Perceptions
3.422 Belief Systems
6.31 Human-Biosphere Relations
SKILL
I. Gaining Information

21

Pioneers in the Wilderness

OBJECTIVE

Students will be able to describe differences between their attitudes toward natural resources and the attitudes of pioneer settlers.

ACTIVITY

Many historical accounts of American conservation practices talk about the "unspoiled continent which was invaded by greedy exploiters who ravaged this virgin land."

It is likely that neither the pioneer resource developers nor their successors saw themselves as unthinking spoilers; they were not regarded as such by most of their contemporaries. Instead, the early settlers tended to act in ways consistent with their environmental circumstances and their intellectual heritage. When our forests seemed limitless, the "cut-out-and-get-out" approach to logging may have seemed a necessary or appropriate response.

Students can attempt to understand why the early settlers acted as they did toward their environment. This activity explores the rationale behind the pioneers' behavior.

Ask your students in small groups to assume the roles of members of pioneer families moving from Philadelphia to the Ohio frontier in the 1780s. The frontier land is covered with dense, deciduous hardwood forests. Wildlife abounds, including bear, deer, bobcat, quail, grouse, passenger pigeon, wolf, and cougar. There is a resident population of Indians, but the settlers have little contact with them.

Each family has brought along vegetable and grain seeds and its livestock, consisting of a milk cow, two pigs, two sheep, a horse, an ox, and ten chickens.

Ask the "families" to make lists of the things they must do in order to establish a home in this wilderness. These tasks should be listed in the order the families plan to accomplish them. For instance, "provide food" might be first and "provide shelter" second.

Then each family should discuss and make a second list describing the environmental impact they could anticipate resulting from each activity. For example, providing food and shelter probably would involve shooting wild game and cutting trees and clearing ground for a cabin and garden.

After the lists are complete, you and the students might discuss:

In your role as a pioneer, how would you describe your attitudes toward the forest when you began establishing your homestead?

What impact would you have been likely to think you were making on the environment?

How does your present attitude toward the forest as a natural resource compare to the attitude you held when you imagined yourself an early settler?

What factors do you think have contributed to changes in Americans' attitudes toward the environment since the 1780s?

Is it appropriate to condemn the pioneers and early industrialists for exploiting the environment? Why or why not?

Do you believe the practices, policies, and traditions of the past are representative of the present behavior of people and industry? Why or why not?

How can we more effectively judge our actions affecting the environment by current standards and conditions as well as by the needs of future generations? State your reasoning.

22

A Day in the Life . . .

OBJECTIVE

Students will be able to describe some ways in which environments influence the cultures and economies of different peoples of the world.

ACTIVITY

Divide your class into several groups. Ask each group to choose one of the major types of forests in the world (examples are rain forest, boreal forest) and develop an oral presentation of "a day in the life of" someone living or working in that forest. The oral communication technique used could be role-playing, a radio play "broadcast" from behind a curtain, a man-in-the-street interview, or something similar. You may suggest as subjects such people as a lumber-mill worker in Wyoming; a member of a non-technical tribe in the Amazon jungles of Brazil; an Appalachian farmer; a ski resort owner in the mountains of Colorado; and a forest ranger on the western slopes of the Olympic Mountains in Washington State.

When the students make their presentations to the class, each group should attempt to convey this information:

1. The appearance of the forest. Students might paint scenery or project slides or movies as background.
2. Who lives and works in this forest and the area's native animals and plants.
3. The forest's physical characteristics including rainfall, terrain, location, altitude, and climate.
4. What happens in the forest. Examples are hunting, logging, skiing, fishing, commercial harvesting.
5. How human action is influencing the environment. This influence might be through planting trees, clearing land, and introducing non-native plants and animals into the forest.

After all the presentations have been made, the students might:

Identify and categorize similarities and differences between the forest types.

Compare the effects of people on each forest.

Determine how the forests' characteristics have affected the economy and culture of the people who live within and near them.

Determine whether each type of forest would be capable of supporting the same number of people.

Describe any correlation between the residents' level of technology and their interaction with the forest.

Identify and describe implications of problems related to management and continued use of each of these forests by human and wildlife populations.

A Letter from Archy

OBJECTIVE

Students will be able to describe conditions which led to the "dust bowl" era of the 1930s and identify possible ways to avoid repeating those conditions.

ACTIVITY

Ask all students to read, or one student to read aloud, "a letter from archy," excerpted below from *the life and times of archy and mehitabel* by Don Marquis.

Then ask the students to discuss questions such as the following, pursuing additional information where necessary to the discussion:

Who was archy? (A cockroach!)

What was taking place in the United States at the time (1935) archy wrote his letter? How accurate was archy's description of the situation?

What did archy predict about the destiny of the human race as a result of humanity's activities? How accurate are his predictions?

How accurate was archy's description of the causes for the downfall of the civilization he describes?

Do you think humanity has taken archy's warning seriously and reformed? What evidence can you cite for your opinion?

What actions are being taken to avoid the conditions archy describes? Are there other actions we ought to be taking, but as yet are not?

EXTENSIONS

1. Ask your students to examine the style of writing used by archy (Marquis). Why didn't archy capitalize? (As a cockroach, archy couldn't operate the upper-case key on the typewriter!) Ask each student to use the same style to write a reply from mehitabel defending exploitation.

2. Obtain a copy of the film "The River" (See the Resources section of the PLT materials.) which was produced during the 1930s under the auspices of one of the government's public works programs. The film documents the conditions of the people and the land during the dust bowl era with startling realism. Compare archy's description with the film. Do both attribute the problem to the same cause? If so, what is it? Do both attribute improper land use to human greed and lack of foresight?

3. Ask each student to "become" a plant or animal, and, from that living thing's point of view, write a story about an environmental concern or event affecting its life.

SUBJECTS
Language Arts and Humanities
Social Studies
Science

GRADES
9-12

PLT PRINCIPLES
3. Cultural Contexts
5. Management and Interdependence of Natural Resources
6. Life-Support Systems

CONCEPTS
3.32 Historical Effects of Forest Use or Misuse
3.33 Forest Influence on U.S. History
3.412 Cultural Concepts of Forests
5.1 Interdependence of Resources
6.23 Humans' Effect on Environment
6.31 Human-Biosphere Relations

SKILLS
I. Gaining Information
IV. Critical Thinking
II. Communication

23

(Continued)

RESOURCES

A LETTER FROM ARCHY
by Don Marquis

"dear boss i was talking with an ant the other day and he handed me a lot of gossip which ants the world around are chewing among themselves

"i pass it on to you in the hope that you may relay it to other human beings and hurt their feelings with it

"no insect likes human beings and if you think you can see why the only reason i tolerate you is because you seem less human to me than most of them

"here is what they are saying

"it wont be long now it wont be long man is making deserts on the earth it wont be long now before man will have used it up so that nothing but ants and centipedes and scorpions can find a living on it

"man has oppressed us for a million years but he goes on steadily cutting the ground from under his own feet making deserts deserts deserts

"we ants remember and have it all recorded in our tribal lore when gobi was a paradise swarming with men and rich in human prosperity it is a desert now and the home of scorpions ants and centipedes

"what man calls civilization always results in deserts man is never on the square he uses up the fat and greenery of the earth each generation wastes a little more of the future with greed and lust for riches

"north africa was once a garden spot and then came carthage and rome and despoiled the storehouse and now you have sahara sahara ants and centipedes

"toltecs and aztecs had a mighty civilization on this continent but they robbed the soil and wasted nature and now you have deserts scorpions ants and centipedes and the deserts of the near east followed egypt and babylon and assyria and persia and rome and the turk the ant is the inheritor of tamerlane and the scorpion succeeds the caesars

"america was once a paradise of timberland and stream but it is dying because of the greed and money lust of a thousand little kings who slashed the timber all to hell and would not be controlled and changed the climate and stole the rainfall from posterity and it wont be long now it wont be long till everything is a desert from the alleghenies to the rockies the deserts are coming the deserts are spreading the springs and streams are drying up one day the mississippi itself will be a bed of sand ants and scorpions and centipedes shall inherit the earth

"men talk of money and industry of hard times and recoveries of finance and economics but the ants wait and the scorpions wait for while men talk they are making deserts all the time getting the world ready for the conquering ant drought and erosion and desert because men cannot learn

"rainfall passing off in flood and freshet and carrying good soil with it because there are no longer forests to withhold the water in the billion meticulations of the roots

"it wont be long now it wont be long till earth is barren as the moon and sapless as a mumbled bone

"dear boss i relay this information without any fear that humanity will take warning and reform signed archy."

From *the life and times of archy and mehitabel* by Don Marquis, (New York: Doubleday & Co., 1935), Reprinted by permission.

Turn to the Resources section of the PLT materials for additional references.

Economic Web of Life

24

OBJECTIVE

Students will be able to identify interrelationships between specific occupations and natural resources.

ACTIVITY

With the students, generate a list of types of occupations in their community. Invite the students to try to identify the natural resource (or resources) which might act as the ultimate basis for each job listed. (For instance, carpentry in home construction is usually based primarily on the forest resource.) Then, ask the students to create a visual or physical "web of life" showing the interrelationships between the specific jobs and natural resources. (One way of doing this could be to depict both the jobs and the resources on a "mural," connecting them with pins and yarn; another way could be to ask individual students to represent the jobs and resources themselves, and connect themselves with the yarn.)

Discuss:

Upon which natural resources do jobs in this community seem to depend?

Where are these natural resources located?

Are the resources renewable or nonrenewable?

What potential or actual limits may exist now and in the future related to natural resources? Discuss short- and long-term implications of such limits for types of jobs in this community and elsewhere.

Are there occupations identified which do not appear to depend upon a specific natural resource? What relationships do these occupations have with other occupations in the community? How, if at all, might these jobs be affected by possible changes in availability of some natural resources at some point in time?

VARIATION

Map the flow of money into and out of a commercial forest over time. Create a web of relationships between this forest resource and the jobs in the communities where the various kinds of forest workers live; other communities where consumers live who use the forest products; other communities across the nation; the rest of the world. Describe this web of interrelationships and the implications for resource use and management it represents.

EXTENSION

Create a web of relationships showing natural resource, human, and economic inter-connections worldwide.

SUBJECT
Social Studies

GRADES
7-12

PLT PRINCIPLES
3. Cultural Contexts
6. Life-Support Systems
5. Management and Interdependence of Natural Resources
7. Lifestyles

CONCEPTS
3.1 Resource Base for Economy
3.2 Cultural Effects on Resources
3.211 Production Cycles
3.222 Global Context of Resources
5.2 Interdependence of Resources
5.3 Urban-Forest Interdependence
6.3 Interdependence of Living Things and Their Environment
6.31 Human-Biosphere Relations
6.41 Dependency on Environment
7.12 Determination of Resources and Their Values
7.2 Cultural Effects on Resources

SKILLS
IV. Critical Thinking
V. Problem Solving
VI. Valuing

The Power of Literature

OBJECTIVE

Students will be able to identify an author's view of nature as communicated through one of the writer's works.

ACTIVITY

There is increasing public involvement in setting priorities and making decisions on environmental policies. The public attitude, or value system relating to nature, is both affected by and reflected in, literature. This activity is designed to show how nature has been valued by two famous authors and how their views have affected contemporary values.

Ask your students to read "To Build A Fire," by Jack London (see Resources). You and they might then include the following in your discussion:

What is the setting of the story?
Who is the principal figure and what happens to him?
What is the significance of the protagonist's (leading character's) dog?
Why can't the fire be built?
What is London's view of nature as communicated in this story? (He sees it as an adversary which must be conquered before it conquers him.)
When London wrote this story, what was happening at the same time? (The Klondike gold rush.) How might this have influenced the author's attitude toward nature?

As a second example, students could read "The Big Two-Hearted River" by Ernest Hemingway (see Resources) and compare this story with London's.

How does nature (the forest) help the principal character in Hemingway's story?
Does Hemingway's picture of nature differ from London's? If so, how? If these authors had been given the responsibility of managing land, might they have been likely to do their jobs differently?

Ask each student to take the point of view of one author or the other and to write a short paragraph explaining the value of the forest to humankind.

SUBJECTS
  Language Arts and
    Humanities
  Social Studies
GRADES
  7-12
PLT PRINCIPLES
  3. Cultural Contexts
  7. Lifestyles
CONCEPTS
  3.4122 Environmental
    Literature
  3.4121 Cultural
    Artifacts
  7.11 Cultural and
    Resource
    Management
SKILLS
  I. Gaining
    Information
  IV. Critical Thinking
  VI. Valuing

(Continued)

VARIATION

Ask students to read Walt Whitman's poem, "Song of a Redwood" (see Resources). In this poem, Whitman explores an ethical conflict: admiration for the pioneer spirit which conquered land to develop the West vs love of nature and the beauty and majesty of a great tree.

Ask the students to identify value statements and pick out words used to express attitudes in the poem. List these phrases and words on the blackboard in two categories: one for those which convey their values through connotation; the second for those which convey their values through their denotative meaning. Some phrases and words may fit in both categories.

Discuss these and other questions:

Which phrases or words seem to be most effective in communicating their values?

What ethical (value) systems are communicated in the poem? Which system do you think Whitman favors?

Have conditions changed since the poem was written? Would your recognition of these changes alter your opinion of the pioneers?

Could some opposing values be present within the same person? If so, how? Give examples.

Superstitions, Symbols, and Similes

OBJECTIVE

Students will be able to describe influences which cultural traditions and religious beliefs may have on a society's treatment of the natural environment.

ACTIVITY

Natural objects have been used to symbolize many concepts. Many cultures, in the past and present, have close ties with the forest. Therefore the forest has been the focus of many legends, myths, and religious beliefs. This activity explores the ways in which these beliefs have shaped humankind's interaction with the environment.

Ask students to think of concepts which natural objects, such as trees, the forest, and wildlife, have symbolized. Among the many examples are life, death, family ancestry, strength, and flexibility. On the chalkboard list concepts such as these that the students identify.

Each student could select one concept from the list and write a paragraph explaining the characteristics that might have contributed to this natural object having become a symbol for that idea in a given culture. Cross-cultural comparisons can be encouraged. The students could accompany their paragraphs with a visual representation of the natural object as a symbol such as a photograph, or drawing.

Students can try to examine any inconsistencies or imperfect analogies that exist between the concept and its symbol. Ask the students to share their completed projects in class and discuss:

How might cultural traditions or religious beliefs affect the use of natural objects as symbols. For example, would Christians use a tree to symbolize their God? If so, under what conditions?

How might cultural traditions or religious beliefs affect a society's treatment of the natural environment? For example, if a culture uses these objects as religious symbols, is the culture's "environmental ethic" affected? (It would be helpful if students read some of the references cited under Resources.) What is the evidence for your hypothesis?

How do present historians interpret the myths and legends of the ancient Greeks and Romans?

How might future historians interpret a legend such as that of Paul Bunyan or Johnny Appleseed?

If Paul Bunyan were interpreted as a god, what would be his doctrine? How might Johnny Appleseed's religious philosophy be interpreted?

What symbols do we have in our culture today that are derived from nature? What relationship is there between these contemporary symbols representing our beliefs and values, and our lifestyle as a culture? Lifestyles within subcultures?

SUBJECTS
Language Arts and
　Humanities
Social Studies
GRADES
7-12
PLT PRINCIPLES
3. Cultural Contexts
7. Lifestyles
CONCEPTS
3.4111 Forest Model
　for Creative
　Expression
3.412 Cultural
　Concept of Forests
3.4121 Cultural
　Artifacts
3.4122 Environmental
　Literature
7.11 Culture and
　Resource
　Management
SKILLS
I. Gaining
　Information
IV. Critical Thinking
V. Problem Solving

VARIATION or EXTENSION

After reading and/or viewing some of the references cited under Resources, encourage students to try one of the following projects:

Create a myth or legend about a tree or forest from the viewpoint of an American Indian, an early American settler from Europe, an early American settler from the Orient, a New Zealand Maori tribesperson, an Eskimo, or an African tribesperson.

Create a piece of jewelry using forest materials such as parts of cones, feathers, animal bones, wood, seeds, or nuts. Then write a legend which describes the significance of this piece of jewelry in an imaginary or a real culture.

Share the results of the projects in class and discuss some of the questions posed in the initial activity.

Ticky Tacky

27

OBJECTIVE

Students will be able to explore environmental issues and concerns expressed through the medium of music.

ACTIVITY

Play popular recordings of any era that have "environmental" themes. For example, recordings such as John Denver's "To the Wild Country," Joni Mitchell's "Paradise Paved," or Pete Seeger's version of the song, "Little Boxes," by Malvina Reynolds, might be used.

Discussing reactions to the song in small groups and compiling lists of their reactions, students can then compare their lists in the large group discussion which follows.

In the large group, ask the students to hypothesize what conditions might have initiated the composing of such a song. Try to establish an information base to determine the accuracy and reasonableness of the concerns expressed in the song. Establishing this information base may require some research by the students.

If the students determine that the concerns are both accurate and reasonable — and if they determine that the base for those concerns still exists — they can suggest possible means for resolution of the problems involved.

VARIATION

Compose a song expressing real concerns you have — or celebrating aspects you value — about current environmental uses of renewable and/or nonrenewable resources.

SUBJECTS
Fine Arts
Social Studies
GRADES
7-12
PLT PRINCIPLES
3. Cultural Contexts
4. Societal Perspectives on Issues
CONCEPTS
3.2 Cultural Effects on Resources
3.3 History and Environment
3.4 People and Biosphere
3.4121 Cultural Artifacts
3.42 Environmental Perspectives
3.422 Belief Systems
4.311 Influence of Artistic Expressions
SKILLS
I. Gaining Information
VI. Valuing

28 Cartoons and Headlines

OBJECTIVE

Students will write a humorous and unlikely headline about some phase of forest management and related issues and be able to give reasons why the headline is improbable.

ACTIVITY

Ask students to write "not-likely-to-happen-headlines" with an accompanying lead paragraph relating to the origin of some forest issue or use of some forest resource. Examples are:

Lumber Harvested in National Parks
Wilderness Organizations Want Grand Canyon For Landfill
Timber Interests Advocate Raising Home Interest Rates
Allowable Cut Can Exceed Growth Indefinitely, Says Genetic Expert
Decaying Organisms Unnecessary, Says Forest Ecologist

Discuss why each headline is unlikely. What conditions would have to occur before the headlines would be probable? Are any of these conditions likely to happen in the future?

VARIATION

Ask students to study editorial cartoons, and discuss their purpose and value as a form of communication. Then ask the students to draw humorous cartoons about a local or national forest-related environmental issue such as land use, wilderness, or recycling. Students might also take existing cartoons and write new punch lines, then giving reasons why the circumstance or point of view is improbable.

RESOURCE

See "Teaching Environmental Education with a Focus on Values" by Clifford Knapp, *Journal of Environmental Education*, Summer 1972. Also see other Resources listed.

Wasted Words

OBJECTIVE

Students will be able to describe the advantages and disadvantages of using emotionally-loaded language when attempting to communicate effectively.

ACTIVITY

Many people, when hearing or talking about environmental issues, do not have an adequate understanding of the terminology used. A Gallup Poll taken in 1972 interviewed 388 people earning a minimum of $15,000 a year with backgrounds including some college education. Survey results showed that not one person interviewed could define correctly "climax forest," "tree farm," "sustained yield," "conservation," or "solid waste," and 35 percent of the group had no idea of the meaning of "clearcutting."

Another semantic complication is the tendency during heated debate to use words or phrases with connotative meanings which tend to obscure the real issues. The activities suggested here are designed to assist students to recognize and deal with such "loaded" words and phrases.

Ask each student to clip out and bring to class an editorial, newspaper story, or brief magazine article about a forest-related environmental issue. Next ask the students to choose from the examples all the words which carry highly emotional overtones — words such as "ravaged" and "plundered."

List all of these emotion-laden words on the blackboard. Divide your class into small groups of three or four students each and assign several of the words to each group. Ask each group to define its assigned words, both denotatively and connotatively as they were used in the example. You may wish to ask several groups to define some of the same words to get varying interpretations of their connotations.

After the definitions have been completed, share them in class and discuss questions such as these:

Which interpretation, the denotative or the connotative, lends more clarity to the message of the written editorial or article?

Clarify the difference between the accuracy of a message and its purpose.

How do you verify accuracy? What criteria might you use?

Which interpretation appears to more effectively convey the writer's message?

Does the use of words or phrases which evoke emotional responses obscure the issue involved? If so, how?

Do different sources and media have varying responsibilities to be accurate?

SUBJECTS
Language Arts and
   Humanities
Journalism
Social Studies

GRADES
7-12

PLT PRINCIPLES
3. Cultural Contexts
4. Societal
   Perspectives on
   Issues

CONCEPTS
3.42 Environmental
   Perspectives
3.421 Cultural
   Perceptions
4.12 Language as
   Influence Tool
4.13 Value-Loaded
   Language

SKILL
II. Communication

29

Ask each of the students to summarize the advantages and disadvantages of using emotionally-loaded language when attempting to communicate effectively.

VARIATIONS or EXTENSIONS

1. Repeat the preceding activity using spoken words in films instead of written examples. Show some of the films listed under Resources. You might show a film first without the images, listening only to the sound track! Ask the students, working in small groups, to describe the sequence of visuals they think will accompany the narration. They can share their results, showing the images on storyboards and hanging them around the classroom.

   Then watch the film, including both visuals and sound. Discuss the difference in what the filmmakers created and what the students expected, describing the advantages and disadvantages of using emotionally-laden language. Some students may want to make their own films!

2. Ask each student to write two newspaper editorials on a local land-use or environmental issue. The first editorial should be highly emotional and subjective in tone and the second in a "just the facts" objective style. (An alternative is to use a Letters-to-the-Editor format and submit the students' work to the local newspaper.)

   The students might share their editorials in class and discuss: Which style is more effective more often? Why? Which style is the easiest to understand? How do you measure "understanding"?

3. Give students these pairs of words:

Perception — Awareness
Biosphere — Ecosystem
Deciduous — Coniferous
Urban — Rural
Conservation — Preservation
Freedom — Regulation
Government — Corporation
Environment — Nature
Wild — Managed
Supply — Demand
Renewable — Depletable
Harvest — Reforestation
Right — Privilege

Ask each student to write down his definitions of these words as they relate to natural resources and the environment; compare the definitions. Discuss:

How are the definitions similar and how do they differ?

Which definitions are most affected by personal experience?

How do the denotative meanings of the words relate to the connotative meanings? Do some single words or pairs evoke more emotional response than others? Does the intensity of the response appear to be related to a personal experience? How?

Ask each student to find and bring to class a brief editorial or article which uses many of these words. The students are to identify words or phrases with connotative meanings which may tend to obscure the writer's message. Then they could rewrite the editorial or article, eliminating as many of the emotionally-loaded words and phrases as possible. Discuss with your class the impact the rewrites have on effective communication of the article's message.

30

Environmental Editorials

OBJECTIVE

Students will be able to recognize techniques of propaganda and persuasion used in the mass media.

ACTIVITY

Give this background information to your students:

You live in Woodsville, a medium-size community where logging and related occupations are one of the major industries. The West Lumber Co. has announced that timber on the state-owned Dennis Tract will be cut in a few weeks. The cutting method will be "group selection," a process in which all trees (for example, three or four trees) in a small area are removed. The management goal is a sustained yield of timber from the area.

The Dennis Tract is not the only large forested area near Woodsville, but it is the closest and most accessible. It is used by many picnickers, hunters, school study groups, fishermen, and others each year. Because of the energy shortage, this recreational use is expected to increase.

West Lumber Co., which purchased the timber from the state, has agreed to several conditions in response to concerns expressed by the community. It promises to leave certain choice areas untouched and to provide access to them; to conduct logging operations in a way which will minimize aesthetic damage during harvest, and to reforest as soon as possible after logging.

Public opinion is divided in Woodsville. Timber industry employees favor the logging plan. The Board of Education is not sure which is of more value, the natural area for study or the state funds they will receive as revenue from the logging operation. Some sports and wildlife interest groups favor the plan because it may increase the population of certain animals, particularly large game animals such as deer. Other sports, wildlife, and nature study organizations oppose the logging. They believe the site has more value as a natural area and are worried that logging and road-building will harm some wildlife, especially fish, and also the water quality of the streams.

The company's position is that it has met all the legal requirements stipulated in its sales contract and, moreover, has made additional efforts to protect values the community considers important. It plans to go ahead with logging operations but a local citizens' coalition still hopes to be able to prevent the harvest.

(Continued)

Ask students to assume the roles of local editorial researchers on the *Woodsville World*. Their managing editor has not decided which position the respected and influential newspaper should support on this issue. The editor has asked staff members to write two editorials, one for and one against the West Lumber Co. plans.

Students should write their editorials to make them as convincing as possible. They may use freely any value-laden words or phrases which they believe will contribute to the effectiveness of their argument. Other propaganda techniques, such as stating some facts and ignoring others, may be used but students may not say anything which is untrue. Researching factual data should be encouraged.

After the editorials are completed, share them in class to determine how choice of words, selection of facts, and other techniques were used to build a case for one viewpoint or another. Then discuss:

Did the value-laden words or phrases tend to clarify or cloud the issue?

Did you notice any obvious omissions of significant facts in any of the most effective editorials? What were they?

Have you recognized any of the opinion-molding techniques you used also being used by the local media in newspaper, radio, or television editorials?

EXTENSION

Investigate regulations affecting logging practices. Regulations can exist at both national and local levels. Through research including contact with experts representing diverse points of view related to forest management, investigate and discuss issues related to the following questions:

Given the base of information you have established in this hypothetical situation, if you lived in Woodsville, would you support the West Lumber Co. or the citizens' coalition? Might your position be different if you lived somewhere else? Describe the bases for your response to each question.

Would you have a different opinion if the company owned the land instead of the state? Why or why not? How would your opinion change?

Are there other alternatives available for the Dennis Tract besides logging or not logging? If so, how might the community conflict be resolved to the satisfaction of the company, the coalition, and the entire community?

How might this conflict be resolved most reasonably to the maximum long-term benefit for all involved, including wildlife, vegetation, other natural resources, and human interests?

What implications of the problem might there be for people living in other places in the United States? In other parts of the world?

31

Environmental Advertisements

OBJECTIVE

Students will become aware of forest management problems and be able to describe public relations efforts related to these issues which are made by large corporations and other special interest groups.

ACTIVITY

Ask your students to find and bring to class a newspaper or magazine advertisement, or a piece of direct mail dealing with an environmental issue relating to forests. Encourage the students to try to find some of these ads from industry and some from conservation or other special interest groups. If there is a local controversy or a land-use issue before the public, the students may be able to find statements from different groups on the same issue. Sources for advertisements could include newspapers and periodicals such as *Natural History, Smithsonian, Harper's, Fortune, Saturday Review, Newsweek, U. S. News & World Report*, and *Time*, and other references listed in the Resources section of the PLT materials.

In class, ask the students to evaluate each advertisement on (1) its emotional appeal, (2) its factual basis, (3) the value system it conveys, (4) the credibility of the arguments stated, and (5) the use of propaganda techniques to help communicate the desired message or objective of the advertisement.

After students have written their evaluations, discuss:

To which advertisements do you give the most credence? Why?
Of any two opposing advertisements, do you agree entirely with either? If not, why? If so, do you disagree with all the arguments presented in the other ad?
How are the ads similar and how do they differ?
What seems to be the purpose behind each group's ad? For example, is it to provide information, to justify a practice, to counter charges?

VARIATION

Play *Propaganda* with your students (see Resources section) until they can identify several types of persuasive techniques. Then ask each student to collect magazine and newspaper advertisements and articles concerning a subject like local forest/environmental issues, building materials, architecture and home design, and land-use planning.

Ask each student to prepare a scrapbook of the ads and articles, identifying the techniques used to persuade the reader. A written paragraph of explanation could accompany each scrapbook entry discussing its (1) appeal, (2) symbols, (3) effectiveness, (4) purpose, and (5) sponsor.

With your class, talk about how propaganda differs from factual and objective communication and if and when propaganda may be legitimate and acceptable.

EXTENSION

Locate billboards in your community. Take or draw pictures of a representative sample of these billboards, for use as a visual record related to this activity. Also take notes for use in later discussion. Your notes might include the following:

- Purpose of the billboard
- General visual appeal
- Intended audience
- Compatibility with surroundings
- Who the sponsor is
- Your judgment of the billboard's effectiveness

Discuss the economic, aesthetic, and environmental trade-offs related to billboards as communication devices.

SOCIETAL PERSPECTIVES ON ISSUES **4**

32

Participatory Democracy

OBJECTIVE

Students will be able to describe how they can make input into resource management policies and decisions through government agencies, special-interest organizations, and citizen groups.

ACTIVITY

This country was founded on the principle that each of its citizens has the right to participate in the policy-setting and decision-making processes.

Then, as government bureaucracies grew in size and became more centralized, decision making was left increasingly to the "experts." Recently, however, the citizen-group movements exemplified by Common Cause and consumer advocate groups, have sought to regain some of the participatory rights which had atrophied. This trend has clearly been evident in issues and policies affecting the environment. Early in this century, there were only seven national and two state conservation organizations. By 1960, these numbers had grown to 78 national and 236 state organizations, and the 1977 *Conservation Directory*, published by the National Wildlife Federation (see Bibliography) lists 342 international, national, and interstate organizations and commissions and 177 state and territorial agencies and citizens' groups concerned with natural resource use and management.

This activity is planned to help students understand the roles and responsibilities of government agencies and of special-interest groups with regard to forest resource management.

Divide the class into groups of three or four students each. Assign each group the task of designing a coat of arms for a specific citizen conservation group, government resource management agency, or forest industry.

The coat of arms should have six sections, each with a symbol representing the students' opinions on the group's:

- Image it has of itself
- Image the general public has of it
- Its greatest immediate concern
- Its overall goals
- What it sees as its greatest obstacle to achieving its goals
- What it might imagine the world would be like without it

Dear Joy,
I will send
Project Wild
Tomorrow!

9/13/88

The symbols could be arranged on a large pa[...] this:

Use the coat-of-arms designs as a basis for a discussion concerning:

The image of the citizens' conservation groups compared to that of the industrial organizations and of the agencies.

How the way a person perceives these groups might affect one's ability to judge their actions.

Whether the present qualities of any of these groups differ substantially from their past qualities. If so, how and why?

Whether and how the roles of the groups in society differ, and whether the roles have changed over time. How? Why?

Follow up this activity with one of the variations, or ask your students to do research on the groups for which they made shields to find out how closely their perception matches the organization's true goals and behavior. They may then revise their coat-of-arms to reflect the new information. Finally, based on their investigations, ask the students to describe the means by which people can make input into resource management and policies and decisions.

VARIATIONS or EXTENSIONS

Invite a local representative of a citizen conservation or environmental group to visit your class. The guest might be from the Audubon Society, National Wildlife Federation, Sierra Club, Nature Conservancy, Friends of the Earth, outdoor sports group, or any one of other citizens' organizations. (Addresses are listed in the PLT Resources section of these materials.)

Involve the entire class in composing key questions to be asked by four students in a Meet-the-Press type of interview with the guest. Schedule the interview so that there will be time left for other class members to ask spontaneous questions from the floor.

Sample questions are:

1. What is your group's main objective?
2. Is the organization statewide, national, or international?
3. How many members does the organization have?
4. Is membership growing or declining?
5. Does the group lobby elected government officials? If so, how often and in what manner? What percentage of your annual budget is spent on lobbying activities?
6. Does your group publish a newsletter or magazine?
7. What technical expertise does your group have available?
8. What is your group's annual budget?
9. What are some of your group's major accomplishments?
10. On what areas are you currently focusing?

This exercise then could be repeated, substituting as the class guest a representative from a government resource management agency, such as the U.S. Forest Service, National Park Service, or the State Department of Natural Resources. A third interview could be held with a guest from an industrial association or company such as the American Forest Institute, National Forest Products Association, St. Regis, Georgia-Pacific, Boise Cascade, or Weyerhaeuser.

Questions for government agency representatives might include:

1. What are your agency's responsibilities?
2. Do these responsibilities overlap with those of other governmental agencies?
3. If this is a federal agency, in what cabinet level department is it included? Who is the department secretary? Who is the agency's director? Is the director elected or appointed? If appointed, by whom?
4. What is the present director's professional background and how does it relate to the responsibilities of the agency? (For example, is the chief forester a professional forester?)
5. What is the agency's annual budget and how is it allocated?
6. How can the public make input into this agency's policy and decisions?
7. Whose responsibility is it to see that the agency carries out the will of the public?
8. How does the agency know the will of the public?
9. Does the agency attempt to educate or inform the public? How?

(Continued)

Some suggested questions for industry representatives are:

1. How large is your organization? (For a company, this could include its rank in national sales and the number of states in which it has operations.)
2. How long has your organization been in business?
3. Does your company (or association) lobby or in other ways attempt to influence legislation? If so, how much do you spend on lobbying in dollars or in percentage of sales or profit?
4. Does your company (association) attempt to influence public opinion? How?
5. What technical expertise do your employees have which qualifies them to deal with the areas of resource management in which your company (association) is involved?
6. Have conditions or policies affecting resource management changed significantly since the beginning of the so-called "environmental decade?" What, in your opinion, caused these changes?
7. What are the major environmentally related issues and problems facing your company (association)?

Finally, use class discussion to compare each group's resources, expertise, role, responsibility, authority, and attitudes. You might include such questions as the following:

Do citizen groups seem to represent the public interest any better than government agencies do or private industry does? Cite evidence to support your opinion.

Does the decision-making process appear to be improved or impeded by input from a citizens' conservation group?

Are quick decisions good or bad? Are slow decisions good or bad? Support your responses.

What conditions determine whether a decision concerning the environment is good or bad?

Since there is a wide variety in organizations, agencies, and in corporate policies, you may wish to choose a single resource (perhaps forests, wildlife, or wilderness) as the basis for these interviews. This will help students become aware of the many overlapping authorities and concerns involved. Given the interest, you could repeat the process for a significant series of resources; for example, forests, water, oil.

Once the interviews, discussion, and related research have been completed, ask the students to summarize the means by which they as citizens can make input into resource management policies and decisions.

33

Who Runs This Place?

OBJECTIVE

Students will be able to describe the means by which a law might be changed as a result of a change in environmental practice.

ACTIVITY

Some changes that would improve environmental quality require changes in or additions to laws. To initiate these changes, citizens must know which officials have jurisdiction over what areas and the extent of their authority. This activity explores environmentally related laws and government authority at the local level.

Ask your students to devise a question about a current environmental concern in their community. Some possibilities are:

- Why don't we have more trees?
- Why don't we have more parks or open spaces?
- Why isn't paper being recycled?
- Does our community have a land-use plan?

If the students want to identify several problems, they might divide into small groups with each group investigating one of the problems.

Next the students might go to their local government offices to find out:

1. Who is in charge (of planting more trees, establishing more parks or dealing with whatever the problem is)?
2. What statute forms the basis for this person's authority?
3. What branch of community government administers the problem area?
4. What is the source of revenue for this government department? How and when are its funds budgeted?
5. In what ways is the department attempting to solve the problem? If no attempts are being made, why not?
6. Does a proposed solution to the problem require a change in a law or other regulation? If so, would the change be in municipal or county codes, standards, zoning regulations, or what?
7. How is the law or regulation changed?

After students have completed their investigations, the class as a whole can select a single problem from among those studied and attempt to solve it.

(Continued)

VARIATION

Brainstorm with your students to produce a list of factors which might be involved in the improvement of residential environments. Factors mentioned could include zoning, sewage treatment, tree planting, remodeling homes.

Students could use this list to develop a questionnaire for a community survey to find out whether any of the factors are local problems. Sample questions are:

1. Does our community have sufficient greenbelts?
2. Is there a housing shortage?
3. Is a comprehensive land-use plan needed?
4. Are sewage disposal and treatment facilities adequate?

Students can administer the questionnaire to community residents and tabulate the answers they receive. Based on these data, they can select the most frequently mentioned problem. As a class, they might attempt to solve that problem, researching laws and local ordinances — and processes for changing these — related to the problem.

34

Urban Open Space

OBJECTIVE

Students will be able to describe zoning regulations which cover local, natural, open-space areas.

ACTIVITY

Aldo Leopold once summed up his feelings about urban development in these words:

> . . . if in a city we had six vacant lots available to the youngsters of a certain neighborhood for playing ball, it might be development to build houses on the first, and the second, and the third, and the fourth and even the fifth, but when we build houses on the last one, we forget what houses are for. The sixth house would not be development at all, but rather . . . stupidity.

This activity explores some of the reasons for urban open space, methods available for maintaining urban open space, and the implications of the use of various methods.

Ask your students to walk, bicycle, ride the bus or some other form of public transportation — or if there is no other reasonable alternative — drive around their community to locate at least four areas maintained by the community as open space. The areas can include parks, wooded areas, ponds, or similar spaces.

After the students have identified the areas, they should visit the city or county zoning office to determine (1) how the spaces are zoned, (2) whether there are any plans to develop these areas for residential or commercial purposes, and (3) if development is planned, whether the change would require that the area be rezoned, and (4) what zoning regulations affect community open space.

After all the information has been collected, discuss with your class the way in which zoning codes dictate land use by stipulating the type of use a particular piece of land may serve. For example, zoning may classify an area as industrial, commercial, or residential and reserve it for low, medium, or high population density.

(Continued)

Explore some of these questions:

How may zoning laws benefit and how may they hinder planners? Builders? Residents? (Include children, aged, families, transients, others.) Land developers? Landowners?

Is there a correlation between strict zoning laws and desirable environmental and social conditions?

What methods besides zoning could be used to preserve open lands?

If we accept land-use regulation by means of zoning, what must we give up and what do we gain?

If you owned a piece of open-space land, how would you feel if zoning regulations prohibited you from developing it? If development was not prohibited, but most of the other community residents wanted the land to remain as open space, would you go ahead and develop your property anyway? What are the reasons for your decision? Would rising property taxes have an effect on your decision? What other factors might there be reason to consider? What differences are there between short-term and long-term implications of your decisions?

Where To Plant

OBJECTIVE

Students will be able to describe how their local government functions and to demonstrate how citizen input can affect government decisions.

ACTIVITY

If possible, distribute school cameras or provide film for students' cameras. Divide your class into groups with a student photographer assigned to each. As a class-time or after-school project, ask each group to find a publicly owned area in the community that would be enhanced by the addition of trees. Ask them to take pictures of the area. Have the film developed and display the pictures in class. If no cameras are available, students may draw pictures of the area they find instead. Even with use of cameras, it can be useful for the students to sketch and make notes of the area.

Ask each group to submit a written report including the location of the area it photographed or sketched, and the students' reasons for believing trees would improve this area. Ask them to recommend what kinds and how many trees they think should be planted, the exact locations where they should be planted, a statement of any environmental impact, the costs involved in planting and caring for the trees, and an estimate of the continuing care required.

Ask representatives from the groups to then ask permission to attend a meeting of the local governing body in order to present their reports to officials responsible for the public land use.

If the officials agree to supply funds for the tree-planting project, the students might volunteer to supply their labor for the job. If the officials seem to support the idea but have no funds to pay for it, see if other sources can be found if the project is approved. Student photographers could take pictures of the same areas after trees are added and show the "before and after" photos at another city council meeting. Pictures and a short news release about the project also could be submitted to the local newspaper.

If city officials do not approve the idea or the funds for this project, the students might request a formal statement providing reasons for the decision. If the problem is a need for more public support, students might draw up a petition and conduct a door-to-door campaign for signatures. If the campaign is successful, students could go back to the city council, present their petition, and ask again for the trees. If these attempts don't succeed, the students might organize and conduct a fund-raising drive for tree-planting money. Again, an attempt can be made to publicize the students' efforts in the local paper.

(Continued)

EXTENSION

Ask students to read and respond to this situation:

. . . I think it would be great if my neighbor would plant about five rows of evergreen trees along his property line and mine. There isn't any room on my side of the line because my house is too close to it.

Through class discussion consider:

Is it fair to ask my neighbor, at his expense, to plant trees which would be of more benefit to me than to him?

If the property between us were owned by the city, would it be fair to ask other taxpayers to pay for trees to benefit me? Would it be fair if it benefited any group of property owners?

Would it be fair for a group of property owners to join me in asking the community's other taxpayers to plant and care for trees for my benefit? Would this be the situation if the class asked for trees in the areas students have identified?

Is it fair for a group to do what an individual cannot legally do? If not, why not? If so, under what conditions?

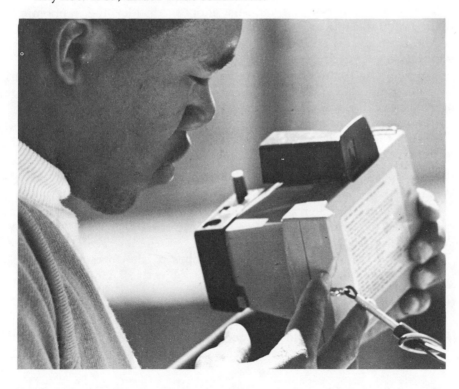

36

Ownership Objectives

SUBJECTS
Social Studies
Vocational
Agriculture
GRADES
11-12
PLT PRINCIPLES
4. Societal
Perspectives on
Issues
2. Diversity of Forest
Roles
CONCEPTS
4.4 Variety in Use
2.1 Forest Uses and
Values
SKILLS
I. Gaining
Information
V. Problem Solving
II. Communication

OBJECTIVE

Students will be able to describe the difference between proprietary and custodial philosophies of land management.

ACTIVITY

Divide your class into three groups. Ask each group to develop a goal statement and ten management guidelines for the same parcel of land.

Assume that this parcel of land is under single ownership, either private or public, and that it is suitable for either a national park and/or wilderness area, a national forest, or a commercial use.

Ask one group of students to create its goal and guidelines from the viewpoint of the National Park Service; the second from the viewpoint of the U.S. Forest Service; and the third from the viewpoint of private industry.

The Park and Forest Service proposals should be in accord with the "Organic Acts" which established these agencies and with any other subsequent mandates established by legislation. (For example, one of these for the Forest Service is the Multiple Use-Sustained Yield Act of 1960.)

The group representing industry should consider the economic realities and social pressures affecting private enterprise.

All three groups should take into account the growing impact of population growth and increasing consumption of resources.

To help your students understand the goals of each of these "ownerships," encourage them to read or view some of the materials listed under Resources and also to interview, if possible, a local representative of the park and forest services and of the forest industry.

When the groups have completed their assignments, ask the students to discuss questions such as the following:

How do the goals and guidelines of the three groups differ?

What other groups might recommend different goals and guidelines; for example, the Sierra Club, the League of Women Voters, the Chamber of Commerce, a Native American tribe?

What forces (such as history, economics, aesthetics, ecology) may determine the values each group attaches to the forest? How do these forces appear to influence their objectives? How are they reflected in the management of their lands?

What are the differences and the similarities between publicly managed and privately managed lands?

Do public and private land management influence each other? What are the effects and pressures of each on the other?

(Continued)

Given that each of these goal and management policies accurately reflects the general tendencies of these major groups today, attempt to create a fourth and "ideal" set of guidelines from the view of the greatest overall good for the greatest number of people.

EXTENSION

Select a real parcel of land in your community and encourage the students to try to apply their ideal guidelines to this area. How is the situation different from the hypothetical one? What considerations will have to be included that did not come up in the discussions of the hypothetical situation?

37

We Can Work It Out?!

OBJECTIVE

Students will be able to identify compatible kinds of land uses and to describe their criteria for judging compatibility.

ACTIVITY

Hold a brainstorming session with your class with the objective of developing four lists relating to land use.

The first list should include *personal uses*, such as fishing, hunting, hiking, camping, rock climbing, and snowmobiling, which can take place in a forest environment.

The second list should include *commercial uses*, such as logging and mining.

The third list should include and reflect *community values*, such as watershed protection, wildlife habitat, and aesthetics, which the same forest might provide.

Focus the fourth list on identifying *interest groups* that would be likely to represent or promote each of the uses or values mentioned in the first three categories. Examples are motorcycle clubs, environmental groups, hunting and fishing clubs, forest industry organizations, ski-resort owners and developers, and real estate brokers. Ask students to role-play members of these groups as they construct a "conflict matrix."

After conflicts have been identified by the matrix, groups with incompatible self-interests can meet to attempt to work out a solution. While attempting to reconcile their conflicts, students could consider:

Are any of the activities always in conflict or does the incompatibility vary with time and in intensity?

What characteristics of the conflicting activities make them incompatible?

What criteria are you using to determine incompatibility?

Do you believe the conflicts will become more or less frequent in the future? Why?

What must each group be willing to sacrifice in order to reach a compromise?

What are the benefits of each compromise to the interest groups, the individual, the community, the rest of the nation?

EXTENSION

Groups which have worked out solutions to their conflicts may submit their recommendations to actual groups in the community which are experiencing similar conflicts "for real." Ask the community organizations to read and comment on the students' proposals.

What Is Wise Use?

OBJECTIVE

Students will be able to define the terms conservation and preservation.

ACTIVITY

A dramatic difference in goals frequently separates those who would preserve the environment from those who would develop its resources for economic purposes, including some kinds of recreation. Both factions often vigorously insist they are conservationist.

This activity explores the value systems represented by each position in an attempt to understand more fully what each means by "wise use." The activity is also designed to assist students in clarifying the meaning of the terms conservation and preservation.

Show students a photographic slide or print of people engaging in some sort of recreational activity — picnicking, taking photos, sightseeing, skiing or backpacking in a forest setting. Discuss:

Do the students know anyone who uses the forest in these ways?

What needs do these experiences and activities satisfy? List the needs, such as "desire for solitude" on the blackboard.

What values are exemplified by these forms of use?

What is conservation? What is preservation? Establish definitions for each.

Repeat the exercise, substituting pictures of other uses of a forest setting, involving "harvesting" the forest resources. Discuss:

How do the needs and values related to the first category of uses differ from those in the second?

Are any of these uses, or the values they represent, in conflict? If so, which?

Is the conflict always present or does it disappear at certain times? For example, while the forest regrows to fill a cut-over area, timber harvesting may no longer conflict with camping, bird-watching, or hunting.

Which of the uses would you classify as:

- wasteful consumption
- reasonable consumption
- a form of preservation
- a form of conservation?

Are there any relationships among these classifications? For example, is it possible for a consumption use also to be an example of preservation? In what circumstances? How might these circumstances differ in different settings? At different times?

Which of these activities appear to be wise uses of the forest resource? For the short term? For the long term? On what criteria do you base your decision?

SUBJECTS
Social Studies
Language Arts and
Humanities
GRADES
7-12
PLT PRINCIPLES
4. Societal
Perspectives on
Issues
2. Diversity of Forest
Roles
5. Management and
Interdependence of
Natural Resources
CONCEPTS
4.13 Value-Loaded
Language
4.14 Consideration of
Reality
2.1 Forest Uses and
Values
2.124 Aesthetic
Benefits
5.1 Interdependence
of Resources
SKILLS
I. Gaining
Information
II. Communication
III. Social
Participation

39

How Much Is Enough?

OBJECTIVE

Students will be able to list reasons for and against the designation of additional wilderness areas.

ACTIVITY

This activity examines the criteria for establishing wilderness areas, particularly in the United States, and addresses the question of how much more land, if any, should be preserved for such areas. At the time of printing of this PLT activity, nationwide hearings were being held in the United States to determine what lands would be designated wilderness, the intent being to establish and protect these lands for posterity. Students can assemble information about the present status of wilderness areas, or the following can be used to introduce the activity. (Refer to "Lovin' It to Death" for related activities.)

In the years between 1900 and 1977, the National Park system has grown from 3,300,000 acres to 31,123,189 acres, with some 20,014,417 acres of this in natural areas. In addition the Wilderness Preservation System has established 14,443,705 acres (approximately one million being held jointly with the Park System). Thus the total of federal land presently legislatively preserved as parks and wilderness is approximately 33,337,900 acres.

The United States has a total of 470 million acres of forest land, or approximately 20.3 percent of the total land area. Urban and paved over areas (cities and roads) cover approximately 72 million acres (3.1 percent of total U.S. land area). Thus the total area devoted to legislated parks and wilderness areas is a little less than one half as much as we are using for cities and roads.

In the spring of 1977, there were before the Congress proposals for an additional 73 wilderness areas totaling another 24,400,000 acres.

Divide your class into two groups. Ask one group to advocate and defend the designation of a new wilderness area based on their perception of the need to preserve such areas. Ask the other to oppose the proposal based on their advocacy of plans for intensive use and development. Using a geologic or road map, help your students locate an area that might be used as the focus for this study, ideally an area in their state that has been or might be proposed as a "forever wild" wilderness area. If students decide there is no suitable area in their state, help them identify one in another part of the country, such as the Everglades in Florida or the North Cascades in Washington State. For information about the proposed areas, write to the addresses given at the end of this activity.

(Continued)

Each group can research and prepare testimony to be considered by a hearing board. Information should include the viewpoints of as many affected groups as possible: motel and restaurant owners, game and fish department personnel, gasoline dealers, guides, lumber companies, campers, backpackers, photographers, hunters and fishermen and women, recreational equipment dealers, miners, off-road vehicle owners, sightseers who travel by car, skiers, natural scientists, and others. Individuals representing strong preservationist points of view should define their positions clearly, as should individuals representing economic interests and concerned about a trend toward establishing wilderness areas.

Once the students have researched their various points of view, convene a meeting of the hearing board. Other students, teachers, or parents could be invited to class to serve on this board. Establish a chairperson to convene the meeting, recognizing participants to make their presentations. Presentations could be limited to no more than five minutes each. Once presentations are made, suggest that questions and discussion include attention to the following:

What activities are allowed and/or encouraged in most wilderness areas? (For example, hunting, grazing, recreation activities, and scientific research.)

What activities are prohibited in most wilderness areas? (For example, skiing, timbering, and road use.)

Are there other lands available where activities prohibited in wilderness areas could be allowed? What lands are these, and under what circumstances are they available?

Are there activities presently allowed in most wilderness areas that possibly should be prohibited? Provide examples, and reasons.

Should the number of visitors to wilderness areas be limited? Why and how?

What would be the impact of the proposed wild areas in this activity on the local economy in the short, and in the long run? How might this differ in different situations?

What are some alternatives to the "forever wild" classification? What are the short-term and long-term implications of such alternatives?

The hearing board members could offer a decision based on the testimony and discussion they have heard. They could also ask the two groups to try to work out a compromise to solve this problem. If a compromise is accepted, continue discussion to determine what each side may have sacrificed. Does the compromise result in the development of the area, or of parts of it, beyond a "forever wild" state? If to achieve a compromise, some type of development is allowed in all situations involving wilderness vs development, what might be the net effect in the long run? Is this an equitable trade-off? Why or why not?

39

(Continued)

EXTENSIONS

1. Create a map of the United States showing all presently established wilderness areas in one color; all areas under consideration for such designation in another. If none are under consideration, all having been established or none pending, contrast wilderness areas from a previous time period to the present. (*Note:* Maps of present parks and wilderness are available from the Government Printing Office. Wall Map of the United States showing Distribution of Federal Lands, in National Parks, Monuments, Forests and Wilderness Areas, U.S. Department of the Interior, Stock No. 024011-00019-4, $3, and National Parks of the United States Map and Guide, Stock No. 2405-00546, 35c)

2. Find out similarities and differences between (a) national wilderness areas, (b) national wildlife refuges, (c) national parks, (d) national forests, (e) national monuments, and (f) national estuaries. What activities are generally allowed in each? What activities are generally prohibited in each? What agencies are responsible for management of each? What problems, if any, are presently affecting the management of each?

(Continued)

RESOURCES

For information about wilderness areas in the National Park System, write to Director, National Park Service, U.S. Department of the Interior, Washington, D.C. 20240; for those in the National Wildlife Refuge System, write to the Director of the Fish and Wildlife Service, U.S. Department of the Interior, Washington, D.C. 20240; for those that may come under the Bureau of Land Management, write to the chief of the Bureau, also in the Department of the Interior; and for the areas within the National Forests, write to the Chief, Forest Service, U.S. Department of Agriculture, Post Office Box 2417, Washington, D.C. 20013.

The article, "Overview of the National Wilderness Preservation System," by Dwight R. McCurdy in the May 1977 issue of the Journal of Forestry provided some of the information for this activity and would be a very useful reference for the activity.

The following is excerpted from the Wilderness Act, September 3, 1964, passed by the U.S. Congress:

"A wilderness, in contrast with those areas where man and his own works dominate the landscape, is hereby recognized as an area where the earth and its community of life are untrammeled by man, where man himself is a visitor who does not remain. An area of wilderness is further defined to mean in this Act an area of undeveloped Federal land retaining its primeval character and influence, without permanent improvements of human habitation, which is protected and managed so as to preserve its natural conditions and which (1) generally appears to have been affected primarily by the forces of nature, with the imprint of man's work substantially unnoticeable; (2) has outstanding opportunities for solitude or a primitive and unconfined type of recreation; (3) has at least five thousand acres of land or is of sufficient size as to make practicable its preservation and use in an unimpaired condition; and (4) may also contain ecological, geological, or other features of scientific, educational, scenic, or historical value."

For additional references, see the Resources section of the PLT materials.

5

MANAGEMENT AND INTERDEPENDENCE OF NATURAL RESOURCES

Soil Compaction

OBJECTIVE

Students will be able to state the relationship between soil compaction and water infiltration rates.

ACTIVITY

Materials:

A dowel rod about 10 inches (25 centimeters) long, sharpened at one end

A tin can, such as a #5 juice can, with top and bottom removed; the bead or lip cut off one end and the edge dulled with emery cloth or sandpaper

A liter or quart measuring container

A stopwatch or a watch with a second hand

Procedure:

Divide your class into groups of three students each. Each group will need the materials listed above. Each group is to test soil compactness in several locations near the school, such as the playground, football field, or other open area. The test method is to push the sharpened end of the dowel rod into the ground by exerting as much force as possible with the flat palm of the hand until the threshhold of pain is reached. *Note:* To avoid the safety hazard this method presents, see the equipment and procedure explanation in *Outdoor Activities for Environmental Studies.* (See Resources.)

(Continued)

Ask each group to measure the depth the dowel rod can be pushed in at each site and record the data.

Next, each group should twist the can, sharp edge down, into the soil, until it extends below the surface vegetation or litter, and pour one liter (or one quart) of water into the can. Ask students to record the length of time needed for the water to sink completely into the soil.

After the field exercises are completed, discuss:

Which type of soil allows the fastest infiltration? Which the slowest?

How does the degree of soil compaction affect the infiltration rate?

What effect does increased compaction have on surface vegetation? On soil erosion?

What effect does surface vegetation have on compaction? On erosion?

Would you expect some soils to be more susceptible to compaction than others? If not, why? If so, which soils would be the most and the least likely to compact? Why?

Is soil more likely to compact when it is wet or dry? (This question may require more experimentation.)

How might soil be compacted? What factors might help soil resist compaction? (Experiment with some factors to see if they work.)

Soil compaction on recreation sites and trails is a problem. What could be done to minimize it? Are such remedies being tried? (Contact your local forest and park recreation officials to find out.)

41

pH and Plants

OBJECTIVE

Students will be able to hypothesize and attempt to verify the relationship between soil pH and plant growth.

ACTIVITY

The pH (hydrogen ion concentration, used in expressing acidity and alkalinity) of the soil has an important bearing on its chemical and microbial activity and significantly influences the growth of plants. The acidity and alkalinity of the soil can be modified both by natural processes such as fire and by cultural treatments such as human activity.

Soils generally lose their alkaline characteristics because of leaching of some minerals and the loss of some to plants. Plant litter also can alter soil pH significantly as it is reincorporated into the soil through decomposition.

As the hydrogen ion concentration increases in proportion to the hydroxide ion, the soil becomes increasingly acid; as the hydroxide ion increases in proportion to the hydrogen ion the soil becomes increasingly alkaline. This scale indicates the range of pH possible.

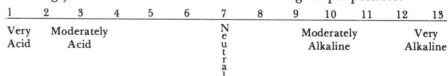

Plants have narrow pH tolerance limits within which they thrive. To demonstrate this in the classroom, suggest students plant a variety of seeds in soils with different pH's.

To minimize the number of variables, the same soil may be used and its pH altered by the addition of lime (to make it more alkaline) or sulfur powder (to make it more acid).

Ask students to prepare a variety of seeds (preferably fast-growing ones such as beans, radishes, lettuce, and marigolds) by soaking them for four to six hours, and then planting several of each kind in each soil of differing pH. Data such as the germination date, growth rate, and observations on general plant vigor and health should be recorded by the students for each test pot.

Discuss with the class which plants seem to prefer more or less acid soils.

Next, assist the students in locating an isolated conifer where needle litter has been allowed to accumulate beneath the tree. Using surface soil samples collected at three-foot (one meter) intervals along a radial from the tree, prepare the soil by leaching the samples with distilled water for 24 hours.

(Continued)

Ask the students to determine the soil pH by titration for each sample and make a graph that plots pH against radial distance from the base of the tree (that is, pH on the Y-axis and distance on the X-axis).

Repeat the experiment using a deciduous (broadleaf) tree from a similar location.

Using the data collected, explore some of these questions with the students:

How does pH differ as one moves outward from the tree?

Under which type of tree does the soil's pH differ more from the surrounding soil?

Observe the plants under the trees. Is there a difference between the species found under the conifer and those found under the deciduous tree?

How does a conifer's litter tend to influence the soil's pH beneath it? How does a deciduous tree's litter tend to influence the soil's pH?

What might we conclude about those plants that are most prominent under a coniferous tree? How might this influence plant succession?

How might the sulfur dioxide (SO_2) which is often produced from the burning of fossil fuels like coal and oil be influencing the soil's pH surrounding plants? What influence might this have on plant succession? How might such influences be offset, and is it appropriate for people to take action to offset such influences?

EXTENSION

Obtain several grams of dry conifer and/or deciduous forest litter. Burn the litter until only ash remains. Fill a test tube one-third full of ash and one-third full of distilled water. Shake and let stand for five minutes (or until the ash settles to the bottom of the tube).

Insert pH paper into the liquid to determine its pH.

What positive and negative effects might a forest fire have on the pH of the soil in a coniferous forest? In a deciduous forest?

42

Growin' Seeds and Savin' Soil

OBJECTIVE

Students will be able to describe the effects of overcrowding on plant growth.

ACTIVITY

These experiments are designed to help students understand how competition for available nutrients influences plant growth.

Materials:

Sunny inside location.

Three identical or nearly identical soil boxes, each approximately 2 feet x 3 feet (65 x 100 centimeters) at the base and 1½ feet to 2 feet in height (45 to 65 centimeters). (See illustration.) Fill each box with soil, forming a slope from one end of the box to the other. Be careful to make the slope and soil compactness the same in all three boxes.

Seeds. Marigold seeds germinate readily. Wheat grass or rice grass will thicken quickly and offer good root systems. Pick a local variety that will grow quickly. The county agricultural extension agent or a nursery that sells lawn and garden products can make suggestions.

Six metric rulers, two for each box.

Sprinkling can.

Procedure:

Plant an equal number of seeds in each of the boxes. One side of the soil area in each box should be planted with seeds at one-inch (three centimeter) intervals and the other side with seeds every two inches (six centimeters). Water equally and place in the sun, being careful to provide each box with as nearly identical growing conditions as possible.

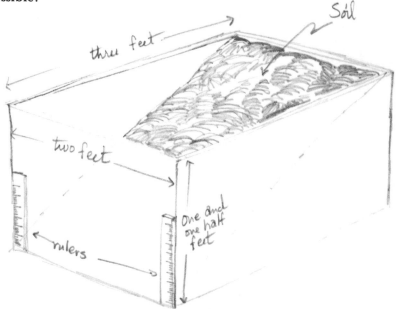

(Continued)

As the seedlings develop, three different management modes should be followed:

1. *Foresters' Box A:* Allow this box to grow untouched. Add water only.

2. *Foresters' Box B:* Thin (remove) every other plant on one end of the box and three out of every four on the other end and add water. Thin twice, once two weeks after the seeds have germinated and a second time four weeks after germination.

3. *Foresters' Box C:* Remove all of the plants from a one-foot (30 centimeter) square area on one side of the box beginning about ⅓ of the way down the slope. On the other side remove all of the plants from a two-foot (65 centimeter) square area beginning about 1/6 of the way down the slope.

Keep records on all of the boxes. Include data on:
- Amount of water supplied and when
- Germination date
- Seeds/square inch (or centimeter) at different intervals of time
- Growth rate — by recording height of plants on a regular basis
- Thinning dates
- Other data which students feel might be useful

Discuss:

1. From this experiment, attempt to make a generalization about the effects of thinning on plant growth.
2. Hypothesize about the productivity of soil relative to nutrients.
3. Is it or is it not possible to generalize from this situation to forest conditions?
4. What are the differences between a forest thinning and this type of thinning?

VARIATION

Prepare six potted-plant containers, each containing an equal amount of the same kind of soil. Bottom sections cut from half-gallon (two liter) paper milk cartons work quite well as containers. Number the containers.

Plant one corn seed in container #1.

Plant 4 corn seeds in container #2.

Plant 8 corn seeds in container #3.

Plant 16 corn seeds in container #4.

Plant 16 corn seeds in container #5 and thin to 8 plants when 5 inches (12 centimeters) tall.

Plant 16 corn seeds in container #6 and thin to 4 plants when 5 inches (12 centimeters) tall.

Place all the containers in a sunny, inside location and keep moist with water. Measure and record (graph) the height of the plants at regular intervals. When the plants are sufficiently high that students can measure their circumferences or diameters, record these statistics also. A piece of string or sewing tape is a good tool for this task.

After a suitable "growing season," use the students' observations and data to discuss:

1. Which container has the tallest plants; which the largest in diameter; whether these containers are the same one; how density (the number of plants/unit area) influences height growth and diameter growth.

2. Whether any of the containers have plants which look less healthy than those in other containers. Whether there is a relationship between density and plant vigor. What you think would happen if you removed one-half of the plants from one of the containers holding 16 plants. If you removed three-fourths of the plants. Try it, using containers #5 and #6. Observe and record any plant responses.

3. Consider what other factors might affect the health and vigor of plants, for instance: soil conditions, nutrients, slope, exposure, climate, species.

4. Compare your removal of one-half and three-fourths of the plants with thinning trees in a forest. Why might foresters plant many small trees close together, knowing they must thin them when they grow larger?

5. To what extent it is possible to generalize from this experiment to conditions and practices in forested areas.

The Value of Wildlife

OBJECTIVE

Students will be able to state some values of wildlife to their community.

ACTIVITY

Divide your class into two groups. Ask one group to investigate the amount of money spent in your community by hunters and fishermen and women; the second, the amount spent by nonconsuming "users" of wildlife, such as photographers, bird watchers, and artists.

Students can use the classified section (yellow pages) of the telephone book as a resource to compile two lists, one of local businesses which cater *directly* to outdoor activities (sporting goods stores, meat processing establishments, photography shops) and the other of businesses *indirectly* related to these "users" of wildlife (motels, service stations, bookstores).

Students can visit businesses on the list and interview the owners or employees to find out what percentage of their income derives from wildlife-related activities. (In smaller communities, particularly in the mountains, this figure may be substantial.)

After students have completed their interviews and tabulated their data, discuss these questions:

Which form of wildlife use, consuming or nonconsuming, contributes the most to the local economy? Will it continue to contribute the most? Why or why not?

Where does the money go which is generated by hunters and fishermen and women? By nonconsuming users?

Does the money spent by either of these groups of users of wildlife represent the real value of wildlife to you? To the community? To the biosphere?

How would you measure the value of an endangered species?

What values, other than economic, do wildlife represent? Design a way other than money to represent the value of wildlife to you; to the community; to the planet.

SUBJECTS
Social Studies
Science
GRADES
9-12
PLT PRINCIPLES
5. Management and Interdependence of Natural Resources
6. Life-Support Systems
7. Lifestyles
CONCEPTS
5.22 Wildlife as a Renewable Resource
6.3 Interdependence of Living Things and Their Environment
6.4 Biological Needs
7.21 Cultural Changes and Resources
SKILLS
I. Gaining Information
IV. Critical Thinking

44

Building For the Birds

OBJECTIVE

Students will be able to plan the procedures necessary to mass-produce birdhouses or feeders, building and locating these appropriate to the species for which they are designed.

ACTIVITY

Ask students to devise a plan for mass-producing birdhouses or feeders. They should consider such problems as materials and equipment needed, logical steps in production, rate of production, and market for product.

Through consultation with the students in a biology class and informed resource people, the students should determine (1) the types of feeders or houses appropriate for the birds in their area, (2) the specifications that the houses should meet (such as hole size, interior dimensions), (3) appropriate locations for and numbers required of the finished product, and (4) exterior finish and color.

Students should set up the "production line" and mass-produce their products. Ask the biology students to work with the other students to distribute the feeders or houses in appropriate locations for optimal use by the species for which the structure was designed. For example, in an urban setting, these locations should be based on a study of the best places in a typical urban backyard which are attractive to and healthful for specific species.

Discuss the implications of mass production of such items as bird feeders and houses. Follow-up the placing of these items over a period of time, in order to determine, if possible, any positive and/or negative impact on bird species.

Snow Use

OBJECTIVE

Students will be able to describe how people use snow, and relationships between these uses, forests, and snow.

ACTIVITY

With your students, generate a list of uses humans make of snow (Snow . . . in some form!). You or one of the students can list these on a blackboard or flip chart, accepting all offerings.

Once the list is fairly extensive, ask the students to group the uses into categories they specify; for example, fun things, useful things, survival things. Divide the students in the class into as many groups as there are categories, and ask each group to investigate, and prepare a report to share with the rest of the class, concerning that category of snow use. Each group can find out and show on a map some places where the snow for that category of use falls. They can also include in their report a discussion of what must happen, and what people must do, to be able to use that snow; how much snow falls in the area(s) each year on the average (from the National Weather Service); and any problems related to the use of the snow, in whatever the form. After allowing sufficient time for the collection of information, ask each group to report its findings to the rest of the students.

Encourage the students to discuss the findings reported. In addition, ask them to ascertain from the reports:

- Which areas of snowfall provide for the greatest number of uses.
- Whether any of these uses conflict with each other.
- How much human use of snow is related to forested areas compared to areas with other kinds of vegetation, or without vegetative cover of any sort.

EXTENSION

Set up an investigation to demonstrate how changes in the forest influence snow pack:

On a board 3 feet (1 meter) square, create a simulated forest. Use pieces of dowel or matchsticks with paper or sponge to simulate trees; use pieces of sponge and other materials to simulate low growing vegetation. Place the "trees" close enough to each other to create a closed crown effect, but also leave some natural, irregular openings with only low-growing vegetation between some groups of trees.

Simulate snowfall by lightly sprinkling the "forest" with powdered laundry detergent to an average depth of about ½ inch (1 centimeter).

SUBJECTS
Science
Social Studies
GRADES
7-12
PLT PRINCIPLES
5. Management and Interdependence of Natural Resources
6. Life-Support Systems
3. Cultural Contexts
CONCEPTS
5.1 Interdependence of Resources
5.2 Depletion Dangers
5.24 Water as a Reusable Resource
5.3 Urban-Forest Interdependence
6.1 Dynamic Biological Systems
6.111 Finite Matter
6.3 Interdependence of Living Things and Their Environment
3.2 Cultural Effects on Resources
SKILL
I. Gaining Information

(Continued)

Observe the forest, with discussion to include:

Where the "snow" cover is deepest.

How the "tree canopy" affects the amount of snow reaching the ground.

What actions could be taken if people wanted to have more snow reach the ground.

How more snow on the ground would affect the uses investigated earlier.

Implications for the forest ecosystem of these changes.

Possible legal and ethical implications of human uses of snow and things done in the forest to influence those uses.

RESOURCES

For information about snowfall and uses of snow in your area, contact the National Weather Service, public information offices of the Bureau of Land Management (district and state offices) or U. S. Geological Survey (state offices), your local utility district or water company, or some recreation group such as ski clubs. Also see the Resources section of the PLT materials.

Water We Doing?

OBJECTIVE

Students will be able to describe the importance of water to living things.

ACTIVITY

Suggest that the students keep track of the ways in which they use water directly during one day — flushing the toilet, drinking, cooking, washing, and so on. The following figures, though approximate, may help in estimating water use.

- Flushing the toilet uses 5 to 7 gallons per flush.
- A shower can use from 5 to 15 gallons per minutes. (An average shower might use 6 to 7 gallons — but it depends on how long you stay in!)
- Filling the bathtub could use from 25 to 30 gallons (but it depends on how full!).
- A clothes washer uses 25 to 30 gallons per load (larger machines use up to 50 gallons).
- A dishwasher uses 15 gallons per load.
- The bathroom faucet left running can use 2 to 5 gallons per minute.

If the students do not have a water meter to read in order to determine the amount of water they use in a given period of time, suggest that they figure out some other way to estimate the total number of gallons they use in a given day.

Ask the students to invent ways to cut their water use in half . . . and then do it! They might try it for three days. Talk about whether trees and other living things can conserve in their water use. Talk about adaptations plants and animals make in their use of water. Discuss the importance of water to all living things.

EXTENSIONS

1. Pick a living thing to "become." Each of your friends can pick other different living things to become. Each of you can find out how much water and for what purposes you use water in a day. For example, you could find out approximately how much water a reindeer uses, a redwood tree, a saguaro cactus, or a dandelion. Find out whether the amount of water and the uses depend on the season of the year. For example, based on availability, your animals and plants may reduce their water demands and needs during some seasons. Compare the varying amounts and uses of water by the different living things. Graph the results.

2. Make a mural of the water cycle. Try it *with* human involvement; *without* human involvement; *with* animal involvement; *without* animal involvement; *with* plant involvement; *without* plant involvement; and *with* human, other animal, and plant involvement.

3. List five examples of "water rights." List five "water wrongs."

47

Loose Knots and Tight Knots

OBJECTIVE

Students will be able to distinguish between natural and human-caused defects in wood and describe probable reasons for the human-made defects.

ACTIVITY

Collect boards with defects which affect the grade of the wood. Divide the sample boards into two categories, one for those with natural defects and one for those with human-caused defects.

Natural defects include knots (loose and tight); wanes; shakes; holes from loose knots or insects; staining from insects, sap, or fungi; cross grain; compression; and decay.

Human-caused defects, which occur during the curing process or from improper handling, include splits; cracking; checking; honeycombing; case hardening and reverse case hardening; crooking; cupping; warping; and collapse.

With help from the references cited under Resources or others you can suggest which deal with common curing defects, ask your students to try to identify the defects on the boards you and they have collected. Discuss:

How can you tell whether these defects were a result of rushing the curing process?

How could some of the natural defects be minimized? Would all people necessarily want these minimized? Suggest reasons why some people might, and others might not, want these minimized.

What are some uses for defective wood? (See related lessons.)

You could make this activity more meaningful by doing it in conjunction with a visit to a sawmill where students could observe the milling and curing process.

VARIATION

Obtain several pieces of lumber which have natural defects produced by such things as insect attack, fungi or parasite attack, and loose knots.

Ask your students to test these boards and matching nondefective boards of the same kinds and dimensions for strength and durability. Some testing methods are:

• Twisting or breaking in a vise.

• Loading between supports until the piece breaks or measuring the distance it sags under the weight

• Nailing to test susceptibility to splitting

(Continued)

Ask your students to suggest other methods of testing. Students should record the results, then discuss:

Are higher grades of lumber always the best buy? Why or why not?
Could we utilize lower quality grades of lumber for some purposes for which only higher grades are used now? What might cause a shift from higher to lower grades for the same purpose? (Scarcity, abundance of lower grades, rising prices for higher grades, changing technology.)
Could we use defective lumber for some useful purposes?

Not all wood uses require strength or durability; some demand, as first priority, an attractive appearance. Suggest that students design and make a project which uses defective lumber for its aesthetic value — a piece of wormy chestnut furniture, for example.

48

Land Allocation

OBJECTIVE

Students will be able to identify advantages and disadvantages related to different methods of land allocation.

ACTIVITY

Ask your students to make a large-scale map of a publicly owned forest which contains 120 acres (approximately 50 hectares) and these features: a scenic area such as a canyon or meadow; a two-lane highway; a prominent stream with a smaller, tributary creek; a stand of old-growth timber.

Ask each student to assume the role of one of the following individuals or groups who wish to lease a portion of the land:

• Timber company executive (40 acres; 15 hectares)
• Seven owners of summer cabins (2½ to 3 acres each; 1 hectare each)
• Private campground developer (12 acres; 5 hectares)
• Mining company executive (20 acres; 10 hectares)
• General store and service station owner (2 acres; 1 hectare)
• Railroad company executive (a 100-foot-wide right-of-way; 30 meter right-of-way)
• Ski resort owner (30 acres; 15 hectares)
• Dude ranch operator (15 acres; 5 hectares)
• Scenic preservation society (amount of land to be decided by the class after the map is drawn)

Each student, either in a predetermined or random pick-a-number order, chooses a site and marks off the area on the map.

As the land is claimed for each use, students with later choices will find the remaining area insufficient or inappropriate for their needs. Some forest users may be left out entirely.

Ask the class to talk about how the land might be allocated in a better way among those who wish to use it. Attempting to use consensus processes, the class may work out a land-use plan to meet the needs of everyone involved. They might also consider whether there is a need to look beyond the people directly involved in this issue. Are there other possible uses and users not yet represented? What seems to be the most just long-term solution? Have some people given up more than others? What does each person or group give up? What does each gain individually or collectively?

Discuss the merits and drawbacks of the two methods of land allocation: "first come, first serve" or consensus.

(Continued)

VARIATION

Assume that the forest land is privately owned and each potential user must *buy* the land he or she requires. (In the first exercise, the land was publicly owned and leased.) Follow the procedures described in the first activity, except when the land "runs out" ask the students to try to reallocate the amount using a free market system. Land can be exchanged or sold. Some users may decide to sell out and locate elsewhere.

Compare the two methods of allocation, identifying the advantages and disadvantages of each. Discuss such ideas as:

Which method seems to create the most controversy, the planning system whereby the land is allocated on the basis of the consensus of the majority or the voluntary system whereby land is allocated on the basis of the individual's ability to pay?

Which system appears to leave the individual owner most satisfied? Explain your response.

Which system appears to be the best for society as a whole? Explain your response.

49

For Better or for Worse

OBJECTIVE

Students will be able to identify trade-offs involved in an environmental issue.

ACTIVITY

Present this hypothetical situation to your students:

Some time ago, Beauwood Paper Co. officials, in order to comply with air- and water-pollution regulations, hired pollution-control technicians to study the company's manufacturing operation. The technicians presented a pollution-reduction plan to Beauwood's board of directors. The new process reduced odorous gas emissions (air pollution) by 95 percent and the B.O.D. (biochemical oxygen demand, a measure of water pollution) added to the river by 94 percent. The control measures cost approximately $11 million to $12 million but the company was able to install the new process within a few years.

The new process had the additional benefit of enabling the company to recover and reuse or sell most of the waste products previously dumped into the river and air.

There is one problem. The new process requires substantial amounts of electricity. The power has been obtained from a coal-fired plant that had to be constructed. This plant also required pollution-control devices but it has had the advantage of generating enough new electricity to meet the increasing energy needs of the community as well as those of the paper plant. Continuing to provide coal to operate the plant, however, has become a problem, affected in part by federal legislation.

Beauwood has proposed an alternative to the coal-fired plant. The company believes it can supply the additional electricity needed by installing a wood- and wood-waste-fired boiler in its plant. Drawbacks are that this boiler would cost three times as much as one using only coal or gas, and it would not produce any excess power for the community. Beauwood believes it would have to raise prices for its products to get the necessary funds, and is also concerned that the community's energy needs will not be met.

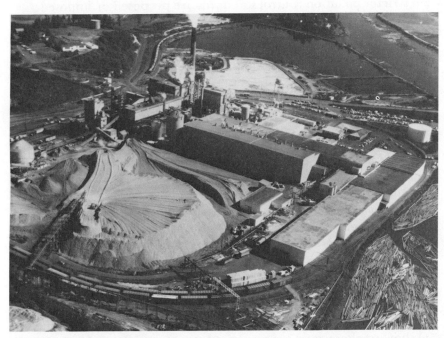

After students have familiarized themselves with the situation, discuss these questions:

What might be the advantages and disadvantages of Beauwood producing its own energy?

What might be the advantages and disadvantages of a coal-fired power plant? A gas-fired power plant? A wood- and wood-waste fired power plant?

What, if any, other options might be available for providing the necessary power both for the plant and for the community, with minimal economic and environmental costs?

If the company installs its own wood- and wood-waste-fired boiler and then raises its paper prices, what effect might there be on sales? Would you be willing to pay more for your paper? Would you be willing to use less?

What implications does the choice of a power source have on the future of the company, the community, and on others beyond the community?

What are the trade-offs involved in this situation?

What options are available to the community?

If you lived in this community, which option would you choose? Why?

How Clean Is Clean?

OBJECTIVE

Students will be able to describe the possible trade-offs involved when stricter pollution control standards are proposed or imposed.

ACTIVITY

Have your students read and react to the following hypothetical situation:

Oxbow is a community located amid the rich forest lands of the Olympic Peninsula in Washington State. It is the largest town on the Peninsula and recently sent a local person, Carol Sears, to Washington, D. C. as a congresswoman from its district. Before her election, Sears was a lawyer in Oxbow and she is well acquainted with the community's people and problems.

Oxbow's economy depends primarily upon a smelting and refining operation which employs several hundred workers and indirectly supports the town's business establishments through its payroll. Because Oxbow is located on the Hemlock River, with easy access to Puget Sound and the Pacific Ocean, its second largest industry is commercial fishing.

Recently, a bill was introduced in Congress to impose stricter pollution-control standards. To meet these standards, the Oxbow smelter would have to spend a substantial sum of money and thereby reduce its profit margin. The smelter owners have asked Sears to oppose the bill because, they say, the profit loss will force them out of business, and hundreds of Oxbow workers will lose their jobs. The president of the local union also opposes the bill and has threatened to withdraw his support for Sears in the next election if the congresswoman votes in favor of the stricter regulations.

On the other hand, townspeople dependent upon the Oxbow salmon industry are urging Sears to vote *for* the new bill. For a long time, they have opposed the pollution of the Hemlock River because they believe it is having an unfavorable impact on the salmon run. In fact, they assert, if control measures aren't imposed soon, they will be forced out of business.

The vote will be close. Sears is under considerable pressure from her constituents on both sides of the issue.

Ask each of your students to imagine he or she is Sears. Pretending to be Sears, each student can go through the process of making a decision as to how to vote. The following might be considered in this process:

(Continued)

1. Identification of the issues at stake.
2. Evidence or data necessary to understand the various issues and their implications.
3. Evaluation of the validity of evidence or data.
4. Analysis of any trade-offs involved in Sear's decision.
5. Alternatives to "clean up or close up" for the smelter owners and the fishermen and women.

   Finally, based on the evidence and his or her view of Sear's role as a member of Congress, each student should cast a vote and explain the reasoning behind the position taken.

51

Mining and Renewable Resources

OBJECTIVE

Students will demonstrate their ability to participate in group processes that are necessary to solve some forest-related environmental problems.

ACTIVITY

This activity uses a simulation technique to involve students in decision making related to mining on the forest- and rangelands surrounding a small community.

Ask the students first to prepare a map of an area 10,000 acres (4,000 hectares) in size, including 25 percent forest and mountains, 25 percent bottomland, 25 percent mountains above the timberline, and 25 percent rangeland. Locate a small community (population 2500) at the foot of the mountains on a stream.

Give your students this background information:

The community of Wildwood is dependent economically upon a small lumber mill, local tourist trade from forest recreation, and a few small farms and cattle ranches. Its water supply comes from Rimrock Creek which flows past the town. The flow of Rimrock Creek meets the present water needs of the town. Additional water for community expansion could be provided by creating a reservoir, but there are no funds available now to do this.

Coal and oil shale recently were discovered in the foothills, in the forested area, and on some of the best rangeland around Wildwood. Some of this rangeland is a part of a large Indian reservation. A large energy company would like to develop these sources of energy. A committee of local citizens has been chosen to decide whether it would be in the best interest of the community to develop these resources.

(Continued)

Now ask your students to brainstorm a list of individuals whom they believe should be appointed to this committee. Though these people may be given fictitious names, make an effort to generate a list of committee members representing diverse points of view and interest.

Committee members might include:

- Rancher who holds the mineral rights to some of the coal and oil shale deposits
- Sawmill owner
- Chamber of Commerce member
- Timberland owners, some of whom own the mineral rights on their land and some who do not
- Newspaper editor
- Banker
- Conservation group representative
- Local Native American Indian tribe council member
- Others?

One group of students is to assume the roles of committee members; another should serve as research staff for the committee, the third and remaining group (the rest of the class) should serve as a city council. Limit the city council group to any odd-numbered size, possibly including a mayor as tie-breaker.

Each student committee member should research and prepare a position statement, stating reasons for supporting or not supporting resource development. Varying degrees of development, as opposed to an all-or-none stand, also may be proposed.

The committee's research staff should be asked to provide information on various issues such as the economic impact on the community; water requirements for oil shale and coal processing; trade-offs involved in committing forest- and rangeland to strip-mining; effects on wildlife; problems involved when the surface rights to the land are held by someone other than the owner of the mineral rights.

The city council should research legal implications of possible decisions they could anticipate the committee to recommend.

The simulation exercise culminates when the committee and its staff report to the city council with its recommendations and plans for resource development for Wildwood . . . and the city council "decides."

Hard Choices

OBJECTIVE

Students will be able to describe some of the environmental and economic trade-offs involved in the use of pesticides in the forest.

ACTIVITY

Ask your students to read and respond to this hypothetical situation:

"Those insects have to be stopped before they destroy our entire forest," Bob Wilcox, president of the Freight Lumber Co., said. "They are killing nearly all of the trees and if we don't spray them soon with DDT our company will be without a continuing lumber supply — and that means the mill will close."

"I agree that you've got a problem," responded Chuck Davis, owner of Oldtown's largest salmon cannery. "But you can't use DDT. A few years back they used it up in New Brunswick on spruce budworm, the same bugs we've got, and it cut their annual salmon run down to about one-sixth of what it had been. If that happens here, my company would be wiped out — and so would all the jobs on the fishing boats."

"But DDT is the only pesticide that will do a quick and thorough job on those budworms," Wilcox argued. "I don't want to destroy your operation and kill all those fish, but I've got my own company, and all those trees to consider. If I don't spray I'll be ruined."

Hold a class discussion on these questions:

How well informed do Mr. Wilcox and Mr. Davis appear to be?

What can these people do to solve their problem? What are their choices?

It is possible that Mr. Wilcox does not have the choice to use DDT, given bans on its use in recent years.

What are the reasons for bans on use of DDT and bans and restrictions on use of other pesticides?

What pesticides are currently allowed, for what reasons, and under what conditions?

What possible positive and negative effects might result from use of specific pesticides you research?

What possible positive and negative effects might result from no use, attempting no chemical treatment of the problem?

How would you resolve the dilemma outlined in this hypothetical situation? What information do you need before making your decision? On what criteria would you base your judgment? What

SUBJECTS
Social Studies
Science

GRADES
9-12

PLT PRINCIPLES
5. Management and Interdependence of Natural Resources
6. Life-Support Systems
7. Lifestyles

CONCEPTS
5.5 Trade-offs
6.23 Humans' Effect on Environment
7.123 Behavior Effects on Environment

SKILLS
VI. Valuing
IV. Critical Thinking
V. Problem Solving

legal constraints must be considered? What alternatives are available which have not been discussed? Which of the alternatives seem most reasonable? Given sufficient information concerning this hypothetical situation, what solution seems most appropriate?

In their search for alternatives and solid criteria, encourage your students to consult the references cited under Resources.

VARIATION or EXTENSION

After students are familiar with the situation described, divide your class into three groups; ask the first to advocate the use of DDT; the second to oppose its use; and the third to represent the United States Environmental Protection Agency.

The first two groups should research and prepare testimony to be heard by the EPA panel. The panel will be asked to decide whether the situation warrants issuing an emergency exemption for the use of DDT, in accordance with the 1972 regulations banning the chemical.

Students preparing for the "hearing" should consider:

• The economic implications and long-range environmental impact of granting or not granting the permit.
• Alternatives or compromise solutions to the problem.
• The EPA criteria which must be met before the use exemption can be approved. (Students role-playing the EPA should research and establish these based on the most current information available.)

RESOURCES

Special Note on sources and dialogue: While the above dialogue represents a hypothetical situation, the data regarding the effects of DDT on salmon runs reflect the results of actual research. For a review of actual case histories see: Rudd, Robert L., *Pesticides and the Living Landscape* (Madison, Wisconsin: University of Wisconsin Press, 1966) p. 106-109. The original research was reported by: Crowter, R.A., and E.H. Vernon, "Effects of Black-Headed Budworm Control on Salmon and Trout in British Columbia," *Canadian Fish Culture* No. 24:23-40 (1959); Keenleyside, M.H. "Effects of Spruce Budworm Control on Salmon and Other Fishes in New Brunswick," *Canadian Fish Culture* No. 24:17-21 (1959); Kerwill, C.J., "Effects of DDT Spraying in New Brunswick on Future Runs of Adult Salmon," *Atlantic Advocate* Vol. 48, No. 8, p. 65-68 (1958).

Moreover, because of the considerable quantity of popular literature available on the effects of DDT (most of it less than objective in its presentation), only a highly selected list is given. Further information is extensively referenced in these documents:

(Continued)

Articles

Edwards, J.G., "One Step Beyond: An Inquiry Into Research On DDT." Available from the Terra Society, P.O. Box 110, Mt. Prospect, Illinois 60056.

Hinckley, A.D., "The Gypsy Moth," *Environment* Vol. 14, No. 2 (March 1972), p. 41-47.

McCaull, Julian, "Questions for an Old Friend," *Environment* Vol. 13, No. 6 (July/August 1971), p. 2-9.

McIntire, Greg, "Spoiled By Success," *Environment* Vol. 14, No. 6 (July/August 1972), p. 14-29.

Pamphlets

U.S. Forest Service, "Major Outbreaks of Douglas Fir Tussock Moth in Oregon and California," (Portland, Oregon: Pacific Northwest Forest and Range Experiment Station, 1973) General Technical Report PNW-5.

U.S. Forest Service, "Surveillance Report 1965 Burns Project Douglas Fir Tussock Moth Control," (Washington: G.P.O., 1968) S/N 994-184.

Other references are listed in the Resources section of the PLT materials.

53

The Value of 100 Acres of Forest Land

OBJECTIVE

Students will be able to describe some of the complex factors that go into determining land values.

ACTIVITY

In this activity, students will attempt to attach values of different kinds (economic, aesthetic, genetic, etc.) to a particular area of forest land.

Divide your class into groups. Ask each group to do research* to determine a land value in one of these categories:

Lumber Value — Choose an area of forest land and count the number of trees. Find out from a local resource agency or forest industry representative how to make a rough estimate of the number of board feet yielded per tree and the number that could be obtained from 100 acres (or 100 hectares). Check with a lumberyard to determine the retail price of lumber per 1,000 board feet. Contact a timber company and ask the cost of converting trees to 1,000 board feet of lumber and transporting the product to the lumberyard. Subtract this amount from the retail price quoted by the lumberyard. What might this 100 acres (or 100 hectares) of forest be worth in dollars for lumber?

Note: This figure does not take into account marketable byproducts; for example, particle board or pressed wood logs.

What might be the value of this forest land and its lumber other than as measured in dollars; for example, as a source of inspiration and solitude.

Watershed Value — Discuss the concept of a watershed and the ways in which a forest affects the amount of water available in an area.

Using the same 100 acres (or 100 hectares) as the sample, check the amount of rainfall in that area and calculate the rainfall on 100 acres (or 100 hectares). Amount of rain in feet x 43,560 square feet/acre = cubic feet of water/acre x 7.5 gallons/cubic feet of water = gallons of water falling on 1 acre. Amount of rain (in meters) x 10,000 square meters = cubic meters of water/hectare ÷ 100 = water falling on 1 hectare. From the local water company, find out the money value of 1,000 gallons of water (or cubic meters). What is the money value of the amount of water that fell on the sample plot?

From the U.S. Weather Service or your local Soil Conservation Service find out what percent of the rainfall they estimate does go into sources (aquifers, streams, etc.) available for human consumption. How would this compare with the same amount of rainfall, falling on a plot of the same size in open prairie, for example?

Calculate approximately what the forest is worth economically to people as a watershed. Attempt to calculate what the forest is worth as a watershed to living things other than people.

Wildlife Value — Find out what types of wildlife inhabit this forest land. How many animals and birds? Are there any, such as deer, turkey, or quail, which are hunted by humans? Determine how much money hunters spend locally on licenses, guns, ammunition, equipment, lodging, travel, and guides. Include any forms of nonconsuming uses related to wildlife (photography and bird watching, for instance) that generate economic income in this area. What is the total wildlife value (as measured in dollars) of this land?

Describe the wildlife value of this land other than in dollars; for example, as a gene pool for future generations.

Recreational Value — Determine what forms of recreation take place in the forest. Find out what camping or parking charges are levied per day. How many people use this forest for camping or other recreation, and how much money do they spend in the area? What is the total recreational value measured in dollars? What recreational values in the forest are not easily measured in dollars?

Forage Value — Determine whether cattle or sheep could use this land for grazing. How many animals could it support? How much are the animals worth on today's market? What are the total forage values, economic and other values?

Note: The forest's intangible values of wildlife, meteorological influences, and aesthetics may be harder to calculate but are nonetheless real and worthy of consideration. Each of the sections above asks the students to invent other ways to determine value than dollar income.

After all the information has been collected, researched, and shared by the class, lead a discussion. Students may not be able to resolve the issues involved, but they may become aware of the complexities of land-use management. Consider specific questions such as:

If the community wanted to clear this 100 acres (or 100 hectares) of forest in order to build homes, provide farm sites, or put in a highway, how would the proposal influence the land's value? Decide which uses make the land more valuable. To whom? Specify how you are measuring value. Find another way to measure value. Does your answer change?

Decide whether the various values determined for this 100 acres (or 100 hectares) could be applied to other areas of the same size but of different forest types. Specify what variables might make a difference in the economic, or the "intangible," values of the area, and from whose viewpoint.

Decide which uses make the land more valuable in the long run, specifying from whose point of view and by what means the value is measured.

What trade-offs are involved when we convert forest land from multiple use or a few dominant uses? Society needs houses, farms, and roads, but we also need forests. Decide whether and how we can have them all.

Find out who determines the uses of forest land.

*Students may find any of the following to be useful in their research:
Newspaper advertisements
Water company/municipal waterworks
Local lumber businesses and foresters
U. S. Soil Conservation Service
U. S. Weather Service
State Department of Wildlife or a similar agency
U. S. Forest Service
State Department of Recreation/Parks or a similar agency
Citizen conservation groups

6 LIFE SUPPORT SYSTEMS

54

Why Do Trees Grow There?

OBJECTIVE

Students will become aware of the differences between the major forest types in the United States and be able to state why these types are located where they are.

ACTIVITY

Divide the class into six groups, with each group to research one of six forest areas — the West Coast Forest, Western Forest, Central Hardwood Forest, Tropical Forest, Northern Forest, Southern Forest.

Ask each group to use maps, charts, pictures, movies, mime, interviews, graphs, or other media to demonstrate why its type of forest exists where it does and what distinguishes its forest region from the others. Illustrations might include geographic features, rainfall, area covered by the forest region, growing season, altitude, highest and lowest temperatures, soil types, population density, resource use, and management.

In presenting their findings to the rest of the students, each group should attempt to answer:

- Why is this forest type where it is?
- Was it always within the boundaries it now has?
- How does the soil type affect the forest type present?
- How does rainfall affect the forest type present?
- How does fire affect the forest type present?
- How have humans influenced the extent and character of this forest type?

VARIATION

Construct a metal tent by folding a piece of sheet metal down the middle (see illustration). Chill it in a refrigerator for two to three hours. (Do not remove the tent from the refrigerator until the rest of the experiment is ready!) Fill a teakettle with water. Heat the water in the teakettle over a hot plate or other burner. Place an electric fan on one side of the heating teakettle.

When the water in the kettle begins to form steam, remove the sheet metal "mountain" from the refrigerator and place it downwind from the fan and kettle. Turn on the fan and direct the steam so that it passes up and over the "mountain." Ask students to observe which side of the "mountain" is the driest. Which do they think would be more favorable for plant growth? Ask them to think of any mountain ranges where there are deserts or near-deserts on one side and lush vegetation on the other (Cascades, Olympics, Sierra Nevadas, Rockies).

On each side of the "mountain" fasten a thermometer. Take the "mountain" and thermometer out on the schoolground. Turn the "mountain" north and south, east and west, northwest and southeast, and so forth, asking the students to record the sunny-side temperature and the shady-side temperature of each setting.

Discuss the following:

Which way do any mountains nearest you in your region lie? Which side of those mountains is the warmest? Coolest? Is this consistent with the temperature differences you found using the model mountain?

Are there differences in plant life on either side of the mountains? Why do you suppose there are, or are not, differences? Is one side more moist than the other? Why?

EXTENSION

Walk around the school yard. What's like a mountain? Find a large boulder, a stump, a car, a tree, a building. (Note: You may wish to introduce the term "microclimates" to refer to these.) What differences in plant life and moisture do you find on the shady and sunny sides of the boulders and stumps? (Mosses, molds, dampness on the shady side — plus the animal life that likes this; less vegetation, less growth, and different wildlife on the dry side.)

RESOURCES

Forests and Trees of the United States map produced by the American Forest Institute, and other materials listed in the Resources section.

55

Wildlife Habitat

OBJECTIVE

Students will be able to calculate the area of a triangle to determine the carrying capacity of a habitat for deer.

ACTIVITY

Using the map of the area and information provided, students may calculate answers to the problems listed. (Forage refers to vegetation taken naturally by herbivorous animals, both wild and domestic.)

Note: You may want to have part of the class use metric measures and compare the ease of calculations. An area of 1.6 x .8 kilometers will be approximately equivalent to the one shown.

Given:

One acre of meadow can produce 500 pounds of forage per year (one hectare can produce 563 kilograms).

One acre of chaparral can produce 300 pounds of forage/year (one hectare, 338 kilograms).

One acre of forest can produce 100 pounds of forage/year (one hectare, 113 kilograms).

One adult deer requires 3,650 pounds (1,652.5 kilograms) of forage/year and for the purposes of this problem, 53 percent of this forage comes from chaparral, 39 percent from meadow, and the remainder from forest.

Note: These figures are realistic but will vary widely, depending upon local conditions, such as rainfall, latitude, etc.

Problems:

1. How many deer could be supported on the area shown? Conversion factor: one acre = 10 square chains.
2. How could vegetation be manipulated if your goal was to support a larger deer population?
3. What percentage of this deer habitat would be lost if the proposed highway is built? How many fewer deer would be supported in this area?
4. If the deer need chaparral, meadow and forest vegetation, how many deer can live east of the highway? What percentage of the total herd would the highway theoretically eliminate?
5. What percentage of this deer habitat would be lost if the proposed summer homes were built? (The development takes up one-eighth of the forest.) How many deer would be eliminated, theoretically, by the summer home development?

(Continued)

6. What vegetative changes would be likely to occur if the timber were harvested by clearcutting? Partial cutting? Section cutting? Shelterwood cutting? (see Glossary and consult local timber and other resource management personnel for definitions of these terms.) What effects would these vegetative changes be likely to have on the total deer herd? What effects might these vegetative changes have on watersheds? On habitat for other plant and animal populations?

7. If you were a Forest Ranger, managing the forest for timber production, and the deer herd increased, what effect might this have on new tree seedlings? What actions might you recommend? What advantages and disadvantages might there be to any action taken?

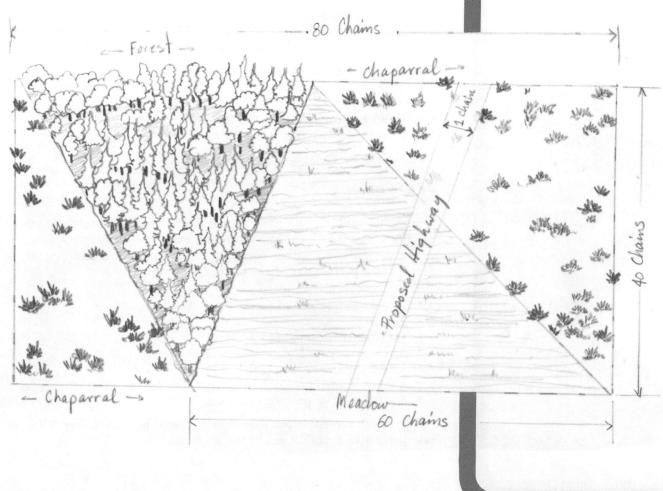

56

The Changing Forest

OBJECTIVE

Students will be able to use audiovisual media to demonstrate their knowledge of the dynamics of the forest.

ACTIVITY

Ask your students to plan and produce multi-media presentations, either as individual or small-group projects, which demonstrate that the forest is a dynamic community.

The choice of media and format should be made by the students. Slides, film, posters, photographs, and tape recordings are examples of communication tools which could be used.

So that students will more fully understand the term "dynamic," they should be encouraged to read or view some of the references cited in Resources.

Ask for volunteers to offer their presentations to the rest of the students. Students in the audience could assume the role of critics, evaluating the presentations according to criteria such as:

1. How effectively the message was communicated.
2. The technical clarity of the medium used to transmit and explain the message.
3. The scientific accuracy of the script or pictures.
4. The appropriateness of the medium to the message.

Include other criteria developed by the students.

VARIATION

Students could create their presentations based on the perceptions of different individuals and interest groups. For example, a multi-media presentation on the forest as a dynamic community could be based on the perspective of any of the following:

- A public utility company
- The Sierra Club
- John Muir
- The United States Forest Service
- A contemporary Native American
- A hunting and fishing club
- A three-year-old child
- A private forest products company

Again, the presentations should be followed by substantive critiques based on criteria established by the students.

57

Climax Forest

OBJECTIVE

Students will be able to identify characteristics of climax plant communities.

ACTIVITY

There is a good deal of disagreement, even among "experts," about what constitutes what is referred to as a *climax* condition in forest and other plant communities; and there is even greater disagreement about the impact and value of management techniques as related to climax conditions.

This activity is designed to enable students to identify characteristics of climax vegetative types, and to consider the implications of management practices related to such vegetative types.

Ask your students to begin by attempting to establish definitions for "sere" and for "climax forest." (See the PLT Glossary.) Suggest that the students contact local resource agencies (for example, Bureau of Land Management, Forest Service, State Department of Natural Resources) or forest industry representatives for information about any existing climax forest areas in your region. The students should also ask for information related to any areas that might be considered dramatically different from a climax forest condition; for example, areas recently burned, clearcut, old fields or vacant lots.

If possible, visit one of each type of vegetative area with your students. Ask the students to record evidence of plant and animal communities in each area. If such a visit is not possible, suggest that the students gather photos representing varying stages of succession in your region. Through study of these photographs and any additional necessary research, ask the students to identify and discuss the stages of sere development represented.

Using the information obtained through either of the above alternatives, discuss questions such as the following with your students:

What is the climax forest type (or other climax vegetative type) in your region?

What impact, if any, have people had on this forest; for example, changing it from a climax type to other stages of succession?

What, if any, are the advantages of climax forests compared to other types of forests? What are possible advantages and disadvantages for wildlife; for water production and use; for human recreation and leisure-time activities; for commercial uses such as grazing and timber production?

What is the relationship of climax forest types to fire? Has human control of fire affected development and maintenance of climax forests?

(Continued)

Related to this discussion and any additional research involved, suggest to the students that they create a mural showing the stages of succession characteristic of the vegetation in their region. They might graph the numbers and types of different plant and animal species present in each stage, comparing these to determine:

Which stage of succession appears to have the greatest variety of plant species; of animal species.

Which stage appears to have the least variety of plant species; of animal species.

Whether any plant or animal species are present in all stages; if so, the apparent role of those species in the food chain.

What happens to some animals and some uses of forest (vegetative) types when succession changes.

In further discussion, ask the students to consider:

When is a climax forest not a climax forest? That is, will it always stay the same, once it has arrived? Imagine what factors could change it from the climax stage. What might happen next? Could these same factors occur at any time before the climax stage? If so, what would happen then? How would or could a person draw a boundary for an area of climax vegetation? Could the planet Earth be considered a climax vegetative type?

VARIATION or EXTENSION

If you are located near a desert area or other unconventional "forest," adapt the above activities for use with the type of "climax forest" — mature plant/animal community — in your area. You might even try the school grounds!

58

Predator Prey

SUBJECTS
Mathematics
Science

GRADES
7-12

PLT PRINCIPLES
6. Life-Support
Systems
5. Management and
Interdependence of
Natural Resources

CONCEPTS
6.42 Carrying
Capacity
5.1 Interdependence
of Resources
5.21 Plants as
Renewable
Resources
5.22 Wildlife as a
Renewable
Resource

SKILL
I. Gaining
Information

OBJECTIVE

Students will be able to make a general statement regarding the impact of land development on wildlife populations.

ACTIVITY

Given the information provided, students may solve the problems posed.

Given:

One mountain lion can eat approximately 1,095 pounds (490 kilograms) of venison (deer meat) each year (in addition to rabbits, porcupines, and other small animals). The lion probably consumes only about 50 percent of each deer he kills; coyotes and other scavengers get the rest.

One deer eats approximately 3,650 pounds (1652.5 kilograms) of vegetation/year in the form of grasses, herbs, brush, and tree leaves.

One square mile (kilometer) of deer habitat produces 800 pounds (320 kilograms) of vegetation acceptable as deer food/year. (Note: This varies depending on the region, condition of the range, and other factors.)

Problems:

1. What is the minimum number of square miles (square kilometers) of habitat needed to support one deer?
2. If each deer averages 150 pounds (70 kilograms) in weight, how many deer are needed to feed one lion for one year?
3. How many square miles (square kilometers) of deer-lion habitat are necessary for one lion to survive? (For the purpose of this problem, assume that one deer and one lion will provide continuation of the species, although of course, in reality, continuation would require many animals.)
4. Use a map of a region you are familiar with and outline an area large enough to serve as habitat for one lion. Ignore all roads, communities, and other developments which do not produce food for deer.
5. On the same map, again outline an area large enough to support one lion but this time take into account the non-deer-food producing areas. How much larger is the second area you outlined?
6. Notwithstanding all the development present in the United States today, there are more deer in this country now than there were when the first European settlers arrived. How could you explain this? Find out what impact the growth of the deer population has had on other species of wildlife.

Endangered Species

59

OBJECTIVE

Students will be able to identify and describe factors that contribute to the endangering of species.

ACTIVITY

Obtain a list of locally rare or endangered animal species from your state wildlife agency or the United States Fish and Wildlife Service; and obtain a list of rare or endangered plant species from the Department of Agriculture. (For addresses, see the *Conservation Directory* listed in the Resources.)

Ask each of your students to select a species from the list and gather information about its problems. Reports might include this information about the species:

- Past and present range and population.
- Length of time it has been endangered.
- Reasons it is endangered.
- Actions currently being taken to improve its chances of survival.
- A list of agencies, interest groups, or others who are working on the problem. Who is contributing money to the effort?
- Activities that the student alone or the entire class might undertake to aid the species.
- Ways in which good land management could slow down or prevent such losses.
- Why it is important that this species survive.

Once the students have each presented their reports, create a chart listing each of the species; length of time endangered; past and present range; past and present population; and outlook for survival. Add any other categories of information and analysis you and the students might find informing. Look for trends. Find practical actions private citizens might take to assist in preservation of species, if they choose. Make these suggestions available to others in your community who might be interested.

VARIATION

Ask your students to design a hypothetical animal or plant with characteristics which would favor extinction. How do the traits of this species compare with those of any real animals or plants? Repeat, except design a species that could resist extinction. (See the Uetz article cited under Resources.)

SUBJECTS
  Science
  Social Studies
GRADES
  7-12
PLT PRINCIPLES
  6. Life-Support Systems
  4. Societal Perspectives on Issues
  5. Management and Interdependence of Natural Resources
  7. Lifestyles
CONCEPTS
  6.22 Changes in Living Things
  6.23 Humans' Effect on Environment
  6.222 Stability with Diversity
  4.43 Constraints on Resource Use
  5.2 Depletion Dangers
  5.22 Wildlife as a Renewable Resource
  7.12 Determination of Resources and Their Value
SKILLS
  I. Gaining Information
  VI. Valuing

60

Build an Ecosystem

OBJECTIVE

Students will be able to design and build a terrarium which simulates a real plant and animal community.

ACTIVITY

Your students can recreate habitats they have observed by making a terrarium. First, take your class on a field trip, asking the students to observe carefully a specific habitat and make notes on what they see there.

A woodland terrarium might contain ferns, mosses, small flowering plants, tiny tree seedlings, a piece of rotting log, rocks, and small animals such as insects and snails.

A grassland terrarium could include native grasses, mosses, insects, forbs, dead grass stems, and leaves.

The students might make one terrarium of a type or make two, one of each of two kinds of simulated habitats, so that they may compare and discuss the things that go into them.

Ask the students to use careful conservation practices if they collect plants for their terrarium. Students should choose small specimens of different kinds and be sure to get their roots. Students should be equipped with small cardboard cartons (milk cartons work well) and garden trowels for collecting specimens from outdoor settings. Show them how to use a trowel to dig a plant without damaging roots and how to transfer a specimen and its soil to a carton.

Plants should *never* be taken unless there are several more of the same kind where students are digging. In many areas there are strict prohibitions against removal of *any* plants. If you can locate an area that is being cleared for construction or logging, you may be able to freely salvage all of nearly any type of plant you want because most will be damaged or destroyed when their environment is altered.

125

(Continued)

Terrarium construction:

As a container for the miniature natural community, students might use a large jar or fish bowl or any container with glass or plastic sides. (If possible, you might ask the school's industrial arts class to build one.) The container may be placed on its side to provide more "floor" space.

Cover the bottom of the container with a one-inch layer of pebbles or charcoal and cover that with a two-inch (four centimeters) layer of soil. Use a soil type appropriate to the needs of your plants. The next step is to make a small hole for each plant; fill the holes with water; put the roots of the plants into the holes and cover them with soil. Plants should not be crowded; they need room to grow.

Add a top layer of twigs, dead leaves, and grass to simulate characteristic natural litter. The students should try to match the terrarium habitat as closely as possible to the real habitat they visited.

Every three or four days, the students should observe the terrarium(s) and note what is happening there. Suggest that the students keep a journal describing any changes. In a spirit of scientific experimentation, the students may wish to alter terrarium conditions (not watering, overwatering, removing plants, adding non-native plants, limiting available light to brief periods, adding salt). If they do so, discuss with the students the effects and talk about what would happen if these same alterations were made or occurred on the earth's surface. Discuss ways and circumstances under which some of these and similar alterations *are* taking place.

61

A Calorie's Cost

OBJECTIVE

Students will be able to compute the monetary cost (price) per Calorie of various foods they consume.

ACTIVITY

Materials needed:

Caloric and nutrition value charts for various foods by grams
Gram scale(s)
Copies of a form like the one suggested here for each student's "Food Log"

Procedure:

This activity is intended to provide students with experience in computing Caloric, nutritional, and monetary values for the various foods they consume. In preparation for this activity, students may find it helpful to practice some of the following skills:

Estimating weight in grams of various foods. (For the purposes of the following activity, stress with the students the importance of consistency rather than absolute accuracy in their estimates. Gram scales can be used to check the accuracy of their estimates.)

Converting from one measurement to another mathematically; for example, from price/pound to price/gram. (See Metric Conversion Charts.)

Computing cost (price) per Calorie, given Calories and cost per some unit of measure.

Ask students to keep track of all the food they eat in a week, including the weight in grams; Caloric value; and cost (using average retail price locally) of each item (even the food they eat at home!). They might use food labels or cookbooks to determine Caloric values; in addition, the Caloric value of some food items may be determined by experimentation. (See the experiments on burning nuts in the Biological Sciences Curriculum Study and the Introductory Physical Sciences textbooks listed in the Resources section of the PLT materials.)

A form for organizing these data might look like this:

Type of food and amount	Cost per unit of measure	Caloric value	Weight in grams	Cost per gram	Cost per Calorie
(for example: 1 apple (½ pound)	40c/lb. (20c)	117 Cal.	360 g.	.056c	.0017c)

Once their data have been collected, ask the students to:

Compare the cost (price) per Calorie of the various food items.

Determine whether there is a general class of foods (such as plant, animal) where a high concentration of Calories per gram is found.

Determine what other nutritional values besides Calories various foods provide for us. (Again, cookbooks or food labels may be helpful; in addition, nutritional information can be obtained from the Cooperative Extension Service in the U.S. Department of Agriculture, as well as from other resources listed in the Resource section of the PLT materials.)

Analyze the monetary cost (price) per unit of various foods in terms of the amount of protein, carbohydrates, specific vitamins, and minerals each provides.

Determine what is the "best buy" based on which nutrients the students consider to be of most value to them.

EXTENSIONS

1. Sometimes food is bought and not consumed — it spoils before being eaten, or gets thrown away as left-over leftovers. Find a way to compute the cost of various foods, taking this factor into consideration. How might this affect decision-making when shopping; for example, related to amounts and types of foods chosen?
2. Are there values to various foods other than nutritive, Caloric, and monetary costs? How important are these values in the process of choosing foods?

62

Food Mobile

SUBJECT
Science

GRADES
7-12

PLT PRINCIPLE
6. Life-Support
   Systems

CONCEPTS
6.3 Interdependence
   of Living Things
   and Their
   Environment
6.222 Stability with
   Diversity
6.112 Sun as the
   Ultimate Energy
   Source

SKILLS
I. Gaining
   Information
V. Problem Solving

OBJECTIVE

Students will be able to describe relationships between primary producers and consumers within a food chain.

ACTIVITY

Ask the students to construct a food pyramid (chain) mobile to observe its complexity and its relationship to their own physical maintenance.

Materials:

Pictures of organisms (producers, consumers, and decomposers)
Wire (or wooden dowels or straws)
Strong thread
Scissors (optional)
Glue (optional)

Procedure:

Either as individuals or in small groups, students can use these materials to construct a mobile representing a simple food chain (pyramid) based upon their understanding of food pyramids and the ecosystem. They will need to assume that the bottom of the mobile represents the sun; however, it is most effective to let them find this out for themselves!

After the mobiles are completed and displayed, you might discuss:

Where in the mobiles are the meat-eaters? Where are the vegetarians?
What is the relationship between the type of animal or plant and its position in the mobiles?
Where are the primary producers in each mobile? What happens when you remove one? When you remove several?
Where are the primary consumers? What happens when you remove one? Several? How does the result compare with the result when you removed one or more producers?
What is the final consumer in each mobile? What other organisms could be at the top of the pyramid?
Does a disturbance at certain levels of a mobile result in greater change than disturbances at other levels? Explain this.
How does the complexity of a mobile affect its susceptibility to change? How do you explain this?
What implications does what you have observed in this exercise have for ecosystem management, particularly as relative to diversity?

Succession on the School Grounds

OBJECTIVE

Students will be able to make a general statement about relationships between diversity and stability in plant communities.

ACTIVITY

Get permission to isolate, by means of temporary fencing, two areas near the school. The first should be a (not black-topped!) playground area (leave it alone) and the second a grassy or cultivated area near a building (stop mowing, watering, or fertilizing this area).

During a class term (for example, semester, trimester, or quarter), ask students to take photographs of these two areas on a regular basis, probably once a week. The camera should be in the same position each time a photo is taken. This accurate pictorial record should be displayed in the classroom as the pictures are ready.

In addition to use of the photographs, ask the students to compare the areas by recording their observations in a journal. Suggest that data like the following be included:

- Which plants and how many go to seed.
- Plant growth rate. (Measure and graph in centimeters per week.)
- Changes in plant density. (Number of stems/square meter.)
- Changes in species composition. (Do some species become more abundant and others less abundant?)
- New species.
- Evidence of animal life or visits, including those of humans.

Ask the students to make a general statement about apparent relationships between diversity and stability in plant communities, based on the data they have acquired.

SUBJECT
Science
GRADES
7-9
PLT PRINCIPLE
6. Life-Support
Systems
CONCEPT
6.221 Succession
SKILL
I. Gaining
Information

64

How Do You Bury a Pile of Dirt?

OBJECTIVE

Students will be able to state the relative biodegradability of various objects and the importance of this characteristic to the biosphere.

ACTIVITY

Ask students, either working in pairs or in small groups, to select one item which commonly is put into garbage cans and subsequently becomes part of the community's solid waste. Typical items are paper towels, glossy magazines, food, tin and aluminum cans, plastic, rubber, grass trimmings, glass, cloth, and cardboard.

Divide each item into two pieces. One half should be buried outdoors, about six inches (15 centimeters) deep and not in a container, for at least a month. The other is to be kept in the classroom as a control.

When the specified time period has elapsed, students can exhume the buried items and compare them with the controls.

Among ideas that might be discussed are:

Which materials seem to decay the most readily and quickly? How can you tell?

Which materials show the least change?

What factors were present which might have caused some items to decay? (Bacteria, insects, and fungus are examples.)

Which substances would appear to be the most appropriate for use in landfills? Which should not be buried in landfills? Why? What can be done with those you determine should not be buried in landfills? Do landfills solve the problem of solid waste? Explain your answer. (Remember: There is no "away"!)

How can society deal with nonbiodegradable solid waste? (Possibilities are recycling, reusing, using as energy sources.)

EXTENSION

With the help of current publications (See the Resources section of the PLT materials.) define the term *recycling*. Divide your class into six groups. Three groups could explore the possible advantages of recycling glass, metal, and paper. The other three could research the disadvantages.

After the research is finished, ask the opposing groups to present their arguments for and against recycling each material. After the debate, the class can vote to decide which materials they think should be recycled and in what order of priority. Encourage them to recycle any materials for which they identify a high priority.

Pollution Search:
A "Sense" of Knowing

OBJECTIVE

Students will be able to identify similarities and differences in kinds of pollution.

ACTIVITY

Students can be divided into six groups, one representing each of the major human senses, sight, touch, hearing, taste, smell (with a sixth group for other possible human senses not yet identified!).

Ask each group of students to go on a "pollution search" attempting to identify the various kinds of pollution to which the sense they represent is or might be particularly vulnerable; for example, human litter in the forest (sight), excessive auto exhaust on a crowded urban street (smell), jet plane or motorcycle (hearing).

Students may identify their examples of pollution over a period of time; for example, one week might be spent with time both in and outside of school in "searching." At the end of the period of "search" time, the students can meet in their small groups and organize their information for a class presentation. In their searching, the students may find examples of pollution that do not relate to the particular "sense" they represent. With all students participating, add any additional examples of pollution the students identified, adding these according to the appropriate category. Create a master list of kinds of pollution according to the senses represented.

For example:

Physical Senses	Pollution
Sight	litter
Touch	
Hearing	
Taste	
Smell	
Other "Senses" or Perceptions	

(Continued)

65

Some kinds of pollution may seem to fit appropriately under more than one category. However, try to limit the listing to the one or more senses most dominantly involved. Students will undoubtedly find some kinds of pollution that seem to involve more than merely the five commonly recognized physical senses. Include their identification, labeling and categorizing them under the title, "OTHER."

As the master list is constructed, encourage this as an opportunity for discussion by the students. If the following do not evolve naturally in your discussion as you create the master list, suggest that the students consider how:

Some things might represent pollution to one person or group of people and not to others.

Some things might represent pollution during one historical period and not in others.

Each of the following are both similar and different to each of the others. List some of the similarities and differences.
- CB airways
- Litter in the forest
- Chemicals in rivers
- Erosion in streams
- Television commercials
- Interruptions

There are varying implications for health involved in different kinds of pollution. Consider health of humans, of wildlife, of plant life, of the national economy, of international relations. How are these last two kinds of health different from the first three?

There may be ways each of these kinds of apparent pollution can be changed into useful forms of energy. Do an analysis of those that might possibly be converted to usefulness; those that apparently could not be. Think of ways to reduce or eliminate those not useful in another form. Think of ways to accomplish the proposed ideas.

134

66

A Treasure Hunt ...for Energy

OBJECTIVE

Students will be able to identify the major present-day sources of energy (the fossil fuels, uranium, and running water) which we use as fuel for space heating, transportation, and generation of electricity; to evaluate the possibility and appropriateness of their continued use for such purposes over time; and to suggest both new uses and better sources in order to meet energy demands.

ACTIVITY

Give this "assignment" to your students:

Map the energy in your community. The students might include visual keys in their maps to show the *sources* of energy used as fuel and electricity; the *locations* where such energy is used; and *how the energy is used.*

Ask the students to check reliable sources to determine the most recent assessment of the available quantity of renewable and nonrenewable resources which are presently used for production of fuel and electricity. The students should distinguish between specific kinds of renewable and nonrenewable resources, and attempt to find information predicting the availability of these resources over time. This kind of prediction will have to include indications of the rate of use.

With this information plus the visual map of their community, you and the students will be able to enter a ranging discussion of the appropriateness and implications for use of renewable and nonrenewable resources over time. The following can be included in the discussion:

- Changes in kinds of uses of specific resources.
- Impact of use of some renewable and nonrenewable resources for fuel and electricity where these resources were previously used for other products and purposes.
- Economic implications of such changes and possible social costs and benefits, including costs to the environment.
- Worldwide implications of such changes.

EXTENSION

Generate a list of possible new sources of energy for fuel and electricity purposes. Find local speakers to provide information and materials related to the feasibility of some of those and other alternative sources.

Through guided imagery* or other mind-stretching techniques, attempt to invent suggestions for other possible energy sources — apparently feasible or not. Discuss some of the more feasible of these possibilities.

135

(Continued)

66

Bring the discussion back to the present. Each student can generate a list of "Things I Can Do Today" to make more efficient and appropriate use of the natural resources available to the student for fuel and electricity. Share these lists. Encourage students to modify their lists based on good ideas they learn from other students and then create a final list for their own purposes. With the list in hand, encourage them to try living by it for at least the period of one week. At the week's end, bring out the lists — and engage in a class discussion of what happened. Discussion might include:

- How hard it was to do the things on the list.
- If other people were involved and noticed the efforts.
- If other people were involved and objected to the changes.
- Why other people might have objected.
- If other people noticed, got excited, and joined in following suggestions on the list.
- Possible positive results of the students' actions.
- Possible negative results, such as discomfort.
- Implications for their own continued lifestyles.

If this activity is done for an extended period of time, some other indications of impact might be observed; for example, lower household fuel and gasoline bills, new bicycle tires due to increased use, weight loss from increased exercise, different food bills based on additional motor (body) activity.

VARIATIONS

Ask students to read the following summary of findings compiled by a task force of energy specialists as a report to the Carter administration, or make the information available to the students through a tape recording:

> Traditional methods of producing electricity are *very* costly (capital-intensive). Demand for electricity (and all energy supplies) is still rising, although the rate of rise has been slowed somewhat. Even if the U.S. could become energy-independent, such an effort would cost at least 1 trillion dollars ($1,000,000 x $1,000,000; $1 million x $1 million) over the next ten years.
>
> Energy probabilities for our near future can be summed up in this way:
>
> - Coal-synthetics and oil-shale industries will probably not be workable because they will waste too much energy and money (capital).
> - Massive strip-mining of the West will probably not be publicly acceptable, so coal will cost more than once believed.

7.1 Culture as
Learned Behavior
7.2 Cultural Effects
on Resources
7.3 Resource
Depletion
Prevention
7.4 Creative
Expression and the
Environment
SKILLS
I. Gaining
Information
IV. Critical Thinking
V. Problem Solving
VI. Valuing

- Full exploration of the Arctic seems less probable because of the great costs and the great potential environmental damage.
- The electric utility industry is having severe money problems because utility laws force them to be wasteful of both capital and energy.
- Nuclear power is very expensive because the power plant cost is very high and the process of uranium extraction and enrichment is very costly. Much potential danger also remains because of the radioactive nature of the fuel and "waste" product.
- Geothermal and solar power — at least for the next couple of decades — seem unusable for massive electrical generating projects.
- Hydroelectric power is inexpensive to produce, but other resources are lost when rivers are dammed.

Ask student groups to brainstorm new approaches to producing and using energy — electric and other types. They might present these as a class project. As part of their research, the students might locate solar energy installations in their community and arrange to visit them. These might be in use in public buildings, in experimental buildings, or in homes to heat water or space.

New approaches to producing and using energy might fall into two major categories:

1. New sources
2. Utilization procedures for new and present resources, including conservation techniques

You and the students might further categorize responses according to most appropriate and likely uses; for example, for private homeowners, apartment dwellers, government office buildings, factories.

Students might also discuss the accuracy of information ruling out the use of particular sources of energy; for example, because they will be expensive or not available for the next ten years or so. The students could try to imagine the kinds of energy we will be using by the time they are 40 or 50 years old.

RESOURCES

*See "I Thought That I Would Never Be," by Cheryl Charles and Jan Rensel in *Branch 3* (Tiburon, Ca: Project Learning Tree, 1977).

67

Impact Statements

OBJECTIVE

Students will be able to describe some of the procedures involved in the preparation of an environmental impact statement for a given site and project.

ACTIVITY

On January 1, 1970 the United States National Environmental Policy Act (NEPA) came into being. It created a new preventive mechanism for dealing with environmental problems. The heart of NEPA is found in Section 102. This section requires that all federal agencies prepare a "detailed statement" on "every recommendation or report on proposals or legislation and other federal actions *significantly* affecting the quality of the human environment." Specifically, these statements, now known as Environmental Impact Statements (EIS), are required for all projects directly undertaken by federal agencies; supported in whole or in part by federal agencies, contracts, grants, subsidies, loans, or other forms of assistance; or requiring a federal lease, permit, license, or certificate, which meet the "significance" test.

Since EIS's are intended to assess the impact of a proposed action, a draft statement must be prepared at least 90 days before the proposed action for review by appropriate federal, state, and local agencies as well as the public. Once a statement has been prepared and reviewed, comments received during the review process must be answered. A final statement, incorporating all comments and objections and their resolutions, must then be made public at least 30 days prior to the proposed action.

If any of the reviewing agencies or members of the general public feel that the prepared statement is inadequate, they may file a court suit to require further research into the project's environmental impact. The adequacy and completeness of the EIS is then determined through traditional judicial procedures. If the EIS is found inadequate, it may be revised and resubmitted. If the statement is deemed adequate, the proposed action may proceed. However, if the predicted consequences are seriously detrimental, further litigation may be brought to prohibit the proposed action.

Environmental Impact Statements are not intended to be justification for proposed funding or action. They are simply detailed presentations of the environmental impacts of and alternatives to the proposed project. The EIS are not intended to screen alternatives solely on the basis of environmental impact. They are prepared to ensure that environmental amenities as well as technical and economic considerations and public desires are equitably considered.

In this activity students are asked to use the following data to prepare Environmental Impact Statements according to guidelines suggested by the Environmental Protection Agency. The completed statements are then reviewed at a simulated public hearing held by the agency that wrote the statement.

Initial Procedure:

As a class, study the attached suggested guidelines for preparing an EIS. It would be helpful to obtain several actual EIS reports prepared for projects in or near your community. Students could examine these as they review the guidelines.

Divide the class into teams of three to five students each. Then ask each team to prepare an EIS for the Picnic Point Park proposal from the data provided here.

Data:

1. *The situation:* A point of land on nearby Balsam Lake (a federal water impoundment), has been a favorite informal beach for many years. The point is easily accessible although a railroad track on private property must be crossed to get to the beach. It has considerable use because it is one of the few public beach areas left easily reached by residents of the surrounding area. Last year it received 30,000 visitor-days of use.

   After several meetings, the Bureau of Reclamation which administers the area, has decided that Picnic Point should be proposed as a recreational beach site. An EIS must be submitted because the proposed action will be funded by federal money. Responsibility for preparing the EIS rests with those making the proposal, in this case the Bureau of Reclamation. The EIS which is prepared will be reviewed at a public hearing held by the Bureau to meet NEPA's requirements.

2. *The existing environment*: Physical features of Picnic Point include a sandy-gravel beach; a creek running through the park area and emptying into Balsam Lake; and an area graded, but not yet surfaced, for a parking lot.

   Biological characteristics to be considered relate to the lake, the land, and the creek. Balsam Lake is a large, quite deep, manmade lake. It is now relatively unpolluted and contains several kinds of fish with trout the most abundant. However, the water quality is beginning to show some signs of deterioration, possibly because untreated sewage enters the lake from homes and summer cabins on the shore. The lake's edge has algae attached to large pebbles and boulders which attract algae-eating animals and their predators. The shallows serve as a breeding area and habitat for several kinds of animals. Water birds also are lake residents.

The land area once was covered with a forest of western red cedar and hemlock. Since these trees were logged off 50 years ago, bigleaf maple, red alder, a few Douglas firs, and a wide variety of berry and flowering plants have grown up to cover the site.

Picnic Creek is a fast-flowing stream, not very wide or deep. When it floods, it carries silt from bank cuts, sand, and some larger debris into the lake. The water generally is clear and of high quality except for excess numbers of coliform bacteria; the bacteria count is two to three times the number safe in water for human use.

3. *Proposed park development:* The development of Picnic Point would include these features:

Construction and maintenance of an asphalt parking lot for 48 cars, with a bus stop and turn-around; concrete restrooms; a pedestrian railroad underpass 35 feet long, 10 feet wide, 8 feet high and 4 feet below (12 meters long, 3 meters wide, 2.75 meters high, and 1.5 meters below) the tracks; a picnic area on the sandy land between the beach and the railroad; a gravel fill to protect existing trees along the railroad track; walkways; landscaping for shade and sand and soil stabilization; and a settling basin for Picnic Creek located just east of the railroad tracks.

Rules prohibiting camping; horseback riding; motor vehicles; log cutting; fires except in designated facilities; unleashed dogs; excessive noise or congregating of groups; pop-open cans; and damage to vegetation, soil, sand, facilities, or native animal life.

4. *Design considerations*: The development must have plans for sewage disposal from restrooms. Ideally this would be accomplished by building a lift station and force main to transfer sewage to the community's new treatment plant now under construction about 3600 feet (1200 meters) from the restroom location.

The design also must allow for sealed catch basins in the parking lot to prevent hydrocarbon run-off into Picnic Creek and consider the flow increment added to the creek by water run-off from the new asphalt parking lot. Although a large flow is not expected, actual data are unavailable.

The development of the beach area is expected to increase its use from about 30,000 visitor-days annually to 47,000. Facilities must be designed to meet the needs of this greater use.

141

Concluding Procedure:

After the students have completed their EIS reports, the documents should be compared.

Ask the students to discuss:

How the statements differ in their assessment of the significance of the environmental impact, the alternatives they propose, and the evaluation of the short- and long-term benefits of the proposal.

Whether each group considered the project's impact differently. Whether you might have expected all the groups to reach the same conclusion. Why or why not?

Select one member from each of the teams to serve on a simulated Department of Ecology panel which is holding public hearings to receive comments on the EIS prepared. In this hearing, panel members will question the consultants who prepared each EIS to clarify ambiguities or conflicts in conclusions. Students serving on the panel will have the benefit of participating in the process of writing the EIS. Once on the panel, however, they should no longer speak as if they had *prepared* the statements. They are now "respected citizens" questioning consultants about the EIS they have prepared. Another group of students might want to assume the role of interested citizens for the purpose of testifying at the hearing.

VARIATION

In this activity students will prepare an EIS for a hypothetical or actual study site in their community, using either the federal guidelines or their state's statutes.

Here is the hypothetical situation:

An area in your community has been selected as the site for a 100-unit, two-story condominium housing development. The site has sewer and water lines within easy access. All existing trees on the land must be removed, but the developers agree to landscape the site when the building is completed. An excavation for the basement also is necessary.

Through class discussion, try to determine:

An appropriate location for the proposed condominium development. (If an actual project which has filed an EIS statement is underway locally, you may prefer to use this for class study.)

Is a site study (EIS) necessary before development may be approved? If so, why?

What are the important environmental factors which should be measured before preparing an EIS? In other words, what data must be collected? How would these factors be measured?

What is meant by "short-term impact" and "long-term impact"? How long is "long"?

Divide the class into several consultant teams. Each team is to collect part of the necessary data as suggested in the following EIS guidelines and/or according to the state's environmental protection statutes, and write a report.

While doing their research, students could consider:

1. A description of the physical and biological resources of the site.
2. How the existing biotic (life-related) community has adapted to the physical environment.
3. Soil characteristics.
4. Air and water quality.
5. Climatic conditions including average rainfall, seasonal temperature extremes and averages, number of sunny days.
6. Accessibility of utility lines and transportation links to the site.
7. Unique or unusual characteristics of the site.

After the data have been collected, follow the procedure outlined in the first activity. Teams can prepare EIS reports from the same data and present them at a public hearing.

(Continued)

**SUGGESTED GENERAL GUIDELINES FOR PREPARING AN ENVIRON-
MENTAL IMPACT STATEMENT**
Adapted from Preparation of Environmental Impact Statements Guidelines, Revised
Edition, April 1973. Environmental Protection Agency. See also Preparation of
Environmental Impact Statements. Final Regulations. Published in the *Federal
Register*, Monday, April 14, 1975. Volume 40, No. 72, Park II, pp. 16814-16827.

I. DESCRIPTION

A. Describe in qualitative and quantitative terms all biological resources and water
resources. This discussion should include how the biotic communities have adapted
to the physical environment, and should also include the hydrologic cycles of ad-
jacent water bodies.
B. Describe the soil characteristics and geology in the project area.
C. Describe all natural resources in the project area, including wilderness areas.
The statement should recognize that these wilderness areas are a diminishing
resource.
D. Describe existing air quality and any applicable standards or regulations.
E. Include graphic and pictorial information.
F. Describe meteorological conditions in the area.
G. Describe past, present, and proposed land use.
H. Describe accessibility to planning area. Include transportation plans.
I. Describe the socio-economic situation in the community.

II. ENVIRONMENTAL IMPACTS

A. Discuss impacts which may occur to water quality, air quality, noise, solid waste
disposal, and pesticide use.
B. Discuss the impacts the project will have on the physical environment such as
soils, geologic formations, hydrology, drainage patterns, etc.
C. Discuss methodology to be used to minimize adverse environmental impacts.
Where abatement measures can reduce adverse impacts to an acceptable level, the
basis for considering these levels acceptable must be outlined.
D. Discuss the economic impacts of the proposed action.

III. ALTERNATIVES

A. Discuss the full range of management alternatives considered in the course of
planning the action. The null alternative (the alternative of taking no action) must
also be evaluated.
B. Discuss why the proposed alternative was chosen.
C. Discuss alternatives in sufficient detail so others may realize secondary or long-
term environmental impacts.

IV. SHORT-TERM USE VS LONG-TERM PRODUCTIVITY

A. Discuss environmental impact and economic costs and benefits as they relate to
short-term uses and long-term productivity.
B. Discuss how actions taken now will (or will not) limit the number of choices left
for future generations .

V. IRREVERSIBLE AND IRRETRIEVABLE COMMITMENT OF RESOURCES

Discuss resources to be utilized and what the replacement potential of these
resources is.

LIFESTYLES 7

68

What Shall I Use To Build It?

OBJECTIVE

Students will be able to select the most appropriate wood for a project on the basis of the function the project is to serve and the physical properties of the wood.

ACTIVITY

These activities are designed to help students become more aware of the characteristics of different kinds of wood and their advantages and disadvantages for different uses.

Ask your students to examine the classroom looking for uses of wood in either plywood or solid form. Suggest that each student mark off two columns on a sheet of paper. In the first column, the student could record the wood's function (door, beam, desk top) and in the second, whether the wood used is hardwood or softwood.

Then discuss:

Is there any relationship between the type of wood used, its physical characteristics, and its function? (Hardwood, for example, is used where durability is needed, as in oak flooring.)

Is there any relationship between the cost of the wood and its function?

Are some woods used when another type of wood has the physical characteristics which make it more suitable for that function? What might be the reason for the choice? (Perhaps cost or availability.) How might the "wrong" wood be improved? (Suggestions might be to use preservatives or laminations instead of solid wood.)

What are the environmental, economic, and aesthetic implications of substitutions and improvements?

EXTENSION

Suggest that your students build two useful structures, such as bird feeders or birdhouses, one using only softwoods and the other only hardwoods. (In making birdhouses and feeders be sure the necessary research is done to ensure that the birds will find their new home or food source appropriate!) Treat sections of each structure with various types of non-toxic wood preservatives and paints. Leave one section untreated to serve as a control. Expose the structures to the elements for an extended period of time.

After noticeable weathering has occurred, compare the effectiveness of each type of preservative and the durability of each kind of wood.

What Wood Waste?

OBJECTIVE

Students will be able to design, plan, and produce a useful product from shop "waste."

ACTIVITY

Ask your students to brainstorm a list of ways in which materials are frequently wasted during woodworking projects. Then hold a class discussion to talk about ways materials can be used more efficiently and economically. For example, areas such as these might be discussed:

- Project design
- Materials layout
- Reworking of materials (sawing and gluing into laminations)

Demonstrate methods of resawing, gluing, and clamping. Ask each student to design and construct a project using resawing and glue techniques on "waste" wood leftover from a previous project.

Some suggested projects are:

- Candlestick holders, glued, and turned on a lathe
- An inlaid checkerboard using alternating dark- and light-colored woods
- A table or counter top using laminated panels

SUBJECT
Industrial Arts
GRADES
7-9
PLT PRINCIPLE
7. Lifestyles
CONCEPT
7.32 Conservation Through Product Design
SKILLS
IV. Problem Solving
VI. Valuing

70

Which Should I Buy?

OBJECTIVE

Students will be able to identify the trade-offs required to substitute a material derived from a nonrenewable resource for a material derived from a renewable resource.

ACTIVITY

Wood has been abandoned for certain uses and replaced by materials developed by modern technology. Many of the replacements are made from materials derived wholly or predominantly from nonrenewable natural resources, such as plastics from petroleum. This activity explores the advantages and disadvantages of the substitutions.

Help your class brainstorm a list of items which once were usually made from wood and now are usually made from a nonrenewable raw material. Some examples are:

- Metal and plastic furniture for wood furniture
- Plastic bags for paper sacks
- Steel beams for wood beams
- Asphalt floor covering for wood floors
- Metal barrels for wood kegs or casks

Use the list as a starting point for discussing questions like these:

Why were the substitutions made?

What trade-offs were made when the substitution took place?

What are the implications if nonrenewable materials become scarce or too expensive and wood is used again? How might society's energy requirements be affected? What impact would the increased demand for wood have on the other uses and values of our forests? How would employment be affected in wood and nonwood industries?

What renewable materials are more suitable for reuse or recycling than some nonrenewable materials? What nonrenewable materials are more suitable for reuse or recycling than some renewable materials? Is any such recycling going on? What problems are involved in any such recycling?

Would you accept wood or wood products now for any of the items listed? Which ones and why?

In buying and using products derived from natural resources, try to select those that seem to make most effective use of our natural resources.

149

(Continued)

VARIATIONS

Duplicate this questionnaire, or develop your own, and distribute it to your students:

Given the choice, which would you prefer?

• Formica with simulated wood grain	polished solid wood
• Metal sculpture	wood carving
• Plastic toys	wooden toys
• Metal kitchen cupboards	wood kitchen cabinets
• Artificial logs with gas flame	fireplace wood
• Gas burner stove	camp cooking or wood fires
• Aluminum canoe	laminated wood canoe
• Fiberglass-hulled boat	wood-hulled boat
• China bowl	wood salad bowl
• Aluminum ladder	wood ladder
• Chain-link fence	wood-slat fence
• Cement patio	wood decking
• Aluminum outdoor furniture	redwood furniture
• Plaster walls	wood-paneled walls
• Stucco siding	shake shingle siding
• Glass bottle (returnable)	paperboard carton
• Glass bottle (recyclable)	paperboard carton
• Glass bottle (nonreturnable)	paperboard carton
• Metal clothes hangers	wood clothes hangers
• Metal baseball bat	wood baseball bat
• Plastic picture frames	wood picture frames
• Wall-to-wall carpeting	wood floors
• Plastic Christmas tree	a living coniferous Christmas tree
• Aluminum Christmas tree	cut coniferous Christmas tree
• Paper towel	cloth dish towel
• Paper cup	plastic cup

After the students have completed the questionnaires, encourage them to discuss their responses. Explore the feelings, ideas and information they feel affected their selections. Discuss questions such as the following:

What factors influenced your choices?
Did the way in which you planned to use the item influence your decision? Did the item's price influence your choice? Its aesthetics? Its durability or performance?
Can you identify any trends shown by your choices?

70 (Continued)

Then ask your students to find out (1) how much energy is required to manufacture and use one of the products or materials they chose; (2) the relative environmental impact of its manufacture and use; (3) the comparative retail price of each item; (4) its renewability, reusability, and recyclability; and (5) the impact of the item's manufacture and use on the nation's economy.

Follow these investigations with a discussion to include questions such as the following:

How does information related to the energy requirements and environmental impact influence your preference?

On reflection, did you consider these factors when you made your decision?

Would the other item, if you had chosen it, have more or less impact on the environment? On energy consumption? On the economy?

What trade-offs, if any, are involved in the selection of such products?

Which items, if any, do you need to survive? Which could easily be eliminated?

How do your choices reflect your lifestyle and values?

EXTENSIONS

1. Help your students brainstorm a list of comparable items made of renewable and nonrenewable materials to be included on a questionnaire. Then they could use the questionnaire to survey other students or the general public to find out which kind of items are most often preferred. You may wish to include questions to determine the survey respondent's age, sex, education, and socioeconomic level. These could be compiled afterward and compared to see if such factors have an effect on the public's choices. What implications are there to what you have found? How much, if at all, can you generalize from the results of your study?

2. Expand your study to comparison of other renewable and nonrenewable resources commonly used in our society; for example, the substitution of cotton clothing (renewable resource) for synthetics derived from oil (nonrenewable resource).

Biography of a Favorite Thing

71

OBJECTIVE

Students will be able to identify ways they depend on natural resources in their daily lives.

ACTIVITY

Ask students to pick out a favorite object in their life which is a forest product; for example, surfboard, skateboard, wall-poster, kite, clogs, book.

Invite the students to trace their favorite things back to their origins. Encourage them to find out whether their things are entirely forest products. Ask the students to include any resources which were used in the manufacture of each item, and any which contributed in bringing the objects to the students. Then ask the students to make pictures representing all the material and energy inputs in the entire journey of their objects from the forest to its present location. (One could create a wall mural starting with photosynthesis!)

Ask each of the students to count the number of times there was a transfer of energy in the total production and transportation of the favorite thing. Ask each to write an equation to represent all the resource inputs on one side, with the pleasure of the student in having or using the object on the other. Are they equal? Are there other factors to account for?

Suggest that each student look again at the picture of all the resources involved in the production of the favorite thing. What else could have been made from the same materials which made the favorite thing?

Ask the students to continue the pictures to represent where their favorite things will go when they are through with them; for example, through reuse on to eventual decay. The students can determine the life expectancy of their objects, determining how long it will take their objects to be converted through decay into soil. (See, "How Do You Bury a Pile of Dirt?")

EXTENSIONS

1. Decide whether each "favorite thing" could have been made out of some other, nonrenewable material; for example, a petroleum-based product. Create a picture to represent the energy and material inputs involved in the creation of the object in this way. What other things could have been made from these materials? Continue the picture, tracing the rest of the object's journey to eventual decay.

2. As a group of students, do improvisations or charades for the rest of the students expressing the roles your favorite things play in your lives.

SUBJECTS
Science
Social Studies
Mathematics

GRADES
7-12

PLT PRINCIPLES
7. Lifestyles
2. Diversity of Forest Roles
6. Life-Support Systems
5. Management and Interdependence of Natural Resources

CONCEPTS
7.123 Behavior Effects on Environment
7.32 Conservation Through Product Design
6.1 Dynamic Biological Systems
5.5 Trade-offs
2.11 Need for Forest Products
2.242 Forest-Dependent Leisure-Time Activities

SKILLS
I. Gaining Information
II. Communication
IV. Critical Thinking

72

Christmas Trees and the Environment

OBJECTIVE

Students will be able to state their reasons for choosing a living, a fresh-cut, an artificial Christmas tree, or none at all.

ACTIVITY

In December, when Christmas tree sales lots are in operation, ask your students to interview managers of the lots. Students, either alone or in small groups, could talk to the managers to find out:

1. The origin of the trees — nursery, tree farms, or natural forest.
2. The supplier of the trees — local businessperson, local farmer, or out-of-state supplier.
3. The date the trees were cut.
4. The names of the species of trees on sale and their prices.
5. Which species is the best seller. (Students may wish to interview buyers to find out reasons for their choices.)
6. Number of trees usually left unsold after Christmas. What happens to the leftovers?

After the information has been collected and shared, use class discussion to try to answer these questions:

If the trees came from a forest, rather than a nursery or tree farm, could there have been a reason (other than for use as Christmas trees) for cutting them? What positive and negative effects, if any, might their removal have had on the forest; for example, on the wildlife in the forest?

(Continued)

Do any local people depend upon Christmas tree sales to make a living?

Are there any farms or forests nearby where people are allowed or encouraged to cut their own trees? Why do the owners or managers of these trees allow them to be cut? Is a permit required? If so, does the permit cost anything?

Do you prefer a natural Christmas tree to an artificial one? Why? Do you prefer a living tree that can be replanted after Christmas to a cut tree? Why?

What are the advantages and disadvantages of a living tree compared to a cut tree? Compared to an artificial tree? Compared to none at all? What happens, for instance, to all the unsold cut trees? What natural resources are used in making artificial trees?

What is the significance of the traditional Christmas tree to the celebration of the holiday? Is a tree an essential component of the Christmas celebration?

What would happen if a significant number of people stopped buying Christmas trees?

EXTENSION

Construct a survey instrument for use in interviewing local residents. Interviewing might be done on a random basis using social science data-gathering techniques. You might determine the number of residents who indicate that they regularly decorate a Christmas tree; whether the trees are live, cut, artificial, or some alternative; if live, what kind; if live, from what source; and what is done with the tree after the holiday season. Based on the validity of the data and the size of the sample, see what generalizations, if any, you can make about local Christmas tree practices.

73

Paper Consumption

OBJECTIVE

Students will be able to calculate the quantity of newsprint consumed annually by their families and suggest ways they might minimize its environmental impact.

ACTIVITY

Ask your students to collect the newspapers accumulated in their homes during a period of seven days. At the end of the week they are to weigh the newspapers and multiply the weight by 52 to determine the amount their families use each year. (Compile each individual family's total, and all individual totals combined for class total.)

Students could then attempt to answer these questions:

1. Based on the total circulation of your local newspaper(s), and the average weight of a single newspaper, calculate the total tonnage of newsprint consumed in your community on a given day. Multiply this total by the number of days in a year. (For greater accuracy, two figures could be used and combined — one for daily papers, and one for weekend editions.)

2. In 1970, total newsprint consumed in the United States was 9.7 million short tons. (8.8 million metric tons.) In 1970, U.S. population was approximately 207.1 million.

   What was the average per capita consumption of newsprint?
   Answer: 93.67 pounds (42.5 kilograms)

   In 1976 U.S. consumption of newsprint was 9.6 million short tons. (8.7 million metric tons.) Per capita consumption was 89.25 pounds. (40.52 kilograms.) How many people were there in the United States in 1976?
   Answer: U.S. population in 1976 was 215.12 million.

   What percentage of the total newspapers did your family consume during 1976?

3. The total circulations of newspapers in the United States in 1970 were 62.1 million daily, while in 1976, daily circulations were 61.0 million. Newspaper circulations are directly related to the number of households in the country, because it is the usual practice for all members of the household to read one newspaper. In 1970, there were 63.4 million households in the United States and there were 72.9 million households in 1976. What was the daily circulation per household in 1970 and 1976? What reasons might there be for the change in consumption per household over the 6 year period?
   Answer: 1970 circulation per household was .98 and in 1976, circulation per household was .84.

Examples of possible reasons: Increase in use of TV as a news media, fewer traveling to work using mass transit, increase in time spent on leisure activities outside the home.

4. In 1970, newsprint comprised 16.8 percent of the total consumption of paper and paperboard in the United States. What was the total consumption of paper and paperboard in 1970?

Answer: 57.7 million short tons (52.3 metric tons)

5. The consumption of newsprint per capita in 1970 in the United States was 93.7 pounds, in Canada it was 67.5 pounds and in Japan it was 41.6 pounds. If there are .454 kilograms in a pound, what was the consumption of newsprint per capita for these countries in kilograms?

Answer:

United States	42.5 kilograms
Canada	30.7 kilograms
Japan	18.9 kilograms

6. In 1976, the U.S. paper industry consumed 77.6 million cords of wood, of which 28.7 million represented wastes collected from saw mills and plywood plants. What percentage of total usage of woods was represented by wood wastes?

Answer: 27.0 percent

7. Recycling of waste paper is also important. In 1976, waste paper represented 22.8 percent of the total fiber used in manufacturing. Total U.S. production was 64.5 million tons. How much paper was recycled in 1976?

Answer: 14.7 million tons

8. In the eleven western states wood waste accounted for 75.7 percent of the wood fiber used in paper manufacturing. How many cords of wood in total were used in paper manufacturing in the eleven western states?

Answer: 15.7 million

In further discussion, ask your students to consider how newspapers can be used more efficiently and what impact reduced consumption could have on the amount of municipal waste, on dissemination of news, on employment in the paper industry, on natural resources, and on lifestyles.

Data provided by the American Paper Institute, 260 Madison Avenue, New York, New York 10016.

74

Would You Like That Wrapped?

OBJECTIVE

Students will be able to identify varying packaging practices, and to consider the impact of packaging practices on economics, lifestyles, and natural resources.

ACTIVITY

Packaging is present at all levels of the U.S. economy: in industry, the distribution of products , and the marketplace. Packaging is the country's largest single industrial user of paper and glass; it is one of the two largest users of plastics; and it is the third largest user of steel. The system begins with the use of the nation's raw materials which are made into packaging to be sold to virtually all manufacturers of consumer and industrial goods. The packaged product then moves from the processor's facility to the retail outlet for the consumer to purchase. When the product is used, the system ends with the disposal, reuse, and/or recycling of the package.

Packaging of various kinds has accounted for more than 34 percent of the total volume of solid waste produced in the United States. Packaging certainly is not inherently "bad," but it can be a problem. This activity explores the concept of packaging and its relationship to resource consumption and the American lifestyle.

Ask your students to divide into groups of three to five students each. Each group is to visit a different store near the school. Ask each group to get the permission of the store's proprietor to collect data on the forms of packaging used in one department of the store. Data could include:

1. A list of each type of commodity sold in that department.
2. A description of the type, size and weight of packaging used for the various products such as plastic or glass bottles, cans, boxes, cartons, sacks, or a combination of different types of packaging for one product.
3. A notation indicating the apparent reasons the type and size of packaging was used for each product. For example, product protection, containment, sanitation, communication of product identity and use, prevention against pilferage, availability of specific quantities.
4. A notation showing whether, in the students' opinion, the product is appropriately packaged (appropriately packaged could include *no* packaging), insufficiently packaged, more than sufficiently packaged.

(Continued)

Once back in the classroom, students might discuss:

1. What are the reasons for using glass, metal, paper, paperboard, plastics and foils as a packaging material? What kinds of materials are most commonly used for packaging?
2. What are different materials used for the same packaging application, such as glass and plastic for jars? What are the reasons for using these materials to package the product?
3. What are the major packaging uses for steel, aluminum, glass, and other materials identified? What role does the type of packaging used have in the protection of the products?
4. How many appropriately packaged products did you find? How many insufficiently packaged? How many that were sufficiently packaged? Convert these results to percentages.
5. What are some advantages of appropriately packaged products? (Convenience, sanitation, durability in distribution.)
6. What are some disadvantages to inappropriately packaged products?
7. Based on your findings, what, if any, recommendations would you make to regulatory agencies, producers and consumers relating to packaged materials?

VARIATION

Ask students to keep written records of everything thrown away or disposed of in their homes during one week. They should classify each solid waste item as paper and paperboard products, food waste, wood and garden refuse (grass clippings, leaves), glass, metal, or miscellaneous. Miscellaneous includes plastic, cloth, leather, rubber, dirt, paint, oil and ash. At the end of the week, students should calculate the percentage of the total each type of waste represents.

After all the data have been recorded and compiled, discuss:

1. What materials composed the largest percentage of the waste? How do your figures compare with national averages by weight?
2. Which of the materials discarded were reusable? How many recyclable? How many non-recyclable? Is your family recycling all the items which can be recycled? How could some of the disposable items be reused? What could be done to increase the number of items reused?
3. What are economic and environmental considerations related to the use and reuse of these materials?

(Continued)

As a follow-up activity, students could survey their community to determine how many group recycling programs there are and interview the managers to find out the procedures used and problems encountered in operating the programs.

EXTENSION

Trace the population shift in the U.S. over the past one hundred years from an agrarian to a semi-rural country to our current predominantly urbanized society.

• How has the population shift changed the methods used to market products and affected the kind of products sold?

• What changes over the years have occurred in the handling, processing, transporting and storing of products? How has packaging contributed to these changes?

• What effects did the changes in employment, per capita income level and education over the years have on the packaging of products? Are there indications that packaging will be more significant in the future? Why?

• What are the food industries? (Growers, processors, beverage firms, wholesalers, retail stores, and restaurant/institution.) How has packaging changed food processing and marketing?

• How has packaging changed the consumption of food by consumers? The productivity of farms? Seasonal availability of food? Costs?

75

...And a Side Order of Paper

OBJECTIVE

Students will be able to describe ways in which consumer decisions have far-reaching economic, social, and environmental implications.

ACTIVITY

The take-out, fast-food industry has a big appetite for natural resources. For example, it typically uses hamburger wrappers; boxes for the wrapped hamburgers; cardboard trays for the bag and the box and the wrappers; napkins; straws wrapped in paper; salt, pepper, sugar, and powdered cream in paper packets; coffee cups from petroleum-derived plastics or paper; soft drink cups. And all the packaging is most often discarded within 15 minutes after its contents are consumed, a practice that contributes to the country's solid waste problem.

This activity examines the trade-offs, economic and environmental, involved in the consumption of resources through packaging practices.

Divide the class into small groups. Ask each group to survey a local fast-food restaurant to find out the quantity of each type of disposable packaging it uses in a given period of time, such as a week or a month. Before beginning the survey, ask the students to make up a questionnaire to be used when they interview the restaurant manager. Sample questions are:

1. What items does your establishment use for disposable packaging, and from what renewable and nonrenewable resources are these products derived?
2. How many of each item do you use per [insert time period]?
3. What companies supply these items?
4. Why do you use disposable materials?
5. Do you think you are properly packaging your products? (Remember, you want to keep the restaurant manager friendly, so be careful how this question is phrased!)
6. What percentage of the total cost of your product does the packaging represent?
7. Would it be possible for your restaurant to operate without disposable packaging?
8. How many employees do you have? How much is your total payroll?
9. Where and how do you dispose of your restaurant's solid waste (for example, landfill, incinerate, recycle, etc.)?

(Continued)

When students have completed their interviews and tabulated their data, you might explore some of the following questions with them:

1. What were the principal reasons given for the use of disposable packaging?
2. Are any of the disposable items used by the fast-food outlets produced locally? If so, how many jobs are dependent upon sales of these products? (Don't forget printing, transportation, manufacturing of machines to print, making paper, etc.)
3. If fast-food restaurants made changes to eliminate disposable packaging, who, if any, might lose their jobs? How might it be possible to retrain any affected personnel, rather than simply eliminating their positions?
4. What, if any, alternatives to use of disposable materials are available to the restaurant owners? What are the environmental and economic costs of these alternatives?
5. How might the alternatives affect the cost and convenience of take-out food?
6. What price do we pay for the convenience of fast-food restaurants and, in your opinion, is the convenience worth the price?
7. What changes in jobs and lifestyles might we see if our population continues to grow within a finite resource base?

EXTENSION

1. Students might determine major categories of natural resources used, not just limiting their study to packaging and use of disposable materials, but other uses of natural resources and products in the fast-food industry. Renewable and nonrenewable resources could be identified as part of the analysis.

2. Suggest that students explore use of natural resources by other restaurants. Do these other restaurants appear to use natural resources as efficiently, more efficiently, or less efficiently than fast-food restaurants.

76

The Second Time Around

OBJECTIVE

Students will be able to assess and describe impacts of changing technology on the quality and availability of home furniture, as well as describe monetary, social, and environmental costs related to home furniture.

ACTIVITY

Arrange for your class to visit a second-hand furniture store. Ask students to identify pieces of furniture which are made all, or in part, of wood. Then direct the students to pick out two pieces of furniture of the same kind (two tables or two chairs, for instance) which appear to have been made several years apart. Ask them to examine the furniture carefully and make notes to determine:

Which piece of furniture, the older or the newer, appears to have more solid wood in its construction? Is this true of other furniture in the shop?

Which piece appears to have been made with more care or craftsmanship? In other parts of the shop, do the old or newer pieces show better workmanship?

Which pieces are more durable, the old or the newer?

If both pieces were on sale today, new, which would you choose? Why? Which would cost more initially and which more in the long run? Why?

After you return to the classroom, you might discuss:

Compare the older wooden furniture to that being manufactured today and sold at the same price. Which appears to be better constructed? Which more aesthetically pleasing?

Compare the price of older wooden furniture to that of newer wooden furniture of comparable quality — both handcrafted and assembly-made.

Establish criteria for determining quality and then compare the quality and price of old and new furniture made from different natural resources. Distinguish between furniture made primarily from renewable resources and furniture primarily made from nonrenewable resources.

Does the price of furniture appear to include the social and environmental costs and benefits of its construction? Can we measure these extra costs? Can we measure any benefits? If so, how? If not, why not?

How, if at all, might construction and use of furniture be more consistent with an environmentally sound lifestyle?

You've Come a Long Way, Maybe

OBJECTIVE

Students will be able to describe ways in which changing domestic habits have intensified human impact on the environment.

ACTIVITY

Ask students, either as individuals or in small groups, to find out the equivalents of modern kitchen and laundry equipment frequently used in pioneer and ancient times. For example for washing clothes: ancient — stream and a flat rock; pioneer — cast-iron tub and wash-board; modern — automatic washer. For information and photographs or drawings, try libraries, historical societies, and museums.

You and the students could then discuss:

The resources that went into each type of equipment.

Which time period used the most *nonrenewable* resources and which the most *renewable* resources; which time period used the most reusable resources; which the most durable.

Which time period used the most energy-intensive devices, which the most convenient, and which the most labor-intensive.

Which time period you would prefer to live in. Why?

How would a tremendous decrease in the amount of nonrenewable resources available change the modern families' lifestyles? What about a tremendous decrease in the amount of renewable resources? What might be causes for such decreases even in renewable resources? How would a tremendous increase in the cost of energy affect modern lifestyles?

In order to reduce household costs, which labor-saving devices or products would you be willing to give up first? Which second? Continue to list them all in the order you would be willing to eliminate them.

Invent an alternative method to do the task now handled by the labor-saving device you are giving up. What is the alternative's impact on the environment? Will it cost more? How do you measure the cost in money, time, and environmental impact? Do you think the alternative is a better or worse choice than the original? Describe the reasons for your response.

EXTENSION

Imagine a day in the lives of a family in each time period, including the present. Determine what percentages of each day might have been or are required for tasks using the various kinds of equipment being studied. What kinds of activities might fill the rest of the day?

Compare leisure time available, and amounts and types of energy and equipment typically used in leisure-time activities. Consider the implications of any results you find.

78

The Continuing Adventures of the Truffle Tree Company

OBJECTIVE

Students will be able to discuss and interpret a fictional work related to use and abuse of natural resources.

ACTIVITY

The Lorax, a children's book by Dr. Seuss, tells of the deterioration of an environment because of reckless exploitation of "truffle trees" to produce "thneeds" to meet the incessant demands of consumers. The book has also been made into a film by the same title. *The Lorax* is sometimes shown on television, and is often available through local media centers and organizations.

Make *The Lorax* available to your students in some form, discuss the general story line, and then explore questions like these with them:

1. What seems to be the author's intent in writing this book?
2. Do you equate the ideas in the story with real situations in present-day society? If so, with what people, what resources, and what issues?
3. Describe any values which appear to be important in the story. Identify any present-day counterparts to these values. Are any of these values in apparent conflict? If so, which ones? And for what apparent reasons?
4. Does *The Lorax* appear to have been written for young children, for their parents, or for both?
5. What, if any, significance do ideas presented in *The Lorax* have for you in your daily life?

Ask your students to share *The Lorax* in some form with some younger children they know. Then ask if these younger children appear to equate the people and events in the story with reality? If yes, with whom and what? If not, what might limit the children's ability to do this?

(Continued)

EXTENSION

As a class project, suggest that your students translate the Seuss language into common English to create a Seuss-English dictionary. Students, either alone or in small groups, can use the dictionary to write and illustrate sequels to *The Lorax*. The sequels might explain what the authors, as new presidents of the Truffle Tree Co., are going to do to maintain a quality environment, at the same time ensuring the continuing growth and availability of "truffle trees."

After the sequels are finished, ask the students to share them in class and explore these questions:

1. Do either the original Seuss story or the students' sequels seem to accurately portray the forest industry today? Other industries? Anyone else? What is the evidence for your opinion?
2. Which version appears to describe most realistically the present American lifestyle?
3. What are the social and economic implications of those programs suggested in the sequels to ensure a quality environment? For example, who will pay for the environmental protection? Who will pay for the damage to the environment if a program proves to be unsuccessful?

After careful analysis and discussion, ask each of the students to identify ways, if any, in which they might appropriately modify their own lifestyles to more effectively ensure a long-term quality environment.

79

ORVs and Us

OBJECTIVE

Students will be able to describe ways in which off-road vehicles affect the environment as well as lifestyles, including energy use.

ACTIVITY

Hold a brainstorming session with your class to develop two lists relating to off-road vehicles (ORVs), such as trail bikes, snowmobiles, and dune buggies.

The first list could include possible benefits and positive uses of ORVs. Examples are jobs, rescue missions, and access to remote areas.

The second list could include the effects of ORVs on the environment, particularly as related to water, soil, air quality, wildlife, vegetation, and energy sources. For example, the vehicles compact soil, create noise pollution, and disturb wildlife.

If your students are unfamiliar with ORVs, you might first show a film (see Resources) which describes their use. Local resource people and the students themselves may be able to provide informative background.

Once a base of information has been established, and the lists of possible beneficial and detrimental effects and uses generated, discuss with the students both the long- and short-term implications for their use. Include in your consideration any implications for:

- Wildlife
- Soil
- Plant life
- Noise
- Fire Danger
- Air quality
- Energy consumption (be sure to consider energy required to manufacture, transport to point of use, and operate)
- Lifestyles (the Eskimo culture, for example)
- Entertainment
- Employment
- Safety and rescue operations

After the discussion, students might divide into small working groups to draw up lists of recommendations they believe would help assure that the uses and effects of ORVs will be positive.

Compile a master list of guidelines from the groups' recommendations. Compare it with guidelines established by local or national ORV associations (see Resources) and by state and federal government agencies such as the U.S. Forest Service and the Bureau of Land Management. Discuss similarities and differences.

Lovin' It to Death

SUBJECTS
Social Studies
Physical Education
Driver Education
GRADES
7-12
PLT PRINCIPLES
7. Lifestyles
5. Management and
Interdependence of
Natural Resources
2. Diversity of Forest
Roles
CONCEPTS
7.211 Pressure on
Forest Recreational
Facilities
7.123 Behavior Effects
on Environment
7.122 Desires
Outstripping
Resources
5.2 Depletion Dangers
2.124 Aesthetic
Benefits
SKILLS
V. Problem Solving
IV. Critical Thinking
VI. Valuing

OBJECTIVE

Students will be able to state their recommendations for solving problems of overcrowding and overuse of public recreation areas.

ACTIVITY

Ask your students to read and consider this information:

Public recreation areas — including national and state parks and forests as well as designated wilderness areas, wildlife refuges, and estuaries — are under increasing pressure, as indicated by the following data:

	1950		1975
Visits to the National Park System (all areas)	33,300,000		238,800,000
Population of the United States	150,697,361		212,796,000
	1950	1965	1970
Recreation Use of National Forest Lands (visitor days)	38,932,000	160,336,000	172,555,000

It is obvious that use is increasing at a more rapid rate than population growth, creating problems related to the maintenance and protection of these areas for their established purposes, and affecting such things as wildlife, vegetation, watersheds, and appropriate human activities.

Note: Visits are not exactly equivalent to persons, since the same person may make more than one visit. One visitor day equals 12 hours of use. (Figures given above are from the *Statistical Abstract of the United States 1976* and Bureau of Census population figures.)

People seeking to spend some time in natural areas and to enjoy nature and the spectacular scenery of many parts of our country, as well as those trying to escape from the crowds and pressures of cities, are finding the same urban problems in the form of traffic jams, polluted lakes, litter, garbage, and overcrowding in their recreation areas as in the cities.

(Continued)

Hold a class discussion on questions such as the following. You might ask individuals or small groups to be prepared to state a position, which the class could then discuss.

1. Under what circumstances, if any, might citizens appropriately be prevented from entering and using a public recreation area?

2. What circumstances may have caused the tremendous increase in outdoor recreation activities?

3. Should our existing public recreation areas, such as national parks and forests, be managed to accommodate more visitors? If so, how? What problems might be solved and what problems might be created by your proposal?

4. Is recreation the only purpose of the various public recreation areas (national and state parks and forests, wilderness areas, wildlife refuges, estuaries)? Is it the primary purpose? What was the original intent of establishing each of these areas? Has the intent changed? How and why? Does it appear that any other changes are necessary or appropriate? Describe your reasoning.

5. Does it appear that more public recreation areas should be established? If so, what kind, how many, and where? What impact might the increase have on the use of resources for other purposes? What possible trade-offs are involved? Would you be willing to accept these trade-offs? State your reasons. (This issue might warrant a debate if there is sufficient student interest.)

6. It has been advocated that parks be sold and the "park experience" be priced at its "true economic value." The reasoning is that this would eliminate the need for quotas, as the cost would make park use self-regulating. What do you think about this proposal? (See Variation I for expansion on this theme.)

7. If you sleep in a state or national park, do you pay all the costs? If you sleep in a hotel in the city, do you pay all the costs? If there is a difference, why?

8. Other proposed solutions are to increase facilities and to open up the wilderness areas. To these ideas Bob Marshall replied, "Only a small minority enjoy art galleries, libraries and universities. Yet no one would suggest making these facilities into bowling alleys, circuses or hot dog stands just because more people would use them." Do you agree with his rebuttal?

9. If our population and our cities continue to expand, would you anticipate a still greater demand on these recreation areas? What other factors might affect trends in recreation? The Bureau of Outdoor Recreation estimates that recreation demand will triple by the year 2000. However, because of the gasoline shortage, national forest recreation use was less in 1973 than the year before. Does this information alter your opinion?

10. If it were possible to create more parks in urban areas, how might this affect the demand on national parks?
11. What other possible means are there for attempting to most effectively maintain and use our national recreation areas.

EXTENSION

1. Garrett Hardin has termed situations similar to the one described at the beginning of this activity as "The Tragedy of the Commons." (See his article of that title listed in the Bibliography.) Briefly his theme is that in the beginning everyone using a "common" or publicly owned or shared resource benefits from that resource, but as each tries to increase the benefits he or she receives from the commons by making more use of the resource, the use becomes so intensified that no one benefits, not even at the original level. Hardin uses the example of ranchers grazing sheep on a commonly held area and each adding sheep until the common becomes so overgrazed that no one benefits. The theory applies equally well to other resources.

   Two possible solutions to the problem of the commons are (1) regulate its use, or (2) place it in private ownership and charge for its use, letting price set by supply and demand allocate the limited resource.

   To explore the concept of the commons and the proposals for solutions to problems it generates, ask students to read Hardin's article and/or view the film titled, "The Tragedy of the Commons" (also listed in the Resources). Then compare the situation described for this activity with the idea of the commons. Discuss:

   • How does the situation in the national and state parks and forests illustrate the concept of the commons? What other things (such as air and water) has society treated as commons?

   • How have we attempted to solve the problem of the commons (through means such as regulation and price)?

   • Which, if any, of these means could be used to solve problems of overcrowding and overuse in existing parks? Do they offer advantages over expanding or adding more parks? Disadvantages?
   Note: At this point, you may wish to introduce the idea of selling the parks, if this thought has not yet been expressed. If the students show enough interest, divide the class into two groups to debate the question:

   "Pricing the park experience at its fair market value would be the most appropriate solution to overcrowding in our national parks and wilderness areas."

2. In conjunction with the first activity, obtain and show one or all of these films. (See Resources for information on sources.)

   For All to Enjoy
   Pave It and Paint It Green
   The People's Heritage

3. After reading the initial activity, ask each student to create a mock application form for visiting a national park, forest, or other public recreation area. The form could include such things as the student's name; real or fictitious name of the area the student wishes to visit; date of visit; reasons for the visit; and activities the student wishes to pursue in the area.

   On the chalkboard, list the activities mentioned on the application forms. Ask students to devise categories where each might be placed.

   Do any of the activities reflect social needs such as peace and quiet?

   Do the activities reflect interests and abilities of the entire population? Can any be pursued by the elderly or the physically handicapped?

   Are some of the activities in conflict, such as fishing and water-skiing? What methods, such as time and spatial zoning or adding recreational areas, could be used to minimize the conflicts?

   Do your students believe that the reservation system increases or decreases freedom of choice for the individual or for an interest group?

   What are some of the reasons for the need for a reservation system? Can your students suggest ways to solve the problem of overcrowding without using this system? What are the social, economic, and environmental implications of the students' proposals?

Plan a Trip

OBJECTIVE

Students will be able to describe the environmental and economic impact of different kinds of forest recreation.

ACTIVITY

Ask your students to generate a list of the different ways in which they might use a forest site for outdoor recreation; for example, for backpacking, fishing, hunting, car- and tent-camping, recreational vehicle camping, and nature study.

Divide the class into small groups. Ask each group to plan a visit for the same length of time to the same forest recreation area, choosing one of the uses listed above or another use they suggest.

Ask each group to find out what they would need for the visit and what costs would be involved; for example, identify economic costs related to such things as price of equipment, special training, licenses, fees, use or fire permits, and maps. Identify possible environmental costs such as loss of forage for wildlife, soil compaction and erosion, and stress to populations of endangered species.

After all the groups have gathered and organized this information, you and they might compare the costs of the trips by discussing these questions:

Which recreational activity costs the most and which the least?

Which recreational use requires the greatest and which the smallest expenditure of energy? Be sure to take into account energy used in manufacturing and maintaining equipment.

How does the economic cost of these modes of use relate to their environmental cost or impact?

Does the dollar amount spent on the trip or experience represent its full economic cost? For example, who pays for maintenance of the facilities required for outdoor recreational activities?

Follow this discussion by an analysis of the various potential benefits related to each of these recreational uses of and practices within a forest area. Weigh the costs and the benefits related to each. Take a trip that seems to combine the greatest benefits with the fewest negative costs!

SUBJECTS
Social Studies
Physical Education
Driver Education

GRADES
9-12

PLT PRINCIPLES
7. Lifestyles
2. Diversity of Forest Roles

CONCEPTS
7.2112 Impact of Leisure-Time Activities on Forests
2.11 Need for Forest Products
2.1241 Variety of Leisure-Time Activities

SKILLS
I. Gaining Information
III. Social Participation
IV. Critical Thinking
VI. Valuing

82

A Simpler Life

OBJECTIVE

Students will be able to describe humankind's interdependence with modern technological society.

ACTIVITY

There are a number of books and films available which document the lives of various individuals who have left the comforts and constraints of "modern society" and built lives for themselves in wilderness settings. Some of these are listed in the Resource section of the PLT materials. Suggest that students read one or more of the books referenced or others dealing with similar stories. After sharing briefly some of the details of the lives of the individuals read about, ask students to write a composition comparing their lifestyles with that of one of these people.

Some guidelines students might consider in their writing include: food gathering, shelter, communication and the availability of news of the world, energy sources, water supply, entertainment and recreation, work, cultural opportunities, reading, political activities, food consumed, cooking utensils, waste disposal and sewage facilities, skills required to survive, and land area required to support oneself.

Ask the students to share the compositions in class and then discuss the possibilities of modern society reverting "back to nature." They might consider:

1. Could society as a whole emulate any of the individuals studied? What would we gain and what would we sacrifice? What might prohibit us from doing so?
2. How might less drastic changes in our lifestyles contribute to a better environment?
3. What might some of these changes be? How might they help and what problems could they cause?

EXTENSIONS

1. See if you can find out about an historical person from your own region who lived in a fashion similar to any of those individuals studied.
2. Find evidence, if any, for a contemporary person with a lifestyle comparable to any of those individuals studied.

Careers in Forestry

83

OBJECTIVE

Students will be able to describe a forest-related career of interest to them.

ACTIVITY

Ask the students, individually or in small groups, to identify a major forest-related career that interests them. Examples of some forest-related careers are: hydrologist, recreation specialist, land use planner, wildlife specialist, forester, timber manager, and wilderness ranger. Each student or group of students could attempt to arrange a meeting with an individual who works in a similar position.

Suggest that the students prepare questions to ask this individual about his or her career in advance of their meeting. The class as a whole may want to brainstorm a master list of general questions (for example, What kind of training is required?). If a personal interview cannot be arranged, the students could pose their questions in a letter.

Once the interviews have taken place, and the students have a base of information, suggest that they prepare a five- to ten-minute speech about the career they have researched and present it to the class. They may wish to use graphs, pictures, charts, photographs, and tools as visual aids in their oral presentation.

EXTENSION

Expand your list to include vocations related to other natural resources. Have a "Natural Resource Job Fair," designed so that people can learn about a variety of resource-related jobs.

SUBJECTS
Vocational
  Agriculture
Science
Social Studies
Language Arts and
  Humanities

GRADES
7-12

PLT PRINCIPLES
7. Lifestyles
3. Cultural Contexts
2. Diversity of Forest
   Roles

CONCEPTS
7.4 Creative
    Expression and the
    Environment
7.3 Resource
    Depletion Prevention
3.21 Standard of
    Living and Resources
2.13 Community
    Benefits from Forests

SKILLS
V. Problem Solving
II. Communication
I. Gaining
   Information

84

Plan Your Community's Future

SUBJECT
Social Studies

GRADES
10-12

PLT PRINCIPLES
7. Lifestyles
5. Management and Interdependence of Natural Resources
4. Societal Perspectives on Issues

CONCEPTS
7.123 Behavior Effects on Environment
5.1 Interdependence of Resources
5.3 Urban-Forest Interdependence
4.4 Variety in Use
4.47 Zoning and Planning

SKILLS
I. Gaining Information
III. Social Participation
V. Problem Solving
VI. Valuing
II. Communication
IV. Critical Thinking

OBJECTIVE

Students will be able to state land-use planning goals, classifications, and criteria, and will be able to use these goals, classifications, and criteria in developing comprehensive community land-use proposals.

ACTIVITY

Initiate a discussion with your students based on what they want their community to be like in the future. Then ask the students to develop some long-range planning goals for their community, putting these goals in writing. Suggest that they consider, as they formulate their goals, what they think would be the optimum situation regarding such issues as population size and density, percentage of open space, provisions for housing, energy sources and uses, transportation systems, educational and recreational facilities, ecological conditions, and types of industry to be allowed or discouraged.

After they have decided upon a set of goals — working individually, in small groups, or in one large group — ask the students to draw up a list of classifications for current and proposed community land uses; for example, *high density residential, light industrial, commercial.* (*Note:* these are commonly used terms; but do not discourage students from inventing their own new classifications.) Assist them in developing criteria for each classification, including the land uses which would be permitted under it. If students decide to use a zoning system, these classifications could become the zones. Assist the students in identifying factors which should be considered in determining suitable land uses. Example factors to be considered are environmental impact, economic costs and benefits, and social needs. Once these factors have been identified and researched, the information gathered can be used to establish criteria by which the various classifications can be defined. The criteria and classifications should be consistent with the community's goals.

Next, ask the students to take a detailed look at current land uses. This could be done either by obtaining a land-use map of the community (usually available from a local planning agency) or by conducting a walking land-use survey of the community. A suggested procedure for the walking survey would be to:

1. Make large scale maps of small sections of the community. (Resource: local government engineer will have plot maps.)
2. Distribute the maps to members of the class.
3. From on-site observations, designate land uses as defined previously by the class (adding classifications if necessary) and using some kind of key or color-coding.

4. Compile a master map of current community land uses.

At this point it might be useful for students to split up into teams of three to five persons, with each team focusing on one of the goals designated as a priority by the class. Given the information about the current status of community land, and the land use classifications and criteria they have developed, ask them to develop a community land use proposal that would accomplish the goal their group has chosen to work on. After they have had sufficient time to draft or sketch a proposal, the teams can take turns making preliminary presentations outlining their ideas. In this way, two or more teams may find other proposals with which theirs can easily be combined. These teams can work together, possibly delegating various tasks such as making sketches, drawing maps, and composing written explanations, to create ever more comprehensive planning proposals. Eventually, the class may come up with one or more proposals addressing several of the goal statements they set out to accomplish.

Looking at each plan, discuss how it looks in terms of such considerations as:

Provisions for population increase. (For example, housing, industrial growth.) If there are none or few, does this fit with the group's goal concerning optimum population?

Transportation systems. Are they designed primarily for individual or mass transit, or a combination?

Efficiency of energy use. Is the energy base renewable or nonrenewable, or both?

Balance of nature. Have natural cycles been taken into account? For example, are there provisions for plant and animal communities to exist with or near the human community?

Balance of economic, social, and environmental good health. Is it possible for people to live here, make a living, and enjoy their life in harmony with the environment?

Change it represents from the present community land-use situation. What might be implications of the proposed changes in terms of the environment, the local economy, the type of people who live here, and what these people do?

From this the class can proceed to a more general discussion of land-use planning. For example, is planning necessary? Why or why not?

In practical terms, how far ahead can people plan? Should planning be short-term, long-term, or both?

How may land-use planning affect the individual, the family (consider all members separately), the people on fixed incomes, the property owner, the business person?

(Continued)

Assuming the plan(s) developed by the students are based on their priorities for members of the whole community, ask the students to discuss and evaluate the process of land-use planning they experienced. If they were decision-makers for a community, how much input would they want from community members as to their desires for community land-use, and how much weight would they give their opinions? If they did want input, how would they get it? How can an individual in a community most effectively and responsibly affect community planning?

EXTENSION

Take your students to your local planning office to examine the current land-use or zoning map. Compare the plan with those developed by the students, noting the differences and similarities. Invite the students' recommendations to improve the present plan. Find out whether there is a way for students to contribute to future land-use plans.

If your community has no comprehensive land-use plan, your students might wish to submit theirs for consideration or attempt to initiate a planning process using suggestions such as those listed in the Resources section of the PLT materials. They might also contact organizations such as California Tomorrow, the American Society of Planning Officials, the Conservation Foundation, and the League of Women Voters.

A Comparison
of Insulation Efficiencies

85

OBJECTIVE

Students will be able mathematically to compare the relative insulation efficiencies of common building materials.

ACTIVITY

Using the tables provided, ask your students to calculate the answers to these questions:

1. How many times more efficient as insulation are most woods commonly used as building materials than most stones?
2. How many inches of stone would be required to insulate as well as two inches of wood?
3. Is a woodpecker's nest in the heart of a 10-inch tree as well insulated as a bear's den inside a 3-foot thick rock?
4. How thick would the walls of the bear's den have to be to be better insulated than the woodpecker's nest?
5. How many times more efficient as insulation is wood than concrete? Than steel? Than aluminum?
6. How many inches (centimeters) of concrete would be required to insulate a human dwelling as well as two inches (5 centimeters) of wood? How many inches (centimeters) of air space?
7. How many times less energy is required to manufacture one ton (metric tonnes) of lumber than an equal amount of steel?
8. What is the ratio of energy required to produce equal amounts of aluminum to steel? (State in lowest terms.)
9. How many tons (metric tonnes) of lumber could be manufactured using the same amount of energy as it takes to manufacture one ton of aluminum?

(Continued)

TABLE 1

Thermal Properties of Various Building Materials, Per Inch of Thickness[a]

Material	Thermal Conductivity (K)	Thermal Resistance (R)	Efficiency as an Insulator (Percent)
Wood	0.80	1.25	100.0[b]
Air Space[c]	1.03	0.97	77.6
Cinder Block	3.6	0.28	22.4
Common Brick	5.0	0.20	16.0
Face Brick	9.0	0.11	8.9
Concrete (Sand & Gravel)	12.0	0.08	6.4
Stone (Lime or Sand)	12.5	0.08	6.4
Steel	312.0	0.0032	.25
Aluminum	1416.0	0.00070	.06

[a]From *The Energy Conservation Issue*, published by the National Forest Products Association, Washington, D.C. (See Resources.)

[b]For purposes of easy comparison we have assigned wood a rating of 100 and calculated the appropriate values for the other materials in relation to that figure. Actual values for heat transfer resistance of materials can be found in handbooks such as the *Handbook of Fundamentals*, published by the American Society of Heating and Air-Conditioning Engineers.

[c]For air in a space; applies for air spaces ranging from ¾ to 4 inches in thickness (approximately 1.9 to 10 centimeters).

TABLE 2

Energy Required to Manufacture Various Building Materials

Lumber - 453 kilowatt hours (kwh)/ton (.9 metric tonne)
Steel - 3,780 kwh/ton
Aluminum - 10,160 kwh/ton
Source: National Forest Products Association. "The Energy Conservation Issue" (pamphlet). See Resources.

EXTENSION

Design an experiment to test the insulation value of a saguaro cactus compared to that of a specified wood or stone.

180

86

Dome Homes

OBJECTIVE

Students will be able to build a model geodesic dome home and state advantages and disadvantages of a dome home compared with a conventional single family home and multi-family dwellings.

ACTIVITY

As a class project, build scale models of a geodesic home and a conventional single family home using wood. Once completed, compare the two structures and discuss:

What other materials might be used to build the geodesic dome, the single family home? Classify all the materials identified, including wood, as being derived from renewable or nonrenewable resources.

What problems might there be in the future in obtaining the different types of materials?

What would be the effect on the environment if wood were used in home building? Aluminum? Steel? Other materials?

Do you think many people would want to live in dome homes? Conduct an opinion poll of your community and school to determine which style, dome or conventional, might be more popular, and why.

Does the dome home comply with local building codes? If not, how might the structure be changed to meet the codes? Could the codes be changed? How might this be accomplished?

What other possible approaches to forms of housing might be explored? Are there any local groups attempting innovative housing alternatives? If so, what successes and problems are they finding?

EXTENSION

There are problems in providing single family housing for everyone, given the pressures of agriculture and development on our fixed-land base and the differences in family incomes. Ask the students to explore how more economical family housing might be provided for everyone. How would this affect our land base? Are there alternatives in multi-family housing that might be acceptable? How would this affect our use of land? Compare single family and multi-family dwellings:

- Which uses more renewable resources?

- Which uses more nonrenewable resources?

- Which uses more land?

- How does each affect the capacity of road systems, sewage systems, water systems, school systems?

- If only multi-family dwellings were available, what effect would this have on our lifestyles? The makeup of our cities? What has happened in cities where neighborhoods have become overcrowded?

- Considering the effect of different types of housing on the environment, what mix, if any, would you suggest to make adequate housing available for families with different incomes without sacrificing a feeling of privacy and space?

87

Design with Nature

OBJECTIVE

Students will be able to design a segment of one community taking into account environmental, energy, economic, and aesthetic considerations.

ACTIVITY

Join your students in brainstorming a list of reasons trees, shrubs, and other greenery are necessary in urban areas. Some of the reasons might be: to help filter the air, to help muffle noise, to provide beauty and shade, to increase ecological stability and diversity.

Ask students, working individually or in small groups, to design a small residential area within a larger community. In making their designs they might consider factors such as:

- economics (Is the plan practical?)
- privacy of residents
- number and size of lots
- number and size of green areas
- ratio of houses to open space
- placement of vegetation
- environmental impact
- energy efficiency
- educational facilities

When they have finished their designs, students could play the simulation *Land Use* (see Bibliography) and/or read some of the references cited in the Resources section of the PLT materials. After some evaluation and discussion of their designs, encourage the students to make revisions in their plans. Students also could compare their plans with those drawn for an actual housing development in their community, if possible talking with the architect who did the plans.

VARIATION or EXTENSION

1. Conduct the above activity to design commercial or industrial areas within a community.
2. Design an entire model community.

A Look at Lifestyles

OBJECTIVE

Students will be able to identify some of their own uses of renewable and nonrenewable resources, suggesting ways they might appropriately change their own lifestyles to more effectively make use of natural resources.

ACTIVITY

Define the terms "renewable" and "nonrenewable." Ask your students to list the renewable and nonrenewable resources in products they have used or consumed in the past 24 hours, identifying each product as (1) essential for survival, (2) necessary for maintenance of their present lifestyle, or (3) a luxury. This list can be made using words and/or images. For example, students can draw pictures of each of the products they have used in the past 24 hours, accompanying these with images or words identifying each of the natural resources from which the products are made.

After looking at the lists and discussing them, ask each student to propose alternatives for each item listed in categories two and three, making an effort to replace items which they believe are inefficient or wasteful. A master list of the resources used and the proposed alternatives can be created in the form of a display. Questions such as these might be discussed with the students:

Which, if any, items listed in the "essential" category are really not essential? What are your criteria for evaluating an item's necessity?

Which, if any, items listed in the second category are luxuries? On what basis do you judge an item a luxury?

What would be the environmental and economic impact of switching to your alternatives? Would it increase your use of renewable resources? (For example, switching from aluminum foil to cellophane food wrap would accomplish this.) Or, would it increase your use of nonrenewable resources? (Switching from paper cups to most plastic cups would have this effect.) How would changes in the production, and consumption of these products influence the use of energy? How might changes in the production and consumption of these products affect the economy?

Look at the list of luxury items. Which items could you give up without a major change in your lifestyle?

Make a list, beginning with the easiest item to give up and ending with the most difficult. Could you give up the top three items on this list for a day? A week? A month? Try it.

Think of several ways in which to reuse or recycle items you determine you could *not* give up, if any.

Identify the resulting economic, cultural, and environmental repercussions involved in any changes you make or recommend. Consider the implications if your entire family, school, community, and nation made such changes.

SUBJECT
Social Studies
GRADES
7-12
PLT PRINCIPLES
7. Lifestyles
5. Management and Interdependence of Natural Resources
CONCEPTS
7.1221 Conflicts in Consumption Patterns
7.3 Resource Depletion Prevention
5.12 Renewable Resources
5.121 Efficiency of Resource Use
SKILLS
VI. Valuing
V. Problem Solving

GLOSSARY

Note: Words in italics are defined in later entries in the Glossary.

ALLOWABLE CUT   The amount of wood fiber that may be harvested annually or periodically from a specified area over a stated period in accordance with the objectives of management.

ALPINE ZONE   The portion of a mountain that lies above timber line.

ANADROMOUS FISH   Salmon, shad, bass, and others that migrate from the sea up a river to spawn.

ANNUAL   A plant that completes its life cycle from seedling to mature seed-bearing plant during a single growing season, and then dies.

ASSOCIATION   A grouping of plants and animals that repeatedly occur together in a forest region. Associations may be identified in terms of their predominant tree association, as oak-hickory forest.

BIENNIAL   A plant that lives for two growing seasons, producing only leaves during the first season, flowers and seeds during the second.

BIODEGRADABLE   The property of a substance that permits it to be broken down by microorganisms into simple, stable compounds such as carbon dioxide and water.

BIOME   A complex of communities characterized by a distinctive type of vegetation and maintained under the climatic conditions of the regions.

BIOSPHERE   The part of the earth's crust, water, and atmosphere where living organisms can subsist.

BIOTA   The animal and plant life of a region or period.

BIOTIC POTENTIAL   The capacity of a population of animals or plants to increase in numbers under optimum environmental conditions.

BOARD FOOT   (fbm or bf): The amount of timber equivalent to a piece of wood 12 inches square and 1 inch thick. As the forest products industry changes to the metric system, it will probably use cubic meters for trees/logs and lumber in bulk and will measure lumber in retail on a linear and piece basis.

B O D (BIOCHEMICAL OXYGEN DEMAND)   A measure of the amount of oxygen used by microorganisms to consume biodegradable organic strength or waste water in terms of dissolved oxygen that would be consumed if the waste water were discharged into a natural body of water.

BOG   A wet, low area, often an old lake bed, filling or filled with partially decayed matter known as peat.

BOREAL FOREST   Northern conifer forest.

BROADLEAF   The term describing a plant with widebladed leaves, such as an oak or maple; generally refers to flowering trees in contrast to conifers.

BROWSE   To eat the twigs and leaves of woody plants. Deer, moose, and their relatives are browsers.

CANOPY   Layer formed by the leaves and branches of the forest's tallest trees.

CARRYING CAPACITY   The number of organisms of a given species and quality that can survive in a given ecosystem without causing deterioration thereof.

CARNIVORE   Any chiefly flesh-eating mammal of the order Carnivora, comprising dogs, cats, bears, seals, and the like.

CHAPARRAL   Dense scrub vegetation of broadleaf, evergreen, or wintergreen shrubs.

-CIDE   From Latin, meaning kill; used in combination words, such as pesticide.

CHLOROPHYLL   A group of pigments that produce the green hue of plants; essential to photosynthesis.

CLEARCUT   Removal of an entire standing crop.

CLEARCUTTING SYSTEM   A silviculture system in which the old crop is cleared at one time; regeneration by artificial or natural means.

CLIMAX   The relatively stable association that represents the final stage in a *sere* under existing conditions of soil and climate.

COMMERCIAL FOREST LAND   Forest lands capable of bearing merchantable timber currently or prospectively accessible and not withdrawn from such use.

COMMERCIAL THINNING   Any type of thinning producing merchantable material at least to the value of the direct cost of harvesting it.

COMMUNITY   All the plants and animals in a particular habitat that are bound together by *food chains* and other interrelations.

CONE   A structure composed of many spirally-arranged scales in which pollen ovules are produced. Cones differ from flowers in that the ovules are borne on the surface of the scales, or carpels. In a flower the carpels form a container called the pistil inside which the ovules are borne.

CONIFER, CONIFEROUS   A plant that bears its seeds in cones. Usually refers to *needleleaf* trees, although some needleleaf, such as yew, do not bear cones.

CONSERVATION   The use of natural resources in a way that assures their continuing availability to future generations; the intelligent use of natural resources.

CUBIC FOOT(ft^3)   The amount of timber in squared or rounded form necessary to produce the equivalent of 1 cubic foot of wood. One cubic foot equals 0.0283 cubic meters.

CUBIC METER (m^3)   The amount of wood necessary to produce a block 1 meter on a side or the equivalent.

DECIBEL   A unit of intensity of sound, equal to 20 times the common logarithm of the ratio of the pressure produced by the sound wave to a reference pressure. A measurement of 50 decibels is considered moderate sound; 80, loud; and 100, the level beyond which the sound becomes intolerable.

DECIDUOUS   Term describing a plant that periodically loses all its leaves, usually in autumn. Most North American broadleaf trees are deciduous. A few conifers, such as larch and cypress, also are deciduous. See **EVERGREEN**.

DECOMPOSER   A plant or animal that feeds on dead material and causes its mechanical or chemical breakdown.

DENDROLOGY   A branch of botany devoted to the study of trees.

ECOLOGY   The scientific study of the relations of living things to one another and to their environment. A scientist who studies these relationships is called an ecologist.

ECOSYSTEM   All living things and their environment in an area of any size. All are linked together by energy and nutrient flow.

EDAPHIC   Related to or caused by particular soil conditions, as of texture or drainage, rather than by physiographic or climatic factors.

EFFLUENT   The outflows, usually offensive, from sewage or industrial plants, and the like.

ENVIRONMENT The aggregate of surrounding things, conditions, or influences, especially as affecting the existence or development of people or of nature.

ENVIRONMENTAL RESISTANCE The limiting effect of environmental conditions on the numerical growth of a population.

EUTROPHICATION Enrichment of soils and water due to fertilization, sewage effluent, or other waters that carry a high plant-nutrient component.

EVEN-AGE STANDS Forest areas where the trees are all of the same age due to planting or harvesting the entire area at one time. Even-age stands are desirable for species whose young trees do not thrive in the shade of older trees.

EVENFLOW The production from a national forest or other unit of land of the same amount of timber each year for an indefinite period of time.

EVERGREEN A plant that does not lose all of its leaves at one time. Among trees, some broadleaf species, such as live oak, remain green all year, but most North American evergreens are coniferous. See **CONIFER; DECIDUOUS.**

FIBER Any long, narrow cell of wood or bast. Loosely used for wood elements in general.

FOOD CHAIN A series of plants and animals linked by their food relationships. A green plant, a leaf-eating insect, and an insect-eating bird would form a simple food chain. Any one species is usually represented in several or many food chains.

FOOTHILL ZONE Lowest of the vegetation zones in mountainous regions. See **VEGETATION ZONES, VERTICAL.**

FOREST A complex community of plants and animals in which trees are the most conspicuous members.

FOREST FLOOR The layer of decomposing material that covers the soil in a forest.

FOREST MANAGEMENT The practical application of scientific, economic, and social principles to the administration of a forest estate for specified objectives.

FOREST REGION An extensive area of a continent in which the climax-forest associations are closely similar. The major forest regions of North America are West Coast Forest, Western Forest, Central Hardwood Forest, Tropical Forest, Northern Forest, and Southern Forest.

FUNGICIDE Any chemical preparation used to control fungal pests.

GIRDLING Stripping or gnawing a section of bark around the trunk of a tree or shrub; may eventually kill the plant.

GRASSLAND A vegetation community in which grasses are the most conspicuous plants.

GROWING STOCK All the trees growing in a forest or in a specified part of it.

HABITAT The native environment of an animal or plant, or the kind of place that is natural for an animal or plant.

HARDWOOD A deciduous or broadleaf tree. The wood from such trees. See **SOFTWOOD.**

HERB Any flowering plant or fern that has a soft, rather than woody, stem.

HERB LAYER The layer of soft-stemmed plants growing close to the forest floor.

HERBICIDE A substance or preparation for killing plants, and especially weeds. See also **PESTICIDE.**

INCREMENT Growth accretion generally expressed in volume per acre per year. Also spoken of as annual yield.

INSECTICIDE Any chemical preparation used to control insects.

INTENSIVE FORESTRY The practice of forestry so as to attain a high level of volume and quality of out-turn per unit of area, through the application of the best techniques of *silviculture* and management.

KERF The narrow slot cut by a saw as it advances through wood.

LANDFILL   A method of disposing of refuse on land by utilizing the principles of engineering to confine the refuse to the smallest practical area and to reduce it to the smallest practical volume.

LEACHING   The removal of soluble substances from soil by percolating water.

LEADER   The main shoot growing from the top of a tree with a single main trunk.

LIFE CYCLE   The continuous sequence of changes undergone by an organism from one primary form to the development of the same form again.

LIGNIN   The organic substance that holds together the individual fibers of wood. Lignin is responsible for the dark color in pulp mill effluents.

MAST   Trees which produce nuts; for example, oak, walnut.

MAST YEAR   A year of above-average nut production in a forest.

MICROCLIMATE   "Little climate"; the environmental conditions in a restricted area.

MICROHABITAT   A "small habitat" within a larger one in which environmental conditions differ from those in the surrounding area. A hole in a tree trunk or an animal carcass is a microhabitat within the forest.

MIXED FOREST   A forest that includes both coniferous and deciduous trees.

MONOCULTURE   The raising of a crop of a single species, generally even-aged.

MONTANE ZONE   The band of vegetation that occurs at intermediate elevations in mountainous regions between foothill and subalpine zones. See **VEGETATION ZONES, VERTICAL**.

MOR   A type of forest floor formed by a thick mat of slowly decomposing matter, often conifer needles.

MULL   A type of forest floor and soil in which the decomposing matter, usually formed of broad leaves, decays rapidly. The humus is mixed thoroughly with mineral matter by earthworms and other small animals, so there is no sharp boundary between the forest floor and soil.

MULTIPLE-USE FORESTRY   Any practice of forestry fulfilling two or more objectives of management.

MUSKEG   A mossy bog in the northern coniferous forest region.

NATURAL SELECTION   A process in nature resulting in the survival and perpetuation of only those forms of plant and animal life having certain favorable characteristics that enable them to adapt best to a specific environment.

NEEDLELEAF   Bearing needlelike leaves. See **CONIFER**.

NITROGEN-FIXATION   The conversion of elemental nitrogen from the atmosphere to organic combinations or to forms readily utilizable in biological processes. Normally carried out by bacteria, living symbiotically in legumes or by free-living soil bacteria.

NONRENEWABLE RESOURCES   Substances such as oil, gas, coal, copper, and gold, which, once used, cannot be replaced, at least not in this geological age.

NORTH   The North includes New England, the Middle Atlantic States, and the Lake States.

OLD FIELD   Farmland once cultivated, but now untended.

ORGANIC MATTER   Chemical compounds of carbon combined with other chemical elements, and generally manufactured in the life processes of plants and animals. Most organic compounds are a source of food for bacteria and are usually combustible.

ORGANISM   A form of life composed of mutually dependent parts that maintain various vital processes.

PACIFIC COAST STATES   Those states that border the west coast of the United States.

PARTIAL CUTTING   Tree removal other than by clearcutting.

PARTICULATES   Small particles of liquid or solid matter.

PERENNIAL   A plant that lives for several years and usually produces seeds each year.

PESTICIDES   Any chemical preparation used to control populations of injurious organisms, plants, or animals.

PHOTOSYNTHESIS   The process by which green plants convert carbon dioxide and water into simple sugar. Chlorophyll and sunlight are essential to the series of complex chemical reactions involved.

PIGMENT   A chemical substance that reflects or transmits only certain light rays and thus imparts color to an object. For example, a substance that absorbs all but red rays, which it reflects, will appear red. See **CHLOROPHYLL**.

PIONEER   A plant capable of invading bare sites such as a newly exposed soil surface, and persisting there until supplanted by successor species.

PLANTATION   A humanmade forest, usually established by planting seedlings.

PLUS TREE   An elite tree judged but not proven to be superior in some quality or quantity. Often used for seed collection.

PLYWOOD   A composite product made up of crossbanded layers of *veneer*, bonded with an adhesive.

POLE   A young tree usually between 4 and 8 inches (10 and 20 centimeters) in diameter.

POLLUTION   Harmful substances deposited in the air or water or land, leading to a state of dirtiness, impurity, or unhealthiness.

PREDATOR   An animal that lives by capturing other animals for food.

PRESCRIBED BURNING   The planned application of fire to natural fuels including logging *slash* with the intent to confine the burning to a predetermined area.

PULPWOOD   Wood cut and prepared for manufacture into woodpulp.

RAIN SHADOW   An area on the leeward side of a mountain barrier that receives little rainfall.

RANGE   All lands, including forest land, that produce native forage in contrast to land cultivated for agricultural crops or carrying a dense forest. Also applied to the range of individual species of plants and animals.

RECYCLE   The salvage and reprocessing of used materials (such as paper, metals, glass, and cloth).

REFORESTATION   The replanting of trees in forests that have been affected by cutting, fire, disease, or other incursion.

REGENERATION   Renewal of a tree crop whether by natural or artificial means. The regeneration period is the period required or allowed in the plan for regenerating following timber harvest.

ROADING   The provision of roads in an area.

ROCKY MOUNTAIN STATES   Those states between the Pacific Coast States and the Great Plains.

RODENTICIDES   Chemical preparations used against mice, rats, and other rodents that may consume forestry seed or debark trees.

ROTATION   The planned number of years between the formation of a forest crop and its final cutting at a specified stage of maturity.

SANITARY FILL   Used to describe the dumping process whereby the garbage or other refuse is covered with soil, thus controlling smell, rodent activity, etc., and speeding the decay of organic substances.

SAPLING   A young tree normally more than 4½ feet (1.5 meters) high and less than 4 inches (10 centimeters) in diameter.

SAVANNA   A parklike grassland with scattered trees or clumps of trees.

SAWLOG   A log considered suitable in size and quality for producing sawn timber.

SAWTIMBER   Trees fit to yield sawlogs.

SCAVENGER   An animal that eats the dead remains and wastes of other animals and plants.

SCRUB A low, woody vegetation composed principally of shrubs.

SECONDARY FIBER Fiber used as a raw material for making new products. The fibers have been reclaimed from waste paper or collected during the manufacture of paper and paperboard products.

SECTION CUTTING The annual or periodic removal of trees individually or in small groups.

SEEDLING A young tree grown from the seed up to the sapling stage, that is a height of 4½ to 6 feet (1.5 to 2 meters).

SERAL STAGE One community of a sere.

SERE The series of communities that follow one another in a natural succession, as in the change from a bare field to a mature forest.

SHELTERWOOD CUTTING Any regeneration cutting in a more or less regular or mature crop designed to establish a new crop under the protection of the old.

SHRUB A woody plant less than 12 feet (4 meters) tall, usually with more than one stem rising from the ground.

SILVICIDES Any chemical preparations used to control unwanted trees.

SILVICULTURE The science and art of cultivating forest crops based on the knowledge of silvics, the study of the life history and general characteristics of forest trees and stands with particular reference to site factors as a basis for the practice of silviculture.

SITE CLASS A measure of the relative productive capacity of an area for timber or other crops.

SITE INDEX A measure of site class based on height of the dominant trees in the stand at age 50 or 100 years.

SKIDDING Moving logs from the stump to a landing usually with the forward end supported off the ground.

SLASH The residue left on the ground after felling timber.

SMOG Originally a combination of fog and smoke; now applied also to photochemical haze produced by the action of the sun and the atmosphere on automobile and industrial exhausts.

SNAG A standing dead tree from which the leaves and most of the branches have fallen.

SOFTWOOD A coniferous tree. A common but not strictly accurate term; the wood of many conifers is harder than that of some so-called hardwood trees.

SOLID WASTE All items discarded after use in a solid state that must be collected and disposed of separately. Solid waste is collected by municipal collection systems. Solid waste does not include items discarded into sewage systems or those emitted with smoke or gas.

SOUTH The South includes the states to the south of the Middle Atlantic States and the Lake States, notably along the South Atlantic region, across the South Central States, and across the Mississippi into Texas and Oklahoma.

SPECIES A class of organisms having some common characteristics or qualities. The major subdivision of a genus or subgenus, regarded as the basic category of biological classification, composed of related individuals that resemble one another, are able to breed among themselves but are not able to breed with members of another species.

STOMA A microscopic opening in the surface of a leaf that allows gases to pass in and out.

SUBALPINE ZONE The band of vegetation in mountainous regions that occurs below timber line and alpine zone. See **VEGETATION ZONES, VERTICAL**.

SUCCESSION The gradual replacement of one community by another. See **SERE**.

SUSTAINED YIELD The yield that a forest produces continuously at a given intensity of management.

TERRITORY   An area defended by an animal against others of the same species. Used for breeding, feeding, or both.

TIMBER   A general term for forest crops and stands containing trees of commercial size and quality suitable for sawing into lumber.

TIMBERLINE   The upper limit of tree growth on mountains. A band of stunted and usually oddly shaped trees between the subalpine forests and alpine tundra. See **VEGETATION ZONES, VERTICAL**.

TRANSPIRATION   The process by which water evaporates from plant tissues.

TREE   A woody plant 12 or more feet (4 or more meters) tall with a single main stem (trunk) and a more or less distinct crown of leaves.

TREE SEED ORCHARD   A plantation of trees assumed or proven genetically to be superior but isolated so as to reduce pollination from genetically inferior outside sources.

TUNDRA   Treeless vegetation in regions with long winter and low annual temperatures. Arctic tundra extends above timber line on mountains.

UNEVEN-AGED   A forest or stand composed of intermingling trees that differ markedly in age. This contrasts with even-aged stands in which all trees are within 10 to 20 years of the same age.

UNDERSTORY   The layer formed by the crowns of smaller trees in a forest.

VEGETATION   The mass of plants that covers a given area. Flora, a term often wrongly used interchangeably with vegetation, is a list of the species of plants that compose the vegetation.

VEGETATION ZONES, VERTICAL   The horizontal belts of distinctive plant cover in mountainous regions, resulting from climatic changes related to elevation changes. From base to peak, the zones are foothill, montane, subalpine, timberline, and alpine.

VENEER   A thin sheet of wood of uniform thickness produced by rotary cutting, slicing, or sometimes by sawing.

VIRGIN FOREST   Primeval forest or original forest. Primarily a forest undisturbed by people.

VISITOR DAY   The presence of one or more persons (other than staff) on land or water generally recognized as providing outdoor recreation for continuous, intermittent, or simultaneous periods aggregating 12 hours. A group of six persons spending 4 hours in a designated picnic ground would therefore count for 2 visitor days.

WILDERNESS AREA   An area established by the federal government to conserve its primeval character and influence for public enjoyment under primitive conditions in perpetuity.

WILDFIRE   Any fire other than a controlled or prescribed burn occurring on wild land.

WILDLIFE   A loose term that includes nondomesticated vertebrates, especially mammals, birds, and fish.

WINTER-BARE FOREST   A forest composed of deciduous trees.

WOODLAND   A wooded area in which the trees are often small, short bowled, and open grown; farm woodland, any wooded area that is part of a farm.

WOODPULP   Wood fiber separated by mechanical or chemical means used in making paper and other products.

YARD UP   To gather in a sheltered area in winter; used in reference to deer, moose, and their relatives.

ZERO POPULATION GROWTH   The maintenance or holding of population numbers at a fixed level so as to obviate increase.

CURRICULUM FRAMEWORK

1.0 Instill a deep appreciation (love) for the diverse forest environment.

1.1 The maintenance of a varied and beautiful life-support system is essential to both physiological and psychological health.

1.11 Contrast and variety that are important to mental health are available in the forest and elsewhere.

1.12 A recognition of beauty and quiet in the forest environment is necessary for a feeling of well-being in many people.

1.13 Opportunities to experience and enjoy nature are psychologically rewarding to many and important to mental health.

2.0 Develop an awareness of the diversity and importance of forest resources and their concomitant values as they relate to the environmental, economic, and sociological health of the region, the country, and the planet.

2.1 The forest has many uses and values; most of which are compatible with each other, but some of which may be temporarily or permanently incompatible.

2.11 Almost all people in their daily life rely on a significant number of forest-generated products.

2.111 The construction and maintenance of human dwellings is dependent upon the use of considerable quantities of natural resources, many of which are obtained from the forest.

2.112 The forest environment is the source of many raw materials and gene pools of potential value and energy.

2.12 Everyone, in daily life, must rely upon the influence of the forest on the overall community — including both its physical and cultural environment.

2.121 Plants, including trees, influence the composition of the atmosphere which strongly affects human economy and human and other animals' comfort, health, safety, and social structure.

2.1211 Forest plants, in carrying on food production (photosynthesis) affect the balance between supplies of carbon dioxide and oxygen in the atmosphere.

2.1212 Forest plants release into the atmosphere various volatile (evaporable) compounds that have an effect on other living things.

2.1213 Forest plants release pollen, spores, and other light, solid substances into the atmosphere.

2.1214 Plants, including trees, are very effective visual screens, windbreakers, and noise barriers.

2.122 Plants, including trees, have effects on the terrestrial environment.

2.1221 Forest plants and plant litter (leaves and stems) cover the ground to varying degrees, protect the surface from wind and water, slow evaporation of water from the surface, and prevent direct sunlight from reaching the ground.

2.1222 Forest plant roots stabilize the soil by binding it together.

2.1223 Forest plant roots change soil texture by mechanically breaking up particles.

2.1224 Forest plants add organic matter to the soil as leaf, stem, and root litter.

2.1225 Forest plants add and remove chemical elements to soil which may change its chemical composition and structural nature.

2.123 Forests affect the hydrological cycle by influencing the quantity, quality, composition, and distribution of water in the cycle.

2.1231 Forest plants intercept falling rain and snow which decreases the amount reaching the soil and reduces the erosive effect of the precipitation, simultaneously decreasing runoff and/or storage and increasing evaporation.

2.1232 Forest plant roots, stems, and litter mechanically slow water runoff from the land's surface and increase infiltration of the water into the soil.

2.1233 Forest plants increase atmospheric water (humidity) by giving off water through the process of transpiration.

2.1234 Forest plants use water from the soil-for-life processes thus reducing the supply stored in the ground.

2.124 The forest provides intrinsic aesthetic benefits (values) that are assuming increasingly greater significance to individuals and society.

2.1241 The forest environment offers the opportunity for a wide variety of leisure-time activities.

2.1242 Many forms of leisure-time activities are dependent upon the forest environment although they themselves do not physically take place within that environment.

2.1243 Forest plants used in landscaping lend a natural beauty to our communities.

2.1244 Forest plant communities provide natural beauty and spiritual uplift to many people.

2.13 Many communities are highly dependent upon local forest, forest industries, and forest recreation for economic and cultural stability.

3.0 Develop an understanding of the impact of and role played by the forest environment in shaping the political, economic, and sociological events and behaviors of the past, present, and future.

3.1 Natural resources form the basis for every economy.

3.2 Availability and use of natural resources are affected by the social and economic needs of a culture and directly or indirectly by philosophy, religion, government, and the arts.

3.21 The economic level (standard of living) of a region depends upon the utilization of its human, cultural, and natural resources and technology over time.

3.211 Goods and services are produced by the interaction of labor, capital, technology, and natural resources.

3.22 The distribution and location of resources in relation to population and to technological and economic factors are critical to problems of resource conservation and use.

3.221 Natural resources, water and minerals in particular, are unequally distributed with respect to land areas and political boundaries.

3.222 No country is entirely self-sufficient in its natural resources, therefore resources should be understood within the context of a world view of humankind's needs.

3.223 The political and economic strength of a country is often heavily dependent upon its access to domestic and foreign resources and international trade.

3.224 Foreign policy, international trade and relations are greatly influenced by the availability of and access to natural resources.

3.3 The history of a people evolves through the interaction of individuals, groups, cultures, and events with the environment.

3.31 Most cultures had forest-related origins.

3.32 An important factor in the history of many civilizations (including their demise) has been their use or misuse of the forest.

3.33 A major portion of the history of the United States was fundamentally influenced by its citizens' interactions with the forest environment.

3.4 The relationship between people and the biosphere is modified by culture.

3.41 The forest environment has psychological impact on people.

3.411 The need for human beings to turn inward for self-renewal can be stimulated by their external aesthetic experiences.

3.4111 The forest has frequently provided a model for creative expression in music, art, and literature.

3.412 Part of the meaning of a culture can be understood by exploring its concept of and values related to the forest community.

3.4121 Artists record those aspects of the environment which to them have meaning; thus the creative works of a people are an indication of their perception of and response to their environment.

3.4122 Literature provides a unique and significant kind of knowledge about relationships to environment.

3.42 The ability of the individual to perceive forest-societal relationships increases awareness of and contributes to the development of an environmental perspective.

3.421 A person's perception of the environment is largely conditioned by the culture in which the person is raised. The language, literature, and art embodied in that culture contribute significantly to that perception.

3.422 Human beings have developed many belief systems to help them explain environmental mysteries, and these often shape the nature of their interactions with their environment.

4.0 Acquaint students with the perspectives from and by which various interest groups judge contemporary forest/environmental issues, the mechanisms by which these issues are resolved, and ways in which their outcome may be influenced.

4.1 Individuals perceive different self-roles depending upon their position in the social, economic, and environmental contexts.

4.11 The nature of the free enterprise system is such that short-term economic realities should be balanced by long-range resource planning.

4.12 People vary widely in their perception of the forest environment; consequently language and other media used to influence them must be based on knowledge of their values and interests.

4.13 Words and phrases relative to forest/environmental issues carry connotative and emotional impact as well as denotative value and must be used and understood in light of this fact.

4.14 Ideas vary widely in their degree of full representation of reality and must be evaluated in light of this fact.

4.2 Citizenship assumes as informed an understanding as possible of the decision-making process; this necessitates knowledge of the values that enter into a decision, the persons and institutions which are influential, and how the decision may affect long-term policy.

4.21 The responsibility for forest conservation should be shared by everyone.

4.22 Effective citizens need to be informed about pressures and a variety of institution structures (such as agencies, interest groups, money) which influence the planning and management of the forest resource.

4.221 Forest conservation policies are often the result of group action by interest groups (public and private), and such actions are vital to the democratic system.

4.222 Understanding of and participation in the various levels of government (local, regional, state, and national) can help to ensure the development of a society in which all citizens live fruitfully.

4.2221 Citizenship includes the opportunity to participate freely in helping to make and change public policy, if a citizen wishes to do so.

4.2222 Participation is not restricted to voting but may also take the form of joining with others in groups to arouse public interest, to influence policy by lawful means, and communicate in other ways with elected or appointed persons in government.

4.3 Management of natural resources requires the flexibility to respond to changing human needs, technological advances, new scientific knowledge, governmental policies, and unusual conditions.

4.31 Conservation policies come about as a result of interacting social processes, science and technology, government operations, and private and public interest and attitudes.

4.311 All forms of artistic expression based on the natural world can be positively persuasive influences in developing a congenial environment.

4.32 Conservation policies and laws in a democracy are means by which the majority tries to ensure that a few do not impair the resources for all.

4.33 The management of natural resources to meet the needs of successive generations demands long-range planning, since the options available to future generations must not be foreclosed.

4.4 Forest land is used in different ways depending upon its biophysical characteristics, the needs and desires of society, and the preferences of its present owners.

4.41 People have the responsibility to develop an appreciation of and respect for rights and preferences of others.

4.42 In a democracy, basic theory is that restrictions on resource allocation and use are imposed by the consent and/or insistence of the people.

4.43 As populations increase and/or as resource supplies decrease, the freedom of the individual to use the resource as he or she wishes decreases irrespective of the form of government.

4.44 We have legal ownership of some resources like real estate and control others during our lifetime — but ethically we are *stewards* rather than *owners* of the resource base.

4.45 The collective society is the owner of the *public* lands, therefore use of those lands is a *privilege* granted by society through government, not a *right*.

4.46 Conflicts sometimes emerge between *private* land-use rights and the maintenance of environmental quality for the general public.

4.47 People use planning and zoning methods to define and adjust land use because some land or human uses exclude others while some can coexist.

4.48 Action taken for public good sometimes conflicts with individual rights.

5.0 Equip students with sufficient knowledge and skills that they may intelligently predict and evaluate the impact of a specific management policy on the forest environment and its interdependent communities.

5.1 Natural resources are interdependent and the use or misuse of one will affect others.

5.11 The exhaustion of one resource produces new demands on others.

5.12 The renewable resource base can be extended by research and development, improved conservation practices and management.

5.121 The increasingly efficient use of some resources is a result of technical and marketing improvement and changes in consumer-use patterns.

5.2 Most resources are vulnerable to depletion in quantity and/or quality.

5.21 Plants, including trees, are renewable resources within given limits of utilization.

5.22 Wildlife is a renewable resource provided species' populations are maintained above the minimum number necessary for reproduction and suitable habitat is available.

5.23 Soil is classified as a renewable resource, but, because it may take a few years to a few thousand years to be "renewed," it is more practically termed a *depletable* resource.

5.24 Water is a reusable and transient resource, but the available quantity may be increased or reduced and/or quality impaired or improved through use.

5.25 Minerals are nonrenewable resources and are finite in quantity, but can be reused many times in many forms.

5.3 Regions of forest and forest activity are often interdependent with metropolitan regions and therefore each depends upon the other for its existence.

5.4 Some forest *values* can coexist with some forest *uses* while others are not compatible either temporarily and/or spatially.

5.5 All decision making involving natural resources entails the consideration of economic and environmental trade-offs.

6.0 Provide the student with a basic understanding of how the life-support system of planet earth functions and have the necessary skills and knowledge to evaluate the short-term and more importantly the long-range effects that manipulations of segments of this system will have on its integrity.

6.1 Biological systems are described as *dynamic* because the materials and energy involved are parts of continuous cycles; inorganic materials and energy become part of organic materials and subsequently are broken down into simpler substances and energy as a result of the operation of organic systems.

6.11 The forest is a *dynamic* community composed of living and nonliving things and dominated by trees.

6.111 Matter is for all practical purposes finite and is recirculated continuously by such bio-geo-chemical interactions as:
        a. the carbon cycle
        b. the nitrogen cycle
        c. the mineral (rock) cycle
        d. the hydrologic (water) cycle.

6.112 The ultimate source of energy used by all living systems is the stellar system, primarily the sun.

6.1121 Energy is passed unidirectionally through systems and is rapidly dissipated according to the laws of thermodynamics.

6.1122 Energy is supplied to an ecosystem through the photosynthetic activities of green plants.

6.1123 Green plants are the ultimate source of food, clothing, shelter, and energy in most societies.

6.2 All living things are undergoing constant change through genetic variability and evolutionary development.

6.21 The environment is undergoing constant natural change at varying rates of speed because of such factors as:

        a. weathering and erosion
        b. elevation and subsidence
        c. sedimentation
        d. volcanism

6.22 All living things change in response to environmental change either through adaptation or elimination (extinction).

6.221 Succession is the gradual and continuous replacement of one kind of plant or animal complex by another and is characterized by a gradual change in species composition.

6.222 The most stable natural communities are those with the greatest diversity.

6.23 Humankind has been an important factor affecting plant and animal succession and environmental processes.

6.3 Living things are interdependent with one another and their environment.

6.31 People are an integral part of the biosphere , constantly affecting it and being affected by it.

6.32 Heredity and environment interact to determine the characteristics of an organism, and therefore, a population.

6.4 All living things have certain basic needs, such as air, water, food, shelter, and a suitable climate.

6.41 All living things depend on their environment to meet their basic needs.

6.42 The size of population that any environment can support in any given period of time is limited. Such a *carrying capacity* of an area is dependent upon the availability and distribution of food, water, shelter, and space and the extent to which an organism is able to alter its environment to meet its needs.

6.421 In any environment, one component such as water, food, shelter, or air may become a *limiting factor*. When these or other resources are in short supply, or in excess to the tolerance of an organism they are said to be limiting factors.

6.43 Forests exist under a specific set of conditions although these conditions may vary greatly.

6.44 Some lands are currently better suited for the growing of forests than for other uses.

6.5 Pollutants and contaminants are produced by natural and human-made processes.

6.6 The biosphere is irreplaceable.

6.7 Humankind's understanding of the dynamics of the forest and other environments, while increasing, is far from complete.

7.0 **Provide students with the skills and knowledge to evaluate and modify their own lifestyles in light of an acute awareness of the finiteness of planet earth.**

7.1 The culture of a group is its learned behavior in the form of customs, habits, attitudes, institutions, and lifestyles that are transmitted to its progeny.

7.11 The management of natural resources is culture bound.

7.12 Supply and demand in relation to the values and needs held by society determine what things are resources and their economic value.

7.121 A person's needs are often different from wants and desires.

7.122 Human needs and desires are generally greater than the supply of natural resources available to meet them.

7.1221 Choices between needs (essentials) and wants or desires (nonessentials) may come into conflict more frequently as humankind's population and consumption levels rise within finite resource limits.

7.123 Every human activity has an effect upon our environment and the need to weigh degrading activities against the benefits received becomes increasingly important as population and consumption levels rise.

7.2 Increased population, mobility, and affluence are changing the nature of demands on natural resources.

7.21 Changes in the cultural patterns, social and economic values, and mores of a society affect the demand for natural resources through their impact on personal conservation practices.

7.211 Ready transportation, coupled with growing interest, money surpluses, and increased leisure time, creates heavy pressures on existing forest recreation facilities and demands for new ones.

7.2111 Some forms of transportation have considerably greater impact on the forest environment than others.

7.21111 Certain emissions from the internal combustion engine have adverse effects on the forest environment.

7.21112 Road construction and right-of-ways for utilities withdraw substantial areas from the production of other forest uses and values.

7.2112 Some forms of leisure-time activities have a greater impact on the forest than do others.

7.3 Resource depletion and environmental degradation can be slowed by the development and adoption of alternative lifestyles and social expectations.

7.31 Modest changes in consumer preferences and practices can markedly affect the impact of the home and family on the forest environment.

7.32 Modest changes in product design and in planning and manufacturing (shop) practices can markedly influence the conservation of natural resources.

7.4 The creative expression of one's relationship with nature is a significant and satisfying means of clarifying that relationship.

INTELLECTUAL AND VALUING SKILLS

I. Acquisition and/or Verification of Information, including observation, data collection (including library skills), classification, interpretation, inference, extrapolation, hypothesis construction and testing, theory construction and testing (both content and validity), prediction; II. Communication; III. Effective Social (Group) Participation; IV. Critical Thinking; V. Creative Problem Solving; VI. Valuing (skills which assist the student in the processes of recognizing and clarifying problems and in managing and/or resolving them).

RESOURCES

1. SYLVAN SERENADE
Articles: 10
Films: 557
Multi-Media: 697, 706

2. TREE VERSE
Articles: 210, 218
Reference Books: 270, 283, 284, 309, 310, 327, 354, 370, 381, 409, 422, 436, 447
Students' Pleasure Reading and Reference Books: 457, 458, 459, 460, 471, 472, 479, 486, 495, 533, 537, 542
Films: 557, 579, 582, 592, 605, 640, 650, 659
Multi-Media: 688, 689

3. SHADES OF MEANING
Reference Books: 357
Pamphlets: 734

4. NATURAL MATERIALS ART
Reference Books: 258, 311, 314, 327, 378, 394
Films: 610
Pamphlets: 802, 804
Related Curriculum Materials: 853, 861, 864, 866, 874 (especially chapter 1)

5. A CASSETTE TOUR OF NEIGH-BORHOOD TREES
Articles: 151
Reference Books: 232, 279, 290, 355, 356, 383, 388, 396, 425, 453
Students' Pleasure Reading and Reference Books: 466, 473, 478, 480, 491, 524, 528
Films: 549, 640, 642
Multi-Media: 667, 692, 696, 704, 708
Pamphlets: 719, 720, 735, 736, 749a,b,c, 753a,b,c, 784, 791, 793, 800, 802, 814, 825
Related Curriculum Materials: 837, 842, 843, 853, 862, 865, 868, 877
Simulations/Games: 896

6. JOHNNY APPLESEED ON MARS
Articles: 84, 151, 169, 174
Reference Books: 290, 336, 355, 356, 388, 396, 445, 452
Students' Pleasure Reading and Reference Books: 534
Films: 591, 632
Multi-Media: 703, 704, 708
Pamphlets: 793, 799, 801
Related Curriculum Materials: 836, 867, 875
Simulations/Games: 915

7. NATURE'S AIR CONDITIONERS
Articles: 169
Reference Books: 290, 336, 355, 356, 388, 396, 420
Students' Pleasure Reading and Reference Books: 524
Films: 553, 565
Multi-Media: 704, 708
Pamphlets: 720, 791, 793, 809, 814
Related Curriculum Materials: 837, 865, 868, 877
Simulations/Games: 902

8. GREEN MUFFLERS
Articles: 11, 84, 119, 151, 169, 174, 200
Reference Books: 396
Films: 591, 632
Multi-Media: 704, 708
Pamphlets: 793, 801, 819
Related Curriculum Materials: 836, 851, 855, 863, 867, 875

9. FOREST PRODUCTS ALL AROUND US
Articles: 30, 38, 39, 50, 52, 75, 114, 169, 173
Reference Books: 236, 245, 254, 269, 279, 303, 334, 362, 403, 448
Films: 545, 550, 570, 601, 637
Multi-Media: 681, 682, 709

Films: 550, 553, 554, 556, 561, 565, 566, 567, 568, 572, 573, 592, 598, 614, 617, 623, 624, 635, 637, 643, 644, 648
Multi-Media: 664, 665, 671, 672, 680, 685, 687, 688, 698, 699, 712
Pamphlets: 718, 719, 738
Related Curriculum Materials: 847

23. A LETTER FROM ARCHY
Articles: 48, 54, 64, 68, 105, 109, 112, 113, 114, 115, 125, 136, 137, 138, 140, 141, 143, 150, 164, 170, 171, 176, 181, 182, 202, 205, 208, 216
Reference Books: 246, 264, 270, 273, 280, 289, 353, 368, 374, 387, 392, 409, 430, 436
Students' Pleasure Reading and Reference Books: 490, 494, 526
Films: 597, 624, 631
Pamphlets: 718, 761, 762, 790
Related Curriculum Materials: 865, 871, 873 (especially the introduction)
Simulations/Games: 884, 905

24. ECONOMIC WEB OF LIFE
Articles: 63, 66
Reference Books: 238, 259, 278, 296, 299, 321, 333, 334
Students' Pleasure Reading and Reference Books: 461, 469, 509
Films: 589, 590, 638
Multi-Media: 676, 701
Pamphlets: 732
Related Curriculum Materials: 865

25. THE POWER OF LITERATURE
Articles: 42
Reference Books: 327
Students' Pleasure Reading and Reference Books: 471, 537, 540, 542
Films: 592, 598, 631
Multi-Media: 697

26. SUPERSTITIONS, SYMBOLS, AND SIMILES
Articles: 58, 65, 210, 218
Reference Books: 237, 243, 283, 284, 290, 309, 313, 359, 370, 381, 438
Students' Pleasure Reading and Reference Books: 463, 465, 470, 478, 491, 495, 497, 499
Films: 579, 582, 592, 631, 650
Multi-Media: 687, 697, 704, 716
Pamphlets: 784, 811
Simulations/Games: 890

27. TICKY TACKY
Films: 557, 605
Multi-Media: 706
Pamphlets: 796
Related Curriculum Materials: 852

28. CARTOONS AND HEADLINES
Related Curriculum Materials: 858

29. WASTED WORDS
Articles: 16, 17, 55, 64, 97, 160, 161, 202, 216
Students' Pleasure Reading and Reference Books: 461

Films: 545, 552, 573, 584, 593, 622, 626, 637, 649, 651
Multi-Media: 661, 686, 714
Related Curriculum Materials: 847, 858, 859
Simulations/Games: 913

30. ENVIRONMENTAL EDITORIALS
Articles: 29, 40, 43, 66, 100, 101, 125, 146, 149, 202, 207
Films: 570, 573, 607, 615, 637, 642
Multi-Media: 683, 686, 693, 714
Simulations/Games: 892, 899, 903, 913, 915

31. ENVIRONMENTAL ADVERTISE-MENTS
Articles: 52, 115, 143, 190
Students' Pleasure Reading and Reference Books: 461
Films: 547
Pamphlets: 755, 833
Related Curriculum Materials: 858, 871
Simulations/Games: 913

32. PARTICIPATORY DEMOCRACY
Articles: 6, 23, 24, 33, 64, 65, 89, 123, 126, 143, 166, 167, 178, 184, 189, 219, 220
Reference Books: 222, 225, 248, 252, 260, 276, 301, 306, 307, 310, 311, 319, 331, 365, 367, 368, 369, 370, 371, 385, 386, 387, 390, 393, 427, 436, 438, 451
Students' Pleasure Reading and Reference Books: 494, 510, 512, 536, 537
Films: 550, 578, 581, 593, 608
Pamphlets: 790
Related Curriculum Materials: 854, 859, 871
Simulations/Games: 880, 894, 911, 912, 914, 915

33. WHO RUNS THIS PLACE?
Articles: 61, 68, 102, 117, 126, 151, 178, 211
Reference Books: 236, 269, 270, 306, 307, 363, 376, 396, 403, 411, 423, 443
Films: 550, 607, 629, 630, 637
Pamphlets: 726, 744, 776, 777
Related Curriculum Materials: 842, 851, 863, 871
Simulations/Games: 883

34. URBAN OPEN SPACE
Articles: 38, 90, 100, 104, 117, 151, 191, 207, 217
Reference Books: 230, 242, 249, 272, 346, 351, 352, 358, 396, 411, 412, 416, 443
Films: 595, 607, 632, 646, 651
Multi-Media: 669
Pamphlets: 744
Related Curriculum Materials: 842, 847, 851, 859, 863, 871
Simulations/Games: 882, 892, 900, 901, 903, 915

35. WHERE TO PLANT
Articles: 169
Reference Books: 452
Students' Pleasure Reading and Reference Books: 534

Films: 639
Pamphlets: 816, 822

36. OWNERSHIP OBJECTIVES
Articles: 8, 9, 21, 23, 24, 25, 27, 29, 32, 33, 35, 49, 55, 56, 74, 82, 106, 107, 112, 113, 118, 132, 137, 138, 140, 141, 143, 144, 166, 170, 172, 178, 181, 194, 198, 215, 219, 220
Reference Books: 225, 240, 247, 250, 252, 256, 260, 263, 301, 310, 329, 367, 368, 369, 378, 389, 397, 432, 433, 434, 435, 436, 439
Films: 545, 565, 569, 573, 637, 649
Multi-Media: 661, 663, 681, 683, 686, 693
Pamphlets: 721, 758, 761, 782, 790, 792, 796, 803, 812, 818, 827, 833
Simulations/Games: 899, 917

37. WE CAN WORK IT OUT?!
Articles: 8, 16, 18, 26, 40, 43, 45, 55, 82, 86, 87, 88, 89, 94, 96, 99, 116, 132, 140, 143, 149, 156, 168, 170, 184, 192, 194, 196
Reference Books: 222, 225, 227, 244, 248, 262, 265, 290, 301, 303, 324, 336, 351, 355, 356, 367, 368, 370, 372, 388, 389, 392
Students' Pleasure Reading and Reference Books: 526
Films: 545, 553, 569, 570, 583, 593, 604, 611, 637, 649, 654
Multi-Media: 675, 686, 693, 701, 714
Pamphlets: 721, 750, 754c,e, 764, 765, 803, 809, 831, 832, 833
Related Curriculum Materials: 858, 859, 865, 871
Simulations/Games: 896, 897, 899, 914, 915

38. WHAT IS "WISE USE?"
Articles: 65, 74, 79, 89, 129, 132, 143, 189, 215, 219, 220
Reference Books: 244, 248, 252, 301, 310, 319, 331, 345, 365, 367, 368, 369, 370, 374, 382, 385, 386, 387, 390, 405, 419, 427, 428, 436
Students' Pleasure Reading and Reference Books: 490, 494, 512, 517, 532, 536
Films: 573, 580, 583, 609, 618, 622, 631, 637, 645, 649, 654
Multi-Media: 661, 663, 673, 683, 686, 693, 714
Pamphlets: 721, 745, 750, 758, 761, 767, 780, 781, 783, 796
Related Curriculum Materials: 858, 859, 865, 871
Simulations/Games: 884, 911

39. HOW MUCH IS ENOUGH?
Articles: 4, 8, 16, 21, 22, 40, 73, 76, 82, 83, 85, 86, 88, 89, 99, 106, 107, 110, 116, 126, 129, 132, 139, 146, 149, 150, 164, 179, 184, 201, 211
Reference Books: 233, 244, 248, 252, 257, 262, 263, 265, 275, 308, 309, 310, 331, 365, 368, 369, 370, 389, 406, 419, 423, 427, 436, 437
Students' Pleasure Reading and Reference Books: 455, 504, 512, 520
Films: 545, 593, 601, 602, 629, 654
Multi-Media: 686, 693, 710, 714
Pamphlets: 721, 742, 754c, 764, 765, 796, 806,

812, 818, 831, 832
Related Curriculum Materials: 859, 865, 871
Simulations/Games: 899, 903, 914

40. SOIL COMPACTION
Articles: 13, 51, 80, 134, 145, 186, 187, 188, 204
Students' Pleasure Reading and Reference Books: 496, 522
Multi-Media: 678, 707

41. PH AND PLANTS
Reference Books: 227, 228, 288, 290, 291, 336, 345 (especially pp. 190-193), 355, 356, 375, 388, 420, 425 (especially Chapter 8)
Students' Pleasure Reading and Reference Books: 466, 524
Films: 556, 633, 635
Multi-Media: 674, 704, 708
Pamphlets: 791, 795, 797, 799, 808, 814, 816, 822, 834
Related Curriculum Materials: 869, 878

42. GROWIN' SEEDS 'N' SAVIN' SOIL
Articles: 135, 169
Reference Books: 235, 266, 273, 280, 290, 326, 389, 433, 434
Students' Pleasure Reading and Reference Books: 496, 522, 524
Films: 552, 553, 573, 618, 622, 637, 636
Multi-Media: 669, 713
Pamphlets: 717, 754a, 776, 791, 808, 834
Related Curriculum Materials: 837, 857, 871

43. THE VALUE OF WILDLIFE
Articles: 12, 199
Reference Books: 222, 266, 345 (especially the essay "On A Monument to the Pigeon"), 371, 428
Students' Pleasure Reading and Reference Books: 500, 510, 523
Films: 546, 608
Multi-Media: 679, 694
Pamphlets: 769, 773, 776

44. BUILDING FOR THE BIRDS
Reference Books: 222
Film: 585
Multi-Media: 749f,g,h, 770, 772, 773, 810
Pamphlets: 749f,g,h, 770, 772, 773, 810
Related Curriculum Materials: 842, 843, 861, 862, 870

45. SNOW USE
Pamphlets: 748

46. WATER WE DOING?
Articles: 155, 206
Reference Books: 336
Students' Pleasure Reading and Reference Books: 516, 522
Films: 603
Multi-Media: 710(1)
Pamphlets: 776(2), 809
Related Curriculum Materials: 846

47. LOOSE KNOTS AND TIGHT KNOTS
Reference Books: 292, 294, 316, 377, 454
Multi-Media: 681

Pamphlets: 738, 740, 800, 826, 830

48. LAND ALLOCATION
Articles: 50
Reference Books: 365
Films: 578, 630
Simulations/Games: 883, 903, 912

49. FOR BETTER OR FOR WORSE?
Articles: 7, 69, 92, 163, 167, 212
Reference Books: 351, 365
Films: 573, 625, 637, 649
Multi-Media: 676
Pamphlets: 739, 742, 747, 775
Related Curriculum Materials: 836, 851, 855, 858, 859, 865
Simulations/Games: 880, 888, 893, 897, 907, 909, 911, 915

50. HOW CLEAN IS CLEAN?
Articles: 7, 19, 155, 163, 206
Reference Books: 330, 334, 362, 365
Films: 548, 625
Multi-Media: 703
Pamphlets: 739, 742, 743, 747, 775, 799, 813, 815
Related Curriculum Materials: 854, 858, 859
Simulations/Games: 880, 883, 888, 902, 907, 909, 915, 916

51. MINING AND RENEWABLE RESOURCES
Articles: 60, 167, 173
Reference Books: 248, 257, 365, 415
Films: 545, 550, 552, 591, 594, 634
Multi-Media: 709
Related Curriculum Materials: 844, 845, 863
Simulations/Games: 880, 883, 903, 910, 915

52. HARD CHOICES
Articles: 53, 91, 108, 131, 133, 148
Reference Books: 239, 311, 401
Students' Pleasure Reading and Reference Books: 488
Films: 571, 574, 597, 613, 615
Pamphlets: 750, 774, 815
Related Curriculum Materials: 854, 858, 859

54. WHY DO TREES GROW THERE?
Articles: 1, 3, 12, 116, 159
Reference Books: 227, 232, 234, 238, 266, 289, 290, 336, 347, 355, 356, 388, 405, 409, 420, 424, 425, 448
Students' Pleasure Reading and Reference Books: 480, 473, 478, 517, 520, 521, 522, 524
Films: 553, 556, 563, 565, 561, 603, 633, 635, 636, 644
Multi-Media: 670, 671, 672, 673, 674, 675, 680, 685, 687, 698, 699, 704, 708, 710, 712
Pamphlets: 718, 719, 724, 741, 781, 782, 784, 785, 791, 797, 801
Related Curriculum Materials: 837, 865, 868
Simulations/Games: 896

55. WILDLIFE HABITAT
Articles: 94, 140, 156, 168, 197, 199
Reference Books: 222, 328, 372, 389
Students' Pleasure Reading and Reference
Books: 500, 502, 503, 510, 511, 523, 529
Films: 555, 560, 587, 608, 656
Multi-Media: 677, 679
Related Curriculum Materials: 837, 862

56. THE CHANGING FOREST
Articles: 1, 116, 125, 151, 209
Reference Books: 234, 289, 290, 355, 356, 375, 388, 404, 409, 420, 424, 425, 444
Students' Pleasure Reading and Reference Books: 466, 513, 514, 517, 524
Films: 555, 556, 559, 560, 561, 565, 586, 595, 603, 640, 652, 658
Multi-Media: 674, 675, 680, 687, 704, 708
Pamphlets: 735, 736, 768, 784, 785, 791, 797, 808, 814, 829
Related Curriculum Materials: 847, 866, 870
Simulations/Games: 886, 896

57. CLIMAX FOREST
Articles: 27, 81, 125, 202, 208
Reference Books: 290, 303, 313, 413, 441
Students' Pleasure Reading and Reference Books: 513, 517, 522
Films: 565, 567, 575, 603, 633, 636, 658
Multi-Media: 661, 671, 677, 680
Pamphlets: 720, 724, 741, 784, 797, 827, 828, 829, 833, 835
Simulations/Games: 917

58. PREDATOR PREY
Articles: 94, 140, 156, 168, 197, 199
Reference Books: 222, 328, 372, 389
Students' Pleasure Reading and Reference Books: 500, 502, 503, 510, 511, 523, 529
Film: 608
Related Curriculum Materials: 837, 862
Simulations/Games: 895

59. ENDANGERED SPECIES
Articles: 94, 98, 140, 144, 156, 168, 196, 197, 199, 207
Reference Books: 222, 252, 273, 280, 310, 332, 345 (especially "On A Monument to the Pigeon"), 360, 371, 372, 389 (especially Appendix N), 425
Students' Pleasure Reading and Reference Books: 500, 501, 502, 503, 510, 511, 523, 529
Films: 546, 551, 575, 577, 608, 615, 627
Multi-Media: 679
Pamphlets: 754e, 769, 770, 772, 773, 807, 810

60. BUILD AN ECOSYSTEM
Reference Books: 308
Multi-Media: 677
Pamphlets: 749d, 751
Related Curriculum Materials: 837, 861, 875

61. A CALORIE'S COST
Articles: 75, 93, 128, 157
Reference Books: 266, 288, 338, 351, 375, 408, 425
Students' Pleasure Reading and Reference Books: 509
Films: 568
Multi-Media: 674, 690
Related Curriculum Materials: 837, 855
Simulations/Games: 895

62. FOOD MOBILE
Articles: 101, 202, 207
Reference Books: 228, 266, 288, 338, 407, 408, 425, 444
Students' Pleasure Reading and Reference Books: 524
Films: 551, 613
Multi-Media: 674, 690, 670, 675
Related Curriculum Materials: 837, 861, 862, 866, 868
Simulations/Games: 888, 895

63. SUCCESSION ON THE SCHOOL GROUNDS
Articles: 1, 14, 125, 131, 134
Reference Books: 228, 266, 288, 289, 290, 338, 355, 356, 375, 388, 408, 424, 425
Students' Pleasure Reading and Reference Books: 524
Films: 595, 599, 628, 633, 656
Multi-Media: 674
Related Curriculum Materials: 837, 841, 842, 843, 857, 861, 862, 868

64. HOW DO YOU BURY A PILE OF DIRT?
Articles: 2, 30, 31, 38, 72, 75, 142, 152, 162, 212, 213
Reference Books: 254, 285, 291, 365, 375, 425
Students' Pleasure Reading and Reference Books: 493, 524
Films: 619, 620, 647
Multi-Media: 705
Pamphlets: 722, 726, 746, 747, 754d, 834
Related Curriculum Materials: 837, 848, 850
Simulations/Games: 906, 907, 908, 909

65. POLLUTION SEARCH: A "SENSE" OF KNOWING
Articles: 11, 20, 30, 84, 85, 120, 122
Reference Books: 365, 445
Students' Pleasure Reading and Reference Books: 493
Films: 615
Multi-Media: 703
Pamphlets: 742, 743, 813, 819
Related Curriculum Materials: 836, 847, 867
Simulations/Games: 907, 908, 909, 916

66. A TREASURE HUNT ... FOR ENERGY
Articles: 69, 75, 173, 212
Reference Books: 337, 341, 429
Students' Pleasure Reading and Reference Books: 509
Films: 621, 634
Multi-Media: 700, 701
Pamphlets: 757, 766, 767, 787
Related Curriculum Materials: 839, 844
Simulations/Games: 893

67. IMPACT STATEMENTS
Articles: 1, 9, 38, 40, 41, 44, 49, 54, 61, 104, 119, 120, 122, 125, 140, 146, 158, 195
Reference Books: 228, 266, 273, 280, 288, 290, 291, 312, 336, 338, 351, 355, 357, 365, 372, 375, 388, 396, 425

Students' Pleasure Reading and Reference Books: 473, 478, 524
Films: 556, 595, 633
Multi-Media: 674, 675, 690, 701, 704, 708
Pamphlets: 739, 814, 815
Related Curriculum Materials: 836, 837, 841, 842, 843, 851, 857, 859, 861, 862, 863, 868, 871, 875, 878
Simulations/Games: 880, 892, 905, 912, 915

68. WHAT SHALL I USE TO BUILD IT?
Students' Pleasure Reading and Reference Books: 511
Simulations/Games: 887

69. WHAT WOOD WASTE?
Reference Books: 400, 426
Pamphlets: 730, 749g, 810
Related Curriculum Materials: 870

70. WHICH SHOULD I BUY?
Articles: 39, 52, 75, 114, 128
Reference Books: 236, 254, 269, 303, 403, 446, 449
Films: 545, 550, 552, 570, 619, 620, 637, 649
Multi-Media: 681, 682
Pamphlets: 722, 730, 747, 757, 766, 767, 779, 804
Related Curriculum Materials: 859, 871
Simulations/Games: 883, 884

71. BIOGRAPHY OF A "FAVORITE THING"
Reference Books: 373, 391
Multi-Media: 681
Pamphlets: 730, 794, 804

72. CHRISTMAS TREES AND THE ENVIRONMENT
Reference Books: 452
Students' Pleasure Reading and Reference Books: 534
Films: 641
Pamphlets: 784, 816, 820

73. PAPER CONSUMPTION
Articles: 2, 20, 75, 152, 162, 177, 183
Students' Pleasure Reading and Reference Books: 493
Films: 619, 620
Multi-Media: 700, 705
Pamphlets: 722, 726, 727, 728, 746, 754d, 771
Related Curriculum Materials: 859, 848, 850, 871
Simulations/Games: 883, 906

74. WOULD YOU LIKE THAT WRAPPED?
Articles: 2, 20, 30, 38, 72, 75, 102, 142, 152, 162, 177, 183, 212, 214
Reference Books: 226, 254, 282, 285, 361
Students' Pleasure Reading and Reference Books: 502
Films: 562, 609, 619, 620, 621, 647
Multi-Media: 705
Pamphlets: 722, 726, 727, 746
Related Curriculum Materials: 848, 850, 859, 871
Simulations/Games: 884, 906

BIBLIOGRAPHY

ARTICLES

1. Ahlgren, Clifford E. "The Changing Forest, Part I & II." *American Forests*, January 1973, v. 79, n. 1, pp. 40-43; and February 1973, v. 79, n. 2, pp. 16-18.

2. Alexander, Tom. "The Packaging Problem Is a Can of Worms." *Fortune*, June 1972, v. 85, n. 6, pp. 104-107+.

3. Alimi, Richard J., and James P. Barrett. White Pine in Central New England — Its Past — Its Potential." *Forest Notes*, Summer 1976, n. 126, pp. 20-30.

4. Allen, Durward L., "Pressures on Our Outdoor Space." *National Parks & Conservation Magazine*, May 1976, v. 50, n. 5, pp. 2,31.

5. Allen, Eric W., Jr. "Total Support for Total Reforestation." *American Forests*, August 1971, v. 77, n. 8, pp. 30-31.

6. American Forestry Association. "Taking Stock of a Forestry Program — A Conservation Program for American Forestry." *American Forests*, February 1972, v. 78, n. 2, pp. 28-39.

7. American Paper Institute. "API Environmental Statement Cites Achievements, Goals, Commitments." *Pulp and Paper*, January 1971, v. 45, n. 1, pp. 105-106.

8. Arno, Stephen F. "They're Putting the 'Wild' Back in Wilderness." *National Parks & Conservation Magazine*, September 1971, v. 45, n. 9, pp. 10-14.

9. Arnold R. Keith. "Interface Between Man and His Forest Environment." *Journal of Environmental Quality*, April-June 1972, v. 1, n. 2, pp. 117-120.

10. Assaff, Edith. "Ecology Written with Lightning." *American Forests*, September 1973, v. 79, n. 9, pp. 14-17+.

11. Aylor, Donald E. "Plants Filter Noises." *Horticulture*, February 1971, v. 49, n. 2, pp. 28, 48.

12. Barber, John C. "Forestry in the Midsouth." *Journal of Forestry*, August 1976, v. 74, n. 8, pp. 505-511.

13. Beardsley, Wendell G., and J. Alan Wagar. "Vegetation Management on a Forested Recreation Site," *Journal of Forestry*, October 1971, v. 69, n. 10, pp. 729-731.

14. Beardsley, Wendell, et al. "Recreation Site Management: How to Rehabilitate a Heavily Used Campground without Stopping Visitor Use." *Journal of Forestry*, May 1974, v. 72, n. 5, p. 279.

15. Behan, R. W. "Timber Mining: Accusation or Prospect?" *American Forests*, November 1971, v. 77, n. 11, pp. 4-6.

16. Behan, R. W. "Wilderness Purism: Here We Go Again." *American Forests*, December 1972, v. 78, n. 12, pp. 8-11.

17. Behan, R. W. "Police State Wilderness — A Comment on Mandatory Wilderness Permits." *Journal of Forestry*, February 1974, v. 72, n. 2, pp. 98-99.

18. Behme, Bob. "Vehicles and Environmental Responsibility." *Field and Stream*, April 1971, v. 75, n. 12, p. 142.

19. Bolker, Henry I. "Out of the Woods." *Technology Review*, April 1971, v. 73, n. 6, pp. 23-29.

20. Bower, B. T., et al. "Residuals Management in the Pulp and Paper Industry." *Natural Resources Journal*, October 1971, v. 11, n. 4, pp. 605-623.

21. Business Week. "The Timber Industry's Struggle for Wood." *Business Week*, November 25, 1972, n. 2256, pp. 76-77.

22. Burch, William R., Jr. "Wilderness — The Life Cycle and Forest Recreational Choice." *Journal of Forestry*, September 1966, v. 64, n. 9, pp. 606-610.

23. Campbell, J. Philip. "Trees for a Better Environment." *American Forests*, January 1971, v. 77, n. 1, pp. 10, 48.

24. Cannon, Julie. "Timber Supply Act: Anatomy of a Battle." *Sierra Club Bulletin*, March 1970, v. 55, n. 3, pp. 8-11.

25. Carter, Luther J. "Timber Management: Improvement Implies New Land-Use Policies." *Science*, December 25, 1970, v. 170, pp. 1387-1389.

26. Carter, Verlon E. "Forest Management on National Wildlife Refuges." *American Forests*, August 1971, v. 77, n. 8, pp. 22-25.

27. Claiborne, Robert. "When It Is Nature's Way Forest Fires Are Not Bad But in Fact a Benefit." *Smithsonian*, May 1972, v. 3, n. 2, pp. 16-23.

28. Cobb, Tom. "Forestry and the Urban Crisis." *American Forests*, February 1973, v. 79, n. 2, pp. 26-29.

29. Commerce Today. " 'Woodsman, Manage That Tree' Is New Cry As Industry Plans for Future." *Commerce Today*, December 25, 1972, v. 3, n. 6, pp. 11-14.

30. Commoner, Barry et al. "The Causes of Pollution." *Environment*, April 1971, v. 13, n. 2, p. 19.

31. Compost Science. "Let's Drop Tokenism Out of Recycling." *Compost Science*, January-February 1971, v. 12, n. 1, pp. 2-3.

32. Connaughton, Charles A. "Forest Fires Damage More Than Trees." *American Forests*, August 1972, v. 78, n. 8, pp. 30-31 +.

33. Connaughton, Charles A. "Now Is The Time to Develop a National Policy for American Forests." *Journal of Forestry*, April 1976, v. 74, n. 4, pp. 201-205.

34. Corr, Michael, and Dan MacLeod. "Getting It Together." *Environment*, November 1972, v. 14, n. 9, pp. 2-9 +.

35. Craig, James B., and Irene McManus. "Fire in the Environment." *American Forests*, August 1972, v. 78, n. 8, pp. 24-29 +.

36. Craig, James B. "Pluses and Minuses in the National Parks." *American Forests*, June 1976, v. 82, n. 6, pp. 14, 15, 61.

37. Crossland, Janice. "Ferment in Technology." *Environment*, December 1974, v. 16, n. 10, pp. 17-20 +.

38. Daedalus. "The No Growth Society." *Daedalus*, Fall 1973. (Vol. 4, n. 4 of Proceedings of the American Academy of Arts and Sciences.)

39. Dane, C. W. "The Hidden Environmental Costs of Alternative Materials Available for Construction." *Journal of Forestry*, December 1972, v. 70, n. 12, pp. 734-736.

40. Dasmann, Raymond F. "A Rationale for Preserving Natural Areas." *Journal of Soil and Water Conservation*, May-June 1973, v. 28, n. 3, pp. 114-117.

41. Davis, Kenneth P. "ABC's of Even-Aged Management." *American Forests*, August 1971, v. 77, n. 8, pp. 18-21 +.

42. Davis, Millard C. "The Influence of Emerson, Thoreau, and Whitman on the Early American Naturalists — John Muir and John Burroughs." *The Living Wilderness*, Winter 1966-1967, pp. 18-23.

43. Davis, William E. "Society's Needs and Desires Basic to Forestry Management." *Forest Industries*, February 1971, v. 98, n. 2, pp. 38-39.

44. Dawson, George, and Ogden C. Lazenby. "Effects of Fire on the Environment." *American Biology Teacher*, May 1972, v. 34, n. 5, pp. 269-272 +.

45. Ditton, Robert B. "Wreckreaction in Our National Forests." *Parks and Recreation*, June 1971, v. 6, n. 6, pp. 22-26.

46. Dodge, Marvin. "Forest Fuel Accumulation — A Growing Problem." *Science*, July 14, 1972, v. 177, n. 4044, pp. 139-142.

47. Dolan, Edwin. "Why Not Sell the National Parks?" *National Review*, April 6, 1971, v. 23, n. 13, pp. 362-365.

48. Dorsey, George. "The World's Wasteful Woodsmen." *American Forests*, July 1971, v. 77, n. 7, pp. 20, 24 +.

49. Duncan, Donald P. "Managing the Forested Environment: The Role of the Professional." *Journal of Forestry*, January 1971, v. 69, n. 1, pp. 8-11.

50. Dwyer, John F. "Forestry Issues in an Urban Economy." *Journal of Forestry*, January 1976, v. 74, n. 1, pp. 21-23.

51. Dyrness, C. T. "Soil Surface Condition Following Tractor and High-Lead Logging in the Oregon Cascades." *Journal of Forestry*, 1965, v. 63, pp. 272-275.

52. Eber, Ron. "Debunking Madison Avenue." *Environmental Action*, November 13, 1971, v. 3, n. 13, pp. 8-9.

53. Edwards, J. G. "One Step Beyond: An Inquiry Into Research on DDT." In *Terra Facts* series. Available from Terra Society.

54. Enke, Stephen. "The Economic Aspects of Slowing Population Growth." *The Economic Journal*, March 1966, v. 76, pp. 44-56.

55. Evans, Brock. "High Yield Forestry: A New Assault on Our Forests." *Sierra Club Bulletin*, March 1972, v. 57, n. 3, pp. 10-13 +.

56. Everhardt, Gary. "A New Look at Our National Parks." *American Forests*, June 1976, v. 82, n. 6, pp. 22-25 +.

57. Fazio, James R., and Douglas L. Gilbert. "Mandatory Wilderness Permits: Some Indications of Success." *Journal of Forestry*, December 1974, v. 72, n. 12, p. 753.

58. Fertig, Fred. "Child of Nature: The American Indian as an Ecologist." *Sierra Club Bulletin*, August 1970, v. 55, n. 8, pp. 4-7.

59. Fialka, John. "The Off-the-Road Menace!" *Environmental Quality Magazine*, April 1973, v. 4, n. 4, p. 37.

60. Fischer, Virlis. "Storm Signals over the Sawtooth." *American Forests*, January 1971, v. 77, n. 1, pp. 32-35.

61. Fisher, R. Frederic. "Environmental Law." *Sierra Club Bulletin*, January 1971, v. 56, n. 1, pp. 24-28.

62. Forbes. "Forest Products." (Twenty-Fourth Annual Report on American Industry). *Forbes*, January 1972, v. 109, n. 1, pp. 178-182.

63. Forston, James C., et al. "Do Classical Economic Concepts Lead to Environmental Degradation?" *Journal of Forestry*, March 1972, v. 70, n. 3, pp. 152-154.

64. Friends of the Earth. "Special Forestry Issue." *Not Man Apart*, October 1973, v. 3, n. 10.

65. Frome, Michael. "The Story of Conservation Stretches Back to Our Land's Early Inhabitants." *Smithsonian*, March 1971, v. 1, n. 12, pp. 17-27.

66. Galbraith, John K. "Economics and the Quality of Life." *Science*, July 10, 1964, v. 145, pp. 117-123.

67. George, Jean Craighead. "What's Ahead for Our National Parks?" *National Wildlife*, February-March 1972, v. 10, n. 2, pp. 36-41.

68. Graham, Janet. "This Woman Fights the Sahara with Trees." *Science Digest*, January 1971, v. 69, n. 1, pp. 20-23.

69. Grantham, John B., and Thomas H. Ellis. "Potentials of Wood for Producing Energy." *Journal of Forestry*, September 1974, v. 72, n. 9, pp. 552-556.

70. Greiff, Frances. "The Motorized Assault." *National Parks & Conservation Magazine*, July 1973, v. 47, n. 7, pp. 17-19.

71. Greist, David A. "Risk Zoning: A Recreation Area Management System and Method of Measuring Carrying Capacity." *Journal of Forestry*, November 1975, v. 73, n. 11, p. 711-714.

72. Grinstead, Robert R. "The New Resource." *Environment*, December 1970, v. 12, n. 10, pp. 2-17.

73. Habeck, James R. "Glacier's Logan Pass: A Case of Mismanagement." *National Parks & Conservation Magazine*, May 1972, v. 46, n. 5, pp. 10-14.

74. Hagenstein, William D. "Environmental Enigma." *Journal of Forestry*, March 1971, v. 69, n. 3, pp. 147-149.

75. Hannon, Bruce M. "Bottles, Cans, Energy." *Environment*, March 1972, v. 14, n. 2, pp. 11-21.

76. Hardin, Garrett, "The Tragedy of the Commons." *Science*, December 13, 1968, v. 162, pp. 1243-1248.

77. Hardin, Garrett. "We Live on a Spaceship." *Bulletin of the Atomic Scientists*, November 1972, v. 28, n. 9, pp. 23-25.

78. Harnik, Peter. "Logging in Alaska: They Can't See the Forest for the Timber." *Environmental Action*, Part I, August 18, 1973, v. 5, n. 7, pp. 3-6; Part II, "The Biggest Going-out-of-Business Sale of All Time." September 1, 1973, v. 5, n. 8, pp. 9-12.

79. Harper, V. L. "The National Forest

Multiple Use Act of 1960: Excerpts from an Oral History." *Journal of Forestry*, April 1973, v. 71, n. 4, pp. 203-205.

80. Hatchell, G. E., et al. "Soil Disturbances in Logging." *Journal of Forestry*, December 1970, v. 68, n. 12, pp. 772-775.

81. Hartesveldt, Richard J. "Fire Ecology of the Giant Sequoias." *Natural History*, December 1964, v. 73, n. 10, pp. 12-19.

82. Hartzog, George B. "Can the National Parks Meet Your Changing Needs." *Popular Science*, May 1972, v. 200, n. 5, p. 114.

83. Hartzog, George B. "Clearing the Roads — and the Air — in Yosemite Valley." *National Parks & Conservation Magazine*, August 1972, v. 46, n. 8, pp. 14-17.

84. Hay, Edwards. "SMOG — The Tree Killer." *American Forests*, October 1971, v. 77, n. 10, pp. 8-10 +.

85. Hendee, John C., and William R. Catton, "Wilderness Users — What Do They Want?" *American Forests*, September 1968, v. 74, n. 9, pp. 29-31, 60-61.

86. Hendee, John C., and Robert Lucas. "Mandatory Wilderness Permits: A Necessary Tool." *Journal of Forestry*, April 1973, v. 71, n. 4, pp. 206-209.

87. Hendee, John C., and Robert C. Lucas. "Police State Wilderness — A Comment on a Comment." *Journal of Forestry*, February 1974, v. 72, n. 2, pp. 100-101.

88. Hendee, John C., and George H. Stankey. "Biocentricity in Wilderness Management." *Bioscience*, September 1973, v. 23, n. 9, pp. 535-538.

89. Henning, Daniel H. "The Ecology of the Political/Administrative Process for Wilderness Classification." *Natural Resources Journal*, January 1971, v. 11, n. 1, pp. 69-75.

90. Heyman, Ira Michael. "The Great 'Property Rights' Fallacy." *Cry California*, Summer 1968, v. 3, n. 3, pp. 29-34.

91. Hinckley, A. Dexter. "The Gypsy Moth." *Environment*, March 1972, v. 14, n. 2, pp. 41-47.

92. Hirst, Eric. "The Energy Cost of Pollution Control." *Environment*, October 1973, v. 15, n. 8, pp. 37-44.

93. Hirst, Eric. "Living Off the Fuels of the Land." *Natural History*, December 1973, v. 82, n. 10, pp. 20-22.

94. Hooven, Edward F. "A Wildlife Brief for Clearcut Logging of Douglas Fir." *Journal of Forestry*, April 1973, v. 71, n. 4, pp. 210-214.

95. Hope, Jack. "Prosperity and the National Parks." *Natural History*, February 1968, v.

77, n. 2, pp. 6-23.

96. Hope, Jack. "The King Besieged." *Natural History*, November 1968, v. 77, n. 9, pp. 52-56 +.

97. Hope, Jack. "The Invasion of the Awful ORVs." *Audubon*, January 1972, v. 74, pp. 36-43.

98. Hutcherson, Kate. "Endangered Species: The Law and the Land." *Journal of Forestry*, January 1976, v. 74, L. 1, pp. 31-34.

99. Hutchins, H. Clifton. "Uses Can Be Abuses." *Journal of Environmental Education*, Fall 1971, v. 3, n. 1, pp. 43-47.

100. Iltis, Hugh. "Man's Forgotten Necessity: Eco-Variety." *Field and Stream*, June 1970, v. 75, n. 2, pp. 62 +.

101. Iltis, Hugh. Orie L. Loucks, and Peter Andrews. "Criteria for an Optimum Human Environment." *Bulletin of the Atomic Scientists*, January 1970, v. 26, pp. 2-6.

102. Ingersoll, Bruce. "Fast Foods Squandering U.S. Resources." *Chicago Sun Times*, November 12, 1972.

103. Isaacs, Jon. "Environmental Mythology." *Environmental Education Report*, November 1974, v. 2, n. 11, pp. 3-5.

104. Johnson, Warren. "The Case Against Mid-century Spread." *Sierra Club Bulletin*, June 1974, v. 59, n. 6, pp. 14-16 +.

105. Josephson, H.R. "The Outlook for Timber in the United States: *Journal of Forestry*, September 1973, v. 71, n. 9, pp. 560-564.

106. Journal of Forestry. "The Redwood Park Proposals." *Journal of Forestry*, May 1967, v. 65, n. 5, pp. 306-321.

107. Journal of Forestry. "Decision in the North Cascades." *Journal of Forestry*, July 1968, v. 66, n. 7, pp. 521-539.

108. Journal of Forestry. "The Use of Chemical Pesticides for Forestry Purposes." Forest Policies in Action. A Statement by the Gulf States Section of the Society of American Foresters. *Journal of Forestry*, September 1975, v. 73, n. 9, pp. 623-624.

109. Journal of Forestry. "Clearcutting Position Statement on Even-Aged Forest Management Involving Harvesting by Clearcutting Systems." Adopted by the Gulf States Section of the Society of American Foresters. *Journal of Forestry*, September 1975, v. 73, n. 9, pp. 620-623.

110. Journal of Forestry. "Forest Wilderness" Forest Policies in Action. *Journal of Forestry*, February 1976, v. 74, n. 2, p. 124.

111. Journal of Forestry. "The Use of Off-Road Vehicles on Public Forest Lands." *Journal of Forestry*, January 1976, v. 74, p. 123.

112. Keane, John T. "Even Flow — Yes or No?" *American Forests*, June 1972, v. 78, n. 6, pp. 32-35 +.

113. Kimball, Thomas L. " 'Sawdust' Forestry Opposed." *American Forests*, January 1973, v. 79, n. 1, pp. 14-15.

114. Kimmins, J.P. "The Renewability of Natural Resources." *Journal of Forestry*, May 1973, v. 71, n. 5, pp. 209-292.

115. Lahn, Richard. "Debunking Madison Avenue." *Environmental Action*, Part I, July 8, 1972, v. 4, n. 4, pp. 8-9; Part II, July 22, 1972, v. 4, n. 5, pp. 8-9.

116. Lambert, Darwin. "We Can Have Wilderness Wherever We Choose." *National Wildlife*, August-September 1973, v. 11, n. 5, pp. 20-24.

117. Lapping, Mark B., and William B. Kurtz. "Protecting Privately Owned Urban Woodlands: Trends in Municipal Tree Ordinances." *Journal of Forestry*, September 1976, v. 74, n. 9, pp. 622-624.

118. Le Master, Dennis C., and Luke Popovich. "Development of the National Forest Management Act." *Journal of Forestry*, December 1976, v. 74, n. 12, pp. 806-808.

119. Leonard, Raymond E., and Sally B. Parr. "Trees As a Sound Barrier." *Journal of Forestry*, May 1970, v. 68, n. 5, pp. 282-283.

120. Leopold, Luna B. "Landscape Esthetics." *Natural History*, October 1969, v. 78, pp. 36-45.

121. Line, Les, and James D. Perry. "Snowmobiles: Love 'em or Hate 'em." *National Wildlife*, December 1971, v. 10, n. 1, pp. 21-22.

122. Litton, R. Burton, Jr. "Visual Vulnerability of Forest Landscapes." *Journal of Forestry*, July 1974, v. 72, n. 7, pp. 392-397.

123. Living Wilderness. "The Strange Case of Michael Frome, Lover of Trees and Bete Noire of the Lumber Industry." *The Living Wilderness*, Autumn 1971, pp. 22-33.

124. Lucas, Robert C. "Wilderness: A Management Framework." *Journal of Soil and Water Conservation*, July-August 1973, v. 28, n. 4, pp. 150-154.

125. Lutz, H.J. "Forest Ecosystems: Their Maintenance, Amelioration, and Deterioration." *Journal of Forestry*, August 1963, v. 61, n. 8, pp. 563-569.

126. Lynn, Isabelle. "Cougar Lakes Do-It-Yourself Wilderness." *National Parks & Conservation Magazine*, June 1972, v. 46, n. 6, pp. 23-27.

127. Mahoney, Charles L. "Soil Insects as Indicators of Use Patterns in Recreation Areas." *Journal of Forestry*, January 1976, v. 74, n. 1, p. 35.

128. Makhikjani, A.B., and A.J. Lichtenberg. "Energy and Well-Being." *Environment*, June 1972, v. 14, pp. 10-18.

129. Marshall, Robert. "The Universe of the Wilderness Is Vanishing. *The Living Wilderness*, Summer 1971, v. 35, n. 114, pp. 8-14.

130. Matthews, Samuel W. "The Phoenicians." *National Geographic*, August 1974, v. 146, pp. 149-189.

131. McCaull, Julian. "Questions for an Old Friend." *Environment*, July-August 1971, v. 13, n. 6, pp. 2-9.

132. McCurdy, Dwight R. "Overview of the National Wilderness Preservation System." *Journal of Forestry*, May 1977, v. 75, n. 5, pp. 260-261.

133. McIntire, Greg. "Spoiled By Success." *Environment*, July-August 1972, v. 14, n. 6, pp. 14-29.

134. McEwen, Douglas, and S. Ross Tocher, "Zone Management: Key to Controlling Recreational Impact in Developed Campsites." *Journal of Forestry*, February 1976, v. 74, n. 2, pp. 90-93.

135. Megahan, Walter F. "Logging, Erosion, Sedimentation — Are They Dirty Words?" *Journal of Forestry*, July 1972, v. 70, n. 7, pp. 403-407.

136. Miller, James Nathan. "The Nibbling Away of the West." *Reader's Digest*, December 1972, v. 101, pp. 107-111.

137. Minckler, Leon S. "Hardwood Silviculture for Modern Needs." *Journal of Forestry*, January 1972, v. 70, n. 1, pp. 10-17.

138. Minckler, Leon S. "Environmental Forestry in the Eastern Hardwoods." *National Parks & Conservation Magazine*, April 1972, v. 46, n. 4, pp. 18-23.

139. Minckler, Leon S. "Wilderness East? — YES." *American Forests*, December 1972, v. 78, n. 12, pp. 3, 42-44.

140. Minkler, Leon. "Ecological Bookkeeping." *American Forests*, August 1973, v. 79, n. 8, pp. 20-23.

141. Minckler, Leon S., and Peter A. Twight. "Ecological Forestry for the Central Hardwood Forest." *National Parks & Conservation Magazine*, April 1972, v. 46, n. 8, pp. 27-28.

142. Mines, Samuel. "Again and Again and Again and . . . a Report on Recycling." *Ecology Today*, March 1971, v. 1, n. 1, pp. 23-25.

143. Mitchell, John G. "The Best of the S.O.B.'s" *Audubon*, September 1974, v. 76, pp. 48-59.

144. Mobley, Hugh E. "Fire — Its Impact on the Environment." *Journal of Forestry*, July 1974, v. 72, n. 7, pp. 414-417.

145. Mochring, David M., and Ike W. Rawls, "Detrimental Effects of Wet Weather Logging." *Journal of Forestry*, March 1970, v. 68, n. 3, pp. 166-167.

146. Moir, William H. "Natural Areas." *Science*, August 4, 1972, v. 177, n. 4047, pp. 396-400.

147. Momaday, N. Scott. "An American Land Ethic." *Sierra Club Bulletin*, February 1970, v. 55, n. 2, pp. 8-11.

148. Mounts, Jack. "1974 Douglas-fir Tussock Moth Control Project." *Journal of Forestry*, February 1976, v. 74, n. 2, pp. 82-86.

149. Nadel, Michael. "Why Not Unmanaged Forests?" *The Living Wilderness*, Winter 1970-71, v. 34, n. 112, p. 2.

150. National Geographic Staff. "America's Wilderness — How Much Can We Save." *National Geographic,* February 1974, v. 145, n. 2, pp. 151-157.

151. Natural History. "The Metro Forest." *Natural History*, Special Supplement to the November 1973 issue, pp. 45-83.

152. Nelson, Gaylord. "Discarded Packaging." *Ecology Today*, March 1971, v. 1, n. 1, pp. 32-34, 36.

153. Newsweek. "Parks Under Siege." *Newsweek*, July 19, 1971, v. 78, n. 3, p. 47.

154. Owens, John S. "Some Thoughts on Management in National Parks." *Biological Conservation*, July 1972, v. 4, n. 4, pp. 241-246.

155. Pardo, Richard. "Water Quality Workshops: Talking It Over with the EPA." *Journal of Forestry*, August 1976, v. 74, n. 8, p. 539.

156. Pengelly, W. L. "Clearcutting: Detrimental Aspects for Wildlife Resources." *Journal of Soil and Water Conservation*, November-December 1972, v. 27, n. 6, pp. 255-258.

157. Perelman, Michael J. "Farming with Petroleum." *Environment*, October 1972, v. 14, n. 8, pp. 8-13.

158. Peters, Lewis C. "Shade and Ornamental Tree Evaluation." *Journal of Forestry*, July 1971, v. 69, n. 7, pp. 411-413.

159. Peterson, Russell W. "Let's Not Gamble with Our Public Forests." *American Forests*, January 1976, v. 82, n. 1, pp. 6, 49-52.

160. Plumb, James W. "Public Attitudes and Knowledge of Forestry." *Journal of Forestry*, April 1973, v. 71, n. 4, pp. 217-219.

161. Powledge, Fred. "Walden III." *Esquire*, June 1970, v. 73, pp. 101-103, 165-169.

162. Printing Magazine. "Recycling Paper: An Historical Overview with Projections for the Future." *Printing Magazine*, July 1972. Four parts, pp. 24-40.

163. Pulp and Paper. "Pulp and Paper Anti-Pollution Effort Belittled." *Pulp and Paper*, February 1971, v. 45, n. 2, pp. 7, 11.

164. Putnam, John. "Timber — How Much Is Enough." *National Geographic,* April 1974, v. 145, p. 484-511.

165. Randall, Charles E. "You Can Be a Conservationist." *American Forests*, April 1966, v. 72, n. 4, pp. 17-27.

166. Reidel, Carl H. "Environment: New Imperative for Forest Policy." *Journal of Forestry*, May 1971, v. 69, n. 5, pp. 266-270.

167. "Resources Planning Act." *Journal of Forestry*, May 1976, v. 74, n. 5. Five articles: Giltmier, Jim, "A Congressional Perspective," p. 275; Bergoffen, Gene S., "A Process for Choice and Management," pp. 276-278; Manthy, Robert S., "Forest Policy," pp. 279-281; Hyde, William F., "Critique and Alternative Approach," pp. 282-284; Vaux, Henry J., "Problems of Method," pp. 285-287.

168. Resler, Rexford A. "Clearcutting: Beneficial Aspects for Wildlife Resources." *Journal of Soil and Water Conservation*, November-December 1972, v. 27, n. 6, pp. 250-254.

169. Riddler, Jane, et al. "Breaking New Ground in Urban America." *American Forests*, November 1976, v. 83, n. 11, p. 26.

170. Robinson, Gordon. "Responsible Forestry." *Sierra Club Bulletin*, December 1971, v. 56, n. 10, pp. 4-7.

171. Robinson, Gordon. "Our Export Forests." *Sierra Club Bulletin*, January 1973, v. 58, n. 1, pp. 10-14 +.

172. Rockefeller, Laurence S. "People in Our Parks." *American Forests*, June 1976, v. 82, n. 6, pp. 12-13.

173. Rose, Dietmar W. "Fuel Forest vs Strip Mining: Fuel Production Alternatives." *Journal of Forestry*, August 1975, v. 73, p. 489.

174. Science Digest. "Breeding Pollution Resistant Trees for Cities." *Science Digest*, August 1971, v. 70, n. 2, pp. 80-81.

175. Seamon, Jerome F., "Forests — Our Inheritance and Our Legacy." *The Northern Logger and Timber Processor*, June 1976, pp. 6, 7.

176. Sears, Paul B. "Beyond the Forest." *American Scientist*, September 1967, v. 55, n. 3, pp. 338-346.

177. Shorter, W. Wyatt. "Solid Waste — A Serendipitous Opportunity." *American*

Paper Industry, January 1971, v. 53, n. 1, p. 60.

178. Siegel, William C. "Environmental Laws and Forest Management." *Journal of Forestry*. November 1972, v. 70, n. 11, pp. 682-686.

179. Simmons, Fred C. "Wilderness East? — No." *American Forests*, July 1972, v. 78, n. 7, pp. 3, 45, 46.

180. Smithsonian. "Scenes . . . From Which the Hand of Nature Has Never Been Lifted." *Smithsonian*, August 1972, v. 3, n. 5, pp. 34-41.

181. Society of American Foresters. "Forest Policies of the Society of American Foresters." *Journal of Forestry*, April 1974, v. 72, n. 4, pp. 242-244.

182. Soucie, Gary. "How Much Wood Would a Wood Chopper Chop If a Wood Chopper Could Chop Wood?" *Audubon*, January 1974, v. 76, pp. 115-120.

183. Spofford, Walter O., Jr. "Solid Residuals Management, Some Economic Considerations." *Natural Resources Journal*, July 1971, v. 11, n. 3, pp. 561-589.

184. Stankey, G. H. "Myths in Wilderness Decision-Making." *Journal of Soil and Water Conservation*, September-October 1971, v. 26, n. 5, pp. 183-188.

185. Stein, Richard G. "A Matter of Design." *Environment*, October 1972, v. 14, n. 8, pp. 17-20 + .

186. Steinbrenner, E.C., "The Effect of Repeated Tractor Trips on the Physical Properties of Forest Soils." *Northwest Science*, November 1955, v. 29, pp. 155-159.

187. Steinbrenner, E. C., and S. P. Gessel. "Effect of Tractor Logging on Soils and Regeneration in Douglas-fir Region of Southwestern Washington." In Society of American Foresters' 1955 Annual Proceedings, pp. 77-80.

188. Steinbrenner, E. C., and S. P. Gessel. "The Effect of Tractor Logging on Physical Properties of Some Forest Soils in Southwestern Washington." In Soil Scientists of America Proceedings 1955, pp. 372-376.

189. Strong, Douglas H. "The Rise of American Esthetic Conservation: Muir, Mather and Udall." *National Parks & Conservation Magazine*, February 1970, v. 44, n. 269, pp. 4-9.

190. Tanner, R. Thomas. "Environmental Sensitivity and the Mass Media." *Journal of Environmental Education*, Summer 1971, v. 2, n. 4, pp. 34-37.

191. Taylor, Ron. "Subdividing the Wilderness." *Sierra Club Bulletin*, January 1971, v. 56, n. 1, pp. 4-9.

192. Taylor, Ronald B. " 'No Vacancy' in the Wilderness." *Sierra Club Bulletin*, October-November 1972, v. 57, n. 9, pp. 5-8.

193. Thomas, Lowell. "The Painful Lesson of the Cedars of Lebanon." *National Wildlife*, December 1969-January 1970, v. 8, pp. 50-55.

194. Thompson, Roger C. "Preservation, Recreation, and the Premise of Forestry." *Journal of Forestry*, June 1967, v. 65, n. 6, pp. 372-377.

195. Tilden, Paul M. "Planning in the Pine Barrens." *National Parks & Conservation Magazine*, August 1971, v. 45, n. 8, pp. 22-26.

196. Tinker, Jon. "Marrying Wildlife to Forestry." *New Scientist*, June 5, 1969, v. 42, n. 652, pp. 518-520.

197. Trefethen, James B. "The Return of the White Tailed Deer." *American Heritage*, February 1970, v. 21, pp. 97-103.

198. Twight, Peter A., "Environmental Forestry: Fiber Farms or Parks? *American Forests*. May 1976, v. 82, n. 5, 22-23 + .

199. Uetz, George, and Donald Lee Johnson. "Breaking the Web." *Environment*, December 1974, v. 16, n. 10, pp. 31-39.

200. Van Haverbeke, David F., and David I. Cook. "Green Mufflers." *American Forests*, November 1972, v. 78, n. 11, pp. 28-31.

201. Vaux, Henry J. "How Much Land Do We Need for Timber Growing?" *Journal of Forestry*, July 1973, v. 71, n. 7, pp. 399-403.

202. Vogl, Richard J. "Monotonous Monocultures." *Ecology Today*, September 1971, v. 1, n. 7, pp. 43-45.

203. Vogl, Richard J. "Smokey's Mid-Career Crisis." *Saturday Review of Sciences*, February 24, 1973, v. 1, n. 2, pp. 23-29.

204. Wagner, J. Alan. "Recreational Carrying Capacity Reconsidered." *Journal of Forestry*, May 1974, v. 72, n. 5, p. 274.

205. Walker, Clyde M. "Rehabilitation of Forest Land." *Journal of Forestry*, March 1973, v. 71, n. 3, pp. 136-137.

206. "Water Pollution Control and Forestry." Interview with George W. Brown, Raymond M. Rice, and Robert B. Thomas. *Journal of Forestry*, June 1976, v. 74, n. 6, pp. 342-345.

207. Watt, Kenneth F. "Man's Efficient Rush Toward Deadly Dullness." *Natural History*, February 1972, v. 81, n. 10, pp. 74-77.

208. Weyerhaeuser, George H. "Accent on Regeneration." *American Forests*. January 1973, v. 79, n. 1, pp. 22-23 + .

209. "What Forests Mean to America." Two-page spreads of art and words. *American Forests*, Each issue 1976, v. 82.

210. White, Lynn, Jr. "The Historical Roots of Our Ecologic Crisis." *Science*, March 10, 1967, v. 155, n. 3767, pp. 1203-1207.

211. Wieser, Jeff. "We Blew Our Cool but Saved a Woods." *National Wildlife*, April-May 1971, v. 9, n. 3, pp. 32-35.

212. Wilcox, Dennis. "Fuel from City Trash." *Environment*, September 1973, v. 15, n. 7, pp. 36-42.

213. Wilson, Carl C., and John D. Dell. "The Fuels Buildup in American Forests: A Plan of Action and Research." *Journal of Forestry*, August 1971, v. 69, n. 8, pp. 471-475.

214. Wilson, David Gordon. "Present and Future Possibilities of Reclamation from Solid Wastes." *Compost Science*, September-October 1970, v. 11, n. 5, pp. 3-7.

215. Wood, H. W., Jr. "Pinchot and Mather: How the Forest Service and the Park Service Got That Way." *Not Man Apart*, Mid-December 1976, p. 1.

216. Wood, Nancy. "Here Comes a Grim Reaper: Today the Forest, Tomorrow the National Parks." *Sierra Club Bulletin*, September 1971, v. 56, n. 8, pp. 14-19.

217. Wood, William W., Jr. "A Policy for Land Use." *Journal of Soil and Water Conservation*, January-February 1971, v. 26, n. 1, pp. 2-3.

218. Yi-Fu Tuan. "Our Treatment of the Environment in Ideal and Actuality." *American Scientist*, May-June 1970, v. 58, n. 3, pp. 244-249.

219. Zivnuska, John A. "Conservation — For Whom." *American Forests*, July 1971, v. 77, n. 7, pp. 8-9 + .

220. Zivnuska, John A. "The Managed Wilderness." *American Forests*, August 1973, v. 79, n. 8, p. 16.

TEACHER REFERENCE BOOKS

221. Adams, Ansel, and Nancy Newhall. *This Is the American Earth*. San Francisco: Sierra Club, 1960, $15.00.

222. Allen, Durward L. *Our Wildlife Legacy*. New York: Funk & Wagnalls, 1974, $4.95, paper.

223. Bagley, Clarence. *Indian Myths of the Northwest*. Facsimile of 1930 edition. Seattle: Shorey, 1971, $8.50, paper.

224. Barkley, Paul W., and David W. Seckler. *Economic Growth and Environmental Decay*. New York: Harcourt Brace Jovanovich, 1972, $4.95, paper text edition.

225. Barney, Daniel. *The Last Stand: Ralph Nader's Study Group Report on the National Forests*. New York: Grossman, 1974, $7.95.

226. Barnett, Harold J., and Chandler Morese. *Scarcity and Growth: The Economics of Natural Resource Availability*. Baltimore: Johns Hopkins, 1963, $2.95, paper.

227. Bates, Marston. *The Forest and the Sea: A Look at the Economy of Nature and the Ecology of Man*. New York: Random, 1965, $1.95, paper.

228. Benton, Allen H., and William E. Werener, Jr. *Field Biology and Ecology*, 3rd ed. New York: McGraw-Hill, 1974, $16.00.

229. Benton, Allen H., and William E. Werener, Jr. *Manual of Field Biology*, 5th ed. Minneapolis: Burgess, 1972, $6.95.

230. Bosselman, Fred, et al. *Taking Issue: Analysis of Constitutional Limits of Land Use Control*. Washington: Government Printing Office, 1973, $2.70.

231. Boulding, Kenneth E. *The Meaning of the Twentieth Century: The Great Transition*. New York: Harper, 1964, $7.95; Colophon, 1965, $1.95, paperback.

232. Brockman, C. Frank. *Trees of North America*. Golden Field Guide Series. Racine: Western, 1968, $6.95; paper, $4.95.

233. Brooks, Paul. *The Pursuit of Wilderness*. Boston: Houghton Mifflin, 1971, $6.95.

234. Brown, Vinson. *Reading the Woods: Seeing More in Nature's Familiar Faces*. Harrisburg: Stackpole, 1969, $7.95; New York: Macmillan (Collier), 1973, $2.95, paper.

235. Burk, Dale A. *The Clearcut Crisis*. Great Falls: Jursnick, 1971, $3.50.

236. Cailliet, Greg, et al. *Everyman's Guide to Ecological Living*. New York: Macmillan, 1971, $0.95.

237. Capps, Walter, ed. *Seeing with the Native Eye: Essays on Native American Religion*. New York: Harper, 1976, $3.95, paper.

238. Carroll, Charles. *The Timber Economy of Puritan New England*. Providence: Brown University, 1973, $12.50.

239. Carson, Rachel L. *Silent Spring*. Boston: Houghton Mifflin, 1962, $7.95; Sentry, $2.95.

240. Carstensen, Vernon, ed. *The Public Lands: Studies in the History of Public Domain*. Madison: University of Wisconsin, 1963, $6.25.

241. Ciriacy-Wantrup, S. V. *Resource Conservation: Economics and Policies,* 3rd ed. Berkeley: University of California, Division of Agricultural Sciences, 1968, $5.00.

242. Clark, Colin. *Population Growth and Land Use*. New York: St. Martin's, 1967, $17.95.

243. Clark, Ella. *Indian Legends of the Pacific*

Northwest. Berkeley: University of California Press, 1953, $2.45, paper.

244. Clawson, Marion. *An Economic Perspective on National Forest Management.* Baltimore: Johns Hopkins, 1976, $4.50.

245. Clawson, Marion. *Forests for Whom and for What?* Baltimore: Johns Hopkins, 1975, $11.95; paper, $3.65.

246. Clawson, Marion. *The Land System of the United States.* Lincoln: University of Nebraska, 1968, $6.50.

247. Clawson, Marion. *Man and Land in the United States.* Lincoln: University of Nebraska, 1964, $7.95.

248. Clawson, Marion. *Man, Land, and the Forest Environment.* Seattle: University of Washington. 1977, $6.95.

249. Clawson, Marion. *Suburban Land Conversion in the United States: An Economic and Governmental Process.* Baltimore: Johns Hopkins, 1971, $15.00.

250. Clawson, Marion, and Burnell Held. *The Federal Lands: Their Use and Management.* Baltimore: Johns Hopkins, 1957, $16.50; Lincoln: University of Nebraska, $5.95, paper.

251. Clepper, Henry E., ed. *Careers in Conservation: Opportunities in Natural Resources.* New York: Ronald, 1963, $6.95.

252. Clepper, Henry E., ed. *Origins of American Conservation.* New York: Ronald, 1966, $5.95.

253. Clepper, Henry, and Arthur Meyer. *American Forestry: Six Decades of Growth.* Washington Society of American Foresters, 1960, $3.95.

254. Commoner, Barry. *The Closing Circle: Man, Nature and Technology.* New York: Knopf, 1971, $7.95; Bantam, 1972, $1.95, paper.

255. Commoner, Barry. *Science and Survival.* New York: Viking, 1967, $1.65.

256. Conservation Foundation. *National Parks for the Future.* Washington: Conservation Foundation, 1974, $3.50.

257. Cooley, Richard A., and Geoffrey Wandesforde-Smith, eds. *Congress and the Environment.* Seattle: University of Washington, 1970, $8.95.

258. Cutler, Katherine. *From Petals to Pine Cones.* New York: Lothrop, 1971, $5.61.

259. Daly, Herman, ed. *Toward a Steady-State Economy.* San Francisco: Freeman, 1973, $9.95, paper, $4.95.

260. Dana, Samuel T. *Forest and Range Policy: Its Development in the United States.* New York: McGraw-Hill, 1956, $14.50.

261. Daniele, Joseph W. *Building Early American Furniture.* Harrisburg: Stackpole, $14.95.

262. Darling, Frank Fraser. *Wilderness and Plenty.* Boston: Houghton Mifflin, 1970, $4.95.

263. Darling, Frank Fraser, and Noel D. Eichhorn. *Man and Nature in the National Parks: Reflections on Policy*, 2nd ed. Washington: Conservation Foundation, 1969, $1.50.

264. Darling, Frank Fraser, and J. P. Milton, eds. *Future Environments of North America.* Garden City: Natural History, $12.95; paper, $5.95.

265. Dasmann, Raymond F. *A Different Kind of Country.* New York: Macmillan (Collier), 1970, $1.95.

266. Dasmann, Raymond F. *Environmental Conservation*, 3rd ed. New York: Wiley, 1959, $7.95.

267. Davies, Barbara S., and J. Clarence Davies, 3rd. *The Politics of Pollution*, 2nd ed. New York: Pegasus, 1975, $5.95; paper, $3.95.

268. Day, Albert, M. *Making a Living in Conservation: A Guide to Outdoor Careers.* Harrisburg: Stackpole, 1971, $3.95.

269. Dayton Museum of Natural History. *The Do-It-Yourself Environmental Handbook.* Boston: Little, Brown, 1972, $1.95.

270. DeBell, Garrett, ed. *The Environmental Handbook: Prepared for the First National Environmental Teach-In.* Westminster: Ballantine, 1970, $0.95.

271. Deedy, John, and Philip Nobile, eds. *The Complete Ecology Fact Book.* Garden City: Doubleday, 1972, $10.00; Anchor Octavo, $3.95, paper.

272. Delafons, John. *Land-Use Controls in the United States*, 2nd ed. Cambridge: MIT, 1970, $15.00.

273. Detwyler, Thomas R. *Man's Impact on Environment.* New York: McGraw-Hill, 1971, $7.95.

274. Dodd, Ed. *Careers for the Seventies: Conservation.* New York: Macmillan, 1971, $4.95.

275. Douglas, William O. *A Wilderness Bill of Rights.* Boston: Little, Brown, 1965, $7.50.

276. Drucker, Peter F. *Men, Ideas and Politics.* New York: Harper, 1971, $7.95.

277. Dubos, Rene. *So Human an Animal.* New York: Scribners, 1968, $7.95; paper, $2.95.

278. Eckholm, Erik P. *Losing Ground: Environmental Stress and World Food Prospects.* Washington: Worldwatch, 1976, $7.95; paper, $3.95.

279. Edwards, Joan (for the Environmental Action Coalition). *Caring for Trees on City*

Streets. New York: Scribners, 1975. $6.95.

280. Ehrenfeld, David W. *Biological Conservation*. New York: Holt, Rinehart and Winston, 1970, $4.50.

281. Ehrlich, Paul R. *The Population Bomb*. Westminster: Ballantine, 1968, $1.95.

282. Ehrlich, Paul R., and Anne H. Ehrlich. *Population, Resources, Environment: Issues in Human Ecology*, 2nd ed., San Francisco: Freeman, 1972, $11.00.

283. Ekirch, Arthur A., Jr. *Man and Nature in America*. Lincoln: University of Nebraska, 1973, $2.45.

284. Elder, Frederick. *Crisis in Eden: A Religious Study of Man and Environment*. Nashville: Abingdon, 1970, $4.50.

285. Environmental Protection Agency, Bureau of Solid Waste Management. *The Role of Packaging in Solid Waste Management*. 1966-1976. Stock No. 055-002-00057. Washington: Government Printing Office; $0.70.

286. Ewald, Ellen B. *Recipes for a Small Planet*. Westminster: Ballantine, 1973, $1.95.

287. Fanning, Odom. *Opportunities in Environmental Careers*. Louisville: Vocational Guidance, 1975, $3.95, paper.

288. Farb, Peter, and the Editors of Life. *Ecology*. Morristown: Silver Burdett, 1970, $7.50.

289. Farb, Peter. *The Face of North America*. New York: Harper, 1964, $4.50.

290. Farb, Peter, ed. *The Forest*. Morristown: Silver Burdett, 1969, $7.50.

291. Farb, Peter. *The Living Earth*. New York: Harper, 1959, $6.95; 1969, $1.95, paper.

292. Feirer, John L. *Cabinetmaking and Millwork*. Peoria: Bennett, 1970, $19.16.

293. Feirer, John L. *Wood: Materials and Processes*. Peoria: Bennett, 1975, $11.76; school price, $8.82.

294. Feirer, John L. *Woodworking for Industry*. Peoria: Bennett, 1971, $13.28.

295. Ferguson Editorial Staff. *Career Opportunities: Ecology, Conservation and Environmental Careers*. Chicago: Ferguson, 1971, $6.95.

296. Finkler, Earl, and David L. Peterson. *Nongrowth As a Planning Alternative*. Chicago: American Society of Planning Officials; and New York: Praeger, 1974, $13.50.

297. Flader, Susan L. *Thinking Like a Mountain: Aldo Leopold and the Evolution of an Ecological Attitude Toward Deer, Wolves, and Forests*. Columbia: University of Missouri, 1974, $12.50.

298. Flexner, James T. *That Wilder Image: The Paintings of America's Native School from Thomas Cole to Winslow Homer*. Gloucester: Peter Smith, $7.00; Vol. 3, New York: Dover, 1970, $4.00 paper.

299. Fritsch, A. J. *The Contrasumers: A Citizen's Guide to Resource Conservation*. Praeger, 1974, $7.95; paper, $3.50.

300. Fritsch, Albert, and Barry I. Castleman. *Lifestyle Index*. Washington: Center for Science in the Public Interest, 1974, $1.50, paper.

301. Frome, Michael. *The Forest Service*. New York: Praeger, 1971, $8.75.

302. Fuller, R. Buckminster, and Robert W. Marks. *The Dymaxion World of Buckminster Fuller*. New York: Doubleday, Anchor Octavo, 1973, $4.95, paper.

303. Fullerton, Roberta. *Happiness is a Well-Managed Forest*. Laramie: Edward Hines Lumber Co., 1973, $0.35.

304. Galbraith, John K. *The Affluent Society*, 2nd ed. New York: New American Library, 1970, paper, $1.50.

305. Galbraith, John K. *The New Industrial State*, 2nd rev. ed. Boston: Houghton Mifflin, 1971, $8.95; 1972, $3.25, paper.

306. Gardner, John W. *The Recovery of Confidence*. New York: Norton, 1970, $5.00.

307. Gardner, John W. *Self-Renewal: The Individual and the Innovative Society*. New York: Harper, 1971, $1.75.

308. Gillette, Elizabeth. *Action for Wilderness*. San Francisco: Sierra Club, 1972, $2.25.

309. Glacken, Clarence J. *Traces on the Rhodian Shore: Nature and Culture in Western Thought from Ancient Times to the End of the Eighteenth Century*. Berkeley: University of California Press, 1973, $24.00; 1976, paper, $9.95.

310. Graham, Frank, Jr. *Man's Dominion, the Story of Conservation in America*. New York: Evans, 1971, $8.95.

311. Graham, Frank, Jr. *Since Silent Spring*. Boston: Houghton Mifflin, 1970, $6.95; Fawcett World, $1.25, paper.

312. Guenzi, W. D., ed. *Pesticides in Soil and Water*. Madison: Soil Science Society of America (order from American Society of Agronomy), 1974, $14.00.

313. Gunther, Erna. *Ethnobotany of Western Washington*. Seattle: University of Washington, 1973, $5.00; paper, $2.95.

314. Gussow, Alan. *A Sense of Place: The Artist and the American Land*, 2nd ed. San Francisco: Friends of the Earth, 1974, $10.98.

315. Hampton, H. Duane. *How the U.S. Cavalry Saved Our National Parks*. Bloomington:

Indiana University, 1971, $9.50.

316. Hand, Jackson. *Modern Woodworking*. Englewood Cliffs: Reston, distributed by Prentice-Hall, 1975. $12.95.

317. Harrison, C. William. *Conservation: The Challenge of Reclaiming Our Plundered Land*, rev. ed. New York: Messner, 1973, $5.29.

318. Haynie, Paul. *Cabinetmaking*. Englewood Cliffs: Prentice-Hall, 1975, $8.67.

319. Hays, Samuel. *Conservation and the Gospel of Efficiency: The Progressive Conservation Movement*. Cambridge: Harvard University, 1959, $13.00.

320. Heilbroner, Robert L. *Between Capitalism and Socialism: Essays in Political Economics*. New York: Random, 1970, $1.95, paper.

321. Heilbroner, Robert L. *The Making of Economic Society*, 4th ed. Englewood Cliffs: Prentice-Hall, 1972, $8.95; paper, $5.00.

322. Herbert, Fred W. *Careers in Natural Resource Conservation*. New York: Walck, 1965, $4.50.

323. Herfindahl, Orris C., and Allen V. Kneese. *Quality of the Environment: An Economic Approach to Some Problems in Using Land, Water, and Air*. Baltimore: Johns Hopkins, 1965, $2.00.

324. Herman, Richard K., and Dennis P. Lavender. *Even-Age Management: Proceedings of a Symposium Held August 1, 1972*. Corvallis: Oregon State University, 1973, $5.00.

325. *Historical Abstract of the United States*. Colonial Times to 1970. Washington: Government Printing Office, 1976, $26.00. (See also *Statistical Abstract of the United States*.)

326. Horwitz, Eleanor C. *Clearcutting: A View from the Top*. Washington, DC: Acropolis, 1974, $7.95; paper, $3.95.

327. Huth, Hans. *Nature and the American: Three Centuries of Changing Attitudes*. Lincoln: University of Nebraska, 1972, $2.95, paper.

328. International Union for the Conservation of Nature and Natural Resources. *Red Data Book*. Morges, Switzerland: The Union, $20.00.

329. Ise, John. *The United States Forest Policy*. New York: Arno. 1972. Reproduction of 1920 edition. $17.00.

330. Jarrett, Henry, ed. *Environmental Quality in a Growing Economy*. Baltimore: Johns Hopkins, 1971, $7.50; paper, $1.95.

331. Jones, Holway R. *John Muir and the Sierra Club: The Battle for Yosemite*. San Francisco: Sierra Club, 1965, $10.00.

332. Kahn, Lloyd. *Domebook II*. New York: Shelter Publications; distributed by Random, 1971, $4.00.

333. Kaminsky, Ralph, ed. *Introduction to Economic Issues*. Garden City: Doubleday, 1970, $1.45.

334. Kapp, K. William. *Social Costs of Private Enterprise*. New York: Schocken, 1971, $3.95, paper.

335. Kaufman, Herbert. *The Forest Ranger: A Study in Administrative Behavior*. Baltimore: Johns Hopkins, 1960, $7.50.

336. Kittredge, Joseph. *Forest Influences: The Effects of Woody Vegetation on Climate, Water, and Soil*. New York: Dover, 1973 (originally published by McGraw-Hill), 1949, $3.50, paper.

337. Kneese, Allen V., et al. *Economics and the Environment: A Materials Balance Approach*. Baltimore: Johns Hopkins, 1971, $2.50, paper.

338. Kormondy, Edward J. *Concepts of Ecology*. Englewood Cliffs: Prentice-Hall, 1969, $6.25, paper.

339. Krutch, Joseph Wood. *The Measure of Man*. Gloucester: Peter Smith, 1954, $5.75.

340. LaBastille, Anne. *Woodswoman*. New York: Dutton, 1976, $10.95.

341. Landsberg, Hans H. *Natural Resources for U.S. Growth: A Look Ahead to the Year 2000*. Baltimore: Johns Hopkins, 1964, $2.45.

342. Lappe, Frances Moore. *Diet for a Small Planet*, rev. ed. Westminster: Ballantine, 1975, $1.95, paper.

343. Layne, Elizabeth N. *The Natural Environment: A Dimension of Development*. New York: National Audubon, 1976.

344. Leopold, Luna, ed. *Round River: From the Journals of Aldo Leopold*. New York: Oxford University, 1972, $1.95, paper.

345. Leopold, Aldo. *Sand County Almanac*. Westminster: Ballantine, 1970, $1.50, paper.

346. Little, Charles E. *Challenge of Land: Open Space Preservation at the Local Level*. New York: Pergamon, 1969, $7.50.

347. Little, Elbert L., Jr. *Atlas of U.S. Trees: Volume I Conifers and Important Hardwoods*. Stock no. 001-000-00601. Washington: Government Printing Office, 1971, $22.15.

348. Lowdermilk, W. C. *Conquest of the Land Through 7000 Years*. Stock no. 001-000-03446 (Agricultural Information Bulletin 99). Washington: Government Printing Office, 1953, $0.45.

349. MacKaye, Benton. *The New Exploration: A Philosophy of Regional Planning.* Urbana: University of Illinois, 1962, $1.75.

350. Maguire, Bryon W. *Complete Book of Woodworking and Cabinetmaking.* Englewood Cliffs: Prentice-Hall, 1974, $9.56.

351. Mandelker, Daniel. *New Developments in Land and Environmental Controls* (Supplement). Indianapolis: Bobbs-Merrill, 1974, $5.00.

352. Mandelker, Daniel. *The Zoning Dilemma.* Chicago: American Society of Planning Officials; distributed by Bobbs-Merrill, 1971, $10.50.

353. Marsh, George Perkins. *Man and Nature,* edited by David Lowenthal. Cambridge: Harvard University, 1965, $4.95, paper.

354. Marx, Leo. *The Machine in the Garden: Technology and the Pastoral Ideal in America.* New York: Oxford University, 1967, $3.95, paper.

355. McCormick, Jack. *The Life of the Forest.* New York: McGraw-Hill, 1966, $5.50.

356. McCormick, Jack. *The Living Forest.* New York: Harper, 1959, $7.87.

357. McCulloch, Walter F. *Woods Words: A Comparative Dictionary of Logger's Terms.* Portland: Oregon Historical Society, 1958, $3.25, paper.

358. McHarg, Ian L. *Design With Nature.* Garden City: Natural History, 1971, $19.95; paper, $6.95.

359. McLuhan, T. C. *Touch the Earth: A Self Portrait of Indian Existence.* New York: Dutton, 1971, $6.95; Simon & Schuster, 1976, $3.95, paper.

360. McMillan, Ian. *Man and the California Condor.* New York: Dutton, 1968, $6.95.

361. Meadows, Dennis L., et al. *The Limits to Growth.* New York: New American Library, 1972, $1.50, paper.

362. Mishan, Ezra J. *Technology and Growth: The Price We Pay.* New York: Praeger, 1970, $7.95; paper, $2.95.

363. Mitchell, John G., ed. *Ecotactics: The Sierra Club Handbook for Environmental Activists.* New York: Simon & Schuster, 1970, $1.95.

364. Mumford, Lewis. *The City in History: Its Origins, Its Transformations, and Its Prospects.* New York: Harcourt Brace Jovanovich, 1961, $18.50; paper, $5.75.

365. Murdoch, William W., ed. *Environment: Resources, Pollution and Society.* Sunderland: Sinauer, 1975, $10.95.

366. Murie, Olaus. *Field Guide to Animal Tracks.* Boston: Houghton Mifflin, 1954, $5.95.

367. Nash, Roderick. *The American Conservation Movement.* St. Charles: Forum, 1974, $1.25.

368. Nash, Roderick. *The American Environment: Readings in the History of Conservation,* 2nd ed. Reading: Addison-Wesley, 1975, $5.95, paper.

369. Nash, Roderick. *Environment and Americans.* New York: Holt, Rinehart and Winston, 1972, $3.95.

370. Nash, Roderick. *Wilderness and the American Mind,* rev. ed. New Haven: Yale University, 1973, $15.00; paper, $3.95.

371. National Wildlife Federation. *Conservation Directory.* Washington: National Wildlife Federation, 1977, $3.00; updated annually.

372. Natural Resource Council. *Land Use and Wildlife Resources.* Washington: National Academy of Sciences, 1970, $6.95.

373. Needham, Walter. *A Book of Country Things.* Brattleboro: Greene, 1965, $5.95.

374. Nixon, Edgar B., ed. *Franklin D. Roosevelt and Conservation 1911-1945.* 2 vols. Reproduction of 1957 edition. New York: Arno, 1972, $58.00.

375. Odum, Eugene P. *Ecology.* New York: Holt, Rinehart and Winston, 1975, $4.95, paper.

376. Ogden, Daniel M., Jr. "The Struggle for Redwood National Park." In *Public Choice and Public Policy,* Robert S. Ross, ed. Chicago: Rand McNally, 1971, pp. 81-109.

377. Olson, Delmar W. *Woods and Woodworking for Industrial Arts.* Englewood Cliffs: Prentice-Hall, $8.67.

378. Oughton, Frederick. *Creative Crafts.* New York: McKay, 1976, $4.95.

379. Paradis, Adrian A. *Reclaiming the Earth: Jobs That Help Improve the Environment.* New York: McKay, 1971, $4.95.

380. Passell, Peter, and Leonard Ross. *The Retreat From Riches: Affluence and Its Enemies.* New York: Viking, 1973, $6.95.

381. Pearce, Roy Harvey, and Millers, J. H., eds. *The Savages of America: A Study of the Indian and the Idea of Civilization,* rev. ed. Baltimore: Johns Hopkins, 1965, $8.50.

382. Penick, James L., Jr. *Progressive Politics and Conservation: The Ballinger-Pinchot Affair.* Chicago: University of Chicago, 1968, $9.00.

383. Petrides, George A. *A Field Guide to Trees and Shrubs,* 2nd ed. Boston: Houghton Mifflin, $4.95.

384. Philbrick, Helen, and Gregg Richard. *Companion Plants and How to Use Them.* Old Greenwich: Devin-Adair, 1966, $4.95.

385. Pinchot, Gifford. *Breaking New Ground,*

new ed. Reproduction of 1945 edition (American Library series). Seattle: University of Washington, 1972, $10.50.

386. Pinchot, Gifford. *The Fight for Conservation*. (American Library series), Seattle: University of Washington, 1969, $9.50; paper, $2.45.

387. Pinkett, Harold T. *Gifford Pinchot: Private and Public Forester*. Urbana: University of Illinois, 1970, $6.95.

388. Platt, Rutherford. *The Great American Forest*. Englewood Cliffs: Prentice-Hall, 1971, $2.95.

389. President's Advisory Panel on Timber and the Environment. *Report of the President's Advisory Panel on Timber and the Environment*. Stock no. 040-000-00298-7. Washington: Government Printing Office, 1973, $4.80.

390. Pursell, Carroll W., ed. *From Conservation to Ecology: The Development of Environmental Concern*. Northbrook: AHM Publishing, 1973, $3.75, paper.

391. Randall, Charles E., and Henry Clepper. *Famous and Historic Trees*. American Forestry Association, 1976, $3.50.

392. Randall, Janet. *To Save a Tree: The Story of the Coast Redwoods*. New York: McKay, 1971, $4.97.

393. Ridgeway, James. *The Politics of Ecology*. New York: Dutton, 1971, $6.95.

394. Ritchie, Carson. *Papercraft*. New York: McKay, 1976, $4.95.

395. Roberge, Earl. *Timber Country*. Caldwell: Caxton Printers, 1974, $30.00.

396. Robinette, G. O. *Plants/People/and Environmental Quality*. Stock no. 024-005-00479-3. Washington: Government Printing Office, 1972, $4.35.

397. Robinson, Glen O. *The Forest Service: A Study in Public Land Management*. Baltimore: Johns Hopkins, 1975, $4.95, paper.

398. Rodgers, Andrew Denny. *Bernhard Eduard Fernow: A Story of North American Forestry*. Reproduction of 1951 edition. New York: Hafner (Macmillan), 1969, $11.95.

399. Ross, Robert S. *Public Choice and Public Policy*. Chicago: Rand McNally, 1971, $5.95, paper.

400. Rottger, Ernst. *Creative Wood Design*. Princeton: Van Nostrand Reinhold, 1972, $5.95; paper, $3.95.

401. Rudd, Robert L. *Pesticides and the Living Landscape*. Madison: University of Wisconsin, 1964, $15.00; paper, $4.25.

402. Sabol, Kenneth J., ed. *The American Landscape: 1776-1976, Two Centuries of Change*. Washington: Wildlife Management Institute, 1976, $2.50.

403. Saltonstall, Richard, Jr. *Your Environment and What You Can Do About It*. New York: Ace, 1972, $1.25.

404. Scheffer, Victor B. *The Seeing Eye*. New York: Scribners, 1971, $5.95.

405. Schenck, Carl Alwin. *The Birth of Forestry in America — Biltmore Forest School 1898-1913*. Santa Cruz: Forest History Society and the Appalachian Consortium, $4.50.

406. Schmitt, Peter J. *Back to Nature: The Arcadian Myth in Urban America*. New York: Oxford University, 1969, $7.95.

407. Schwartz, George I. and Bernice S. *Food Chains and Ecosystems: Ecology for Young Experimenters*. New York: Doubleday, 1974, $4.95.

408. Scientific American. *The Biosphere*. San Francisco: Freeman, 1970, $3.50, paper.

409. Sears, Paul B. *Deserts on the March*, 3rd rev. ed. Norman: University of Oklahoma, 1967, $4.95.

410. Shepard, Paul, and Daniel McKinley, eds. *The Subversive Science: Essays Toward an Ecology of Man*. Boston: Houghton Mifflin, 1969, $7.50, paper.

411. Shomon, Joseph J. *Open Land for Urban America: Acquisition, Safekeeping, and Use*. Baltimore: Johns Hopkins, 1971, $8.50; paper, $2.50.

412. Siegan, Bernard H. *Land Use Without Zoning*. American Society of Planning Officials. Boston: Heath, 1972, $11.00.

413. Smith, David M. *The Practice of Silviculture*, 7th ed. New York: Wiley, 1962, $18.50.

414. Smith, Guy-Harold, ed. *Conservation of Natural Resources*, 4th ed. New York: Wiley, 1971, $14.25.

415. Society of American Foresters. *America's Renewable Resource Potential — 1975: The Turning Point*. From the 1975 convention of the Society of American Foresters. Washington: The Society, 1976, $10.00.

416. Society of American Foresters. *Foresters in Land Use Planning: Proceedings of the 1973 Annual Convention*. Washington: The Society, 1974, $5.00.

417. Soil Science Society of America. *Soil Surveys and Land Use Planning*. Madison: The Society, 1966, $3.00.

418. Springer, John S. *Forest Life and Forest Trees*, rev. ed. (Reproduction of 1851 Edition). Portland: O'Brien, 1971, $7.50.

419. Spurr, Stephen H. *American Forest Policy in Development*. Seattle: University of Washington, 1976, $6.95.

420. Spurr, Stephen H., and Burton V. Barnes. *Forest Ecology*, 2nd ed. New York: Ronald, 1973, $13.50 .

421. *Statistical Abstract of the United States*. National Data Book and Guide to Sources. Updated annually. Washington: Government Printing Office. $10.50; paper, $8.00. (See also *Historical Abstract of the United States*.)

422. Stefferud, Alfred. *Christians and the Good Earth*. New York: Friendship, 1969, $2.50, paper.

423. Stone, Christopher D. *Should Trees Have Standing?: Toward Legal Rights for Natural Objects*. Los Altos: Kaufman, 1974, $6.95; paper, $2.95.

424. Storer, John H. *Man in the Web of Life: Civilization, Science and Natural Law*. New York: New American Library, 1968, $0.95, paper.

425. Storer, John H. *The Web of Life*. New York: New American Library, 1972, $2.75, paper.

426. Sunset. *Woodcarving Techniques and Projects*, rev. ed. Menlo Park: Lane, 1971, $2.45, paper.

427. Swain, Donald C. *Wilderness Defender — Horace M. Albright and Conservation*. Chicago: University of Chicago, 1970, $10.75.

428. Teale, Edwin Way, ed. *The Wilderness World of John Muir*. Boston: Houghton Mifflin, 1976, $4.95.

429. Terry, Mark, and Paul Witt. *Energy and Order*. San Francisco: Friends of the Earth, 1976, $3.00, paper.

430. Thomas, William J., Jr., ed. *Man's Role in Changing the Face of the Earth*. Chicago: University of Chicago, 1956, $20.00; paper, vol. 1, $4.75; vol. 2, $6.95.

431. Trefethen, James B. *The American Landscape: 1776-1976, Two Centuries of Change*. Washington: Wildlife Management Institute, 1976.

432. Twight, Peter A. *Ecological Forestry for the Central Hardwood Forest*. Washington: National Parks and Conservation Association, 1972, $1.00.

433. Twight, Peter A. *Ecological Forestry for the Coast Redwoods*. Washington: National Parks and Conservation Association, 1973, $1.00.

434. Twight, Peter A. *Ecological Forestry for the Douglas Fir Region*. Washington: National Parks and Conservation Association, 1973, $1.00.

435. Twight, Peter A. *Ecological Forestry for the Northern Hardwood Forest*. Washington: National Park and Conservation Association, 1972, $1.00.

436. Udall, Stewart. *The Quiet Crisis*. New York: Holt, Rinehart and Winston, 1963; Avon, 1964, $1.75, paper.

437. U. S. D. A. *Outdoors U. S. A.: The Yearbook of Agriculture 1967*. Stock no. 001-000-00114. Washington: Government Printing Office, 1967, $6.20.

438. U. S. D. A. *Trees: The Yearbook of Agriculture 1949*. Stock no. 001-000-00097. Washington: Government Printing Office, 1949, $9.10.

439. U. S. D. A. Forest Service. *The Outlook for Timber in the United States*. Stock no. SN 0101-00375. Washington: Government Printing Office, 1974, $3.70.

440. U. S. D. A. Forest Service. *Silvics of the Forest Trees of the United States*. Stock no. SN 001-000-02946. Washington: Government Printing Office, 1965, reprinted 1976, $10.00.

441. U. S. D. A. Forest Service. *Silvicultural Systems for the Major Forest Types of the United States*. Stock no. 001-100-02816-2. Washington: Government Printing Office, 1973, $1.30.

442. Van Dyne, George M. *The Ecosystem Concept in Natural Resource Management*. New York: Academic, 1969, $19.50.

443. Vosburgh, John. *Living With Your Land: A Guide to Conservation for the City's Fringe*. New York: Scribners, 1972, $6.95; paper, $2.65.

444. Walker, Laurence C. *Ecology and Our Forests*. Cranbury: Barnes, 1973, $7.95.

445. Warren, J. L. *Green Space for Air Pollution Control*. School of Forest Resources, North Carolina State University Technical Report No. 50, 1973.

446. Weiner, Michael. *Earth Medicine — Earth Foods*. New York: Macmillan (Collier), 1972, $4.95, paper.

447. White, Lynn, Jr. *Machina Ex Deo: Essays in the Dynamism of Western Culture*. Cambridge: MIT Press, 1971, $3.95, paper.

448. Widner, Ralph R. *Forests and Forestry in the American States*. Raleigh: National Association of State Foresters, 1968.

449. Wigginton, Eliot, ed. *The Foxfire Book, Foxfire Book 2, Foxfire Book 3*, Garden City: Anchor/Doubleday, 1975, boxed set $13.50; *Foxfire Book 3*, $4.95, paper.

450. Wilkins, Thurman. *Thomas Moran: Artist of the Mountains*. Norman: University of Oklahoma, 1969, $8.95.

451. Worster, Donald, ed. *American Environmentalism: The Formative Period 1860-1915*. New York: Wiley, 1973, $9.00; paper, $4.95.

452. Yepsen, Roger B., Jr. *Trees for the Yard, Orchard, and Woodlot*. Emmaus: Rodale, 1976, $8.95.

453. Zim, Herbert S. *Trees: A Guide to Familiar American Trees*. Golden Book series. Racine: Western, 1952, $5.50; paper, $1.95.

454. Zimmerman, Fred W. *Exploring Woodworking*. South Holland: Goodheart-Willcox, 1976 ed., $4.98.

STUDENTS' PLEASURE READING AND REFERENCE BOOKS

455. Abbey, Edward. *Desert Solitaire: A Season in the Wilderness*. Westminster: Ballantine, 1971, $0.95, paper.

456. Anderson, Charles R. *Thoreau's World: Miniatures From His Journal*. Englewood Cliffs: Prentice-Hall, 1971, $2.95, paper.

457. Atwood, Ann. *The Kingdom of the Forest*. New York: Scribners, 1972, $5.95.

458. Atwood, Ann. *Haiku: The Mood of the Earth*. New York: Scribners, 1971, $5.95.

459. Behn, Harry, compiler. *Cricket Songs: Japanese Haiku*. New York: Harcourt Brace Jovanovich, 1964, $3.95.

460. Behn, Harry, compiler. *More Cricket Songs: Japanese Haiku*. New York: Harcourt Brace Jovanovich, 1971, $4.50.

461. Bendick, Jeanne and Robert. *The Consumer's Catalog of Economy and Ecology*. New York: Webster/McGraw Hill, 1974, $3.96.

462. Borland, Hal. *Beyond Your Doorstep: A Handbook to the Country*. New York: Knopf, 1962, $6.95.

463. Borland, Hal. *When the Legends Die*. Philadelphia: Lippincott, 1972; Bantam Books, $0.95, paper.

464. Bradbury, Ray. *Martian Chronicles*. Garden City: Doubleday, 1958, $5.95.

465. Brandon, William. *The Magic World: American Indian Songs and Poems*. New York: Morrow, 1972, $2.95, paper.

466. Brown, D. G. *Exploring and Understanding Plant Structure*. Westchester: Benefic, 1974, $3.30.

467. Burton, Maurice. *Animal Partnerships*. New York: Warne, 1970, $4.95.

468. Carrighar, Sally. *One Day on Beetle Rock*. Westminster: Ballantine, 1973, $1.25, paper.

469. Chamberlain, Furnas Joseph. *The Americans, A Social History of the United States*. New York: Putnam, 1969, $12.95.

470. Clark, Ann N. *Circle of Seasons*. New York: Farrar, 1970, $4.95.

471. Clough, Wilson O. *The Necessary Earth: Nature and Solitude in American Literature*. Austin: University of Texas, 1964, $8.50.

472. Cole, William, compiler. *A Book of Nature Poems*. New York: Viking, 1969, $7.95.

473. Collins, Stephen. *Forest and Woodland*. The Community of Living Things series. Mankato: Creative Educational Society, 1967, $5.95.

474. Demmon, E. L. *Opportunities in Forestry Careers*. Louisville: Vocational Guidance Manuals, 1975, $4.25; paper, $2.45.

475. de Saint-Exupery, Antoine. *The Little Prince*. New York: Harcourt Brace Jovanovich, 1968, $1.25, paper.

476. Dodge, Bertha S. *Plants That Changed the World*. Boston: Little, Brown, 1959, $4.95.

477. Dowdell, Dorothy and Joseph. *Careers in Horticultural Sciences*, rev. 1975. New York: Messner, 1975, $6.95.

478. Dudley, Ruth H. *Our American Trees*. New York: Thomas Y. Crowell, 1956, $4.50.

479. Dunning, Steven, et al. *Reflections on a Gift of Watermelon Pickle and Other Modern Verse*. New York: Lothrop, 1967, $5.95.

480. Earle, Olive L. *State Trees*, rev ed. New York: Morrow, 1973, $4.84.

481. *Early Country Furniture*. Washington: Photo Lab, $2.25.

482. Eckert, Allan W. *Incident at Hawk's Hill*. Boston: Little, Brown, 1971, $6.95.

483. Eiseley, Loren. *The Immense Journey*. New York: Random, 1957, $1.95, paper.

484. Eiseley, Loren. *The Invisible Pyramid*. New York: Scribners, 1972, $6.95; paper, $2.95.

485. Felton, Harold W., ed. *Legends of Paul Bunyan*. New York: Knopf, 1947, $6.99.

486. Frost, Robert. *You Come Too: Favorite Poems for Young Readers*. New York: Holt, Rinehart and Winston, 1959, $4.50.

487. Geisel, Theodor (Dr. Seuss). *The Lorax*. New York: Random, 1971, $3.95.

488. George, Jean C. *Who Really Killed Cock Robin?: An Ecological Mystery*. New York, Dutton, 1971, $4.95.

489. Hardin, Garrett. *Exploring New Ethics for Survival: The Voyage of the Spaceship Beagle*. Baltimore: Pelican, 1973, $1.45.

490. Helfman, Elizabeth S. *Land, People and History*. New York: McKay, 1962, $4.19.

491. Helfman, Elizabeth S. *Maypoles and Wood Demons: The Meaning of Trees*. New York: Seabury, 1972, $6.95.

492. Hemingway, Ernest. *The Big Two-Hearted River.* In Woollcott, A., *Second Reader.* New York: Viking, 1937.

493. Hilton, Suzanne. *How Do They Get Rid of It?* Philadelphia: Westminster, 1970, $5.25.

494. Hirsch, S. Carl. *Guardians of Tomorrow: Pioneers In Ecology.* New York: Viking, 1971, $4.95.

495. Jones, Hettie. *Trees Stand Shining: Poetry of the North American Indians.* New York: Dial, 1971, $4.95.

496. Keen, Martin L. *The World Beneath Our Feet: The Story of Soil.* New York: Messner, 1974, $6.25.

497. Kroeber, Theodora. *Ishi in Two Worlds: A Biography of the Last Wild Indian in North America.* Berkeley: University of California Press, 1961, $2.45, paper.

498. Krutch, Joseph W. *The Great Chain of Life.* Boston: Houghton Mifflin, 1957 $5.95.

499. La Farge, Oliver. *Laughing Boy.* Boston: Houghton Mifflin, 1963, $7.95; Sentry, $2.45, paper.

500. Laycock, George. *America's Endangered Wildlife.* New York: Grosset & Dunlap, 1969, $4.99.

501. Laycock, George. *Animal Movers: A Collection of Ecological Surprises.* Garden City: Natural History, 1971, $4.50.

502. Laycock, George. *Never Pet a Porcupine.* New York: Grosset & Dunlap, 1965, $4.51.

503. Laycock, George. *Never Trust a Cowbird.* New York: Grosset & Dunlap, 1966, $4.51.

504. Lewin, Ted. *World Within a World: Everglades.* New York: Dodd, Mead, 1976, $5.95.

505. London, Jack. *To Build a Fire.* In Burrell, John A. *An Anthology of Famous American Stories.* New York: Modern Library, 1953; Kielty, B. *Treasury of Short Stories,* Simon and Schuster, 1947; Maugham, W. S., *Teller of Tales,* Doubleday, 1939.

506. Lorenz, Konrad Z. *King Solomon's Ring.* New York: Thomas Y. Crowell, 1952, $6.95; Apollo, $1.95, paper.

507. Marquis, Don. *The Life and Times of Archy and Mehitabel.* Garden City: Doubleday, 1935, $6.95.

508. McCall, Virginia and Joseph R. *Your Career in Parks and Recreation,* rev. 1974. New York: Messner, 1974, $5.79.

509. McCloud, D. E., ed. *A New Look at Energy Sources.* Madison: American Society of Agronomy, 1974, ASA Special publication 22; single copy free; nominal charge for quantities.

510. McClung, Robert. *Lost Wild America: The Story of Our Extinct and Vanishing Wildlife.* New York: Morrow, 1969, $7.50.

511. McCoy, J. J. *Nature Sleuths: Protectors of Our Wildlife.* New York: Lothrop, 1969, $5.49.

512. McPhee, John. *Encounters with the Archdruid.* New York: Farrar, 1971, $6.95.

513. McPhee, John. *The Pine Barrens.* Westminster: Ballantine, 1971, $0.95, paper.

514. Michener, James. *Centennial.* New York: Random, 1974, $12.50.

515. Millard, Reed. *Careers in Environmental Protection.* New York: Messner, 1974, $5.79.

516. Miller, G. Tyler. *Replenish the Earth: A Primer in Human Ecology.* New York: Wadsworth, 1972, $4.50, paper.

517. Milne, Lorus and Margery. *The Phoenix Forest.* New York: Atheneum, 1968, $3.95.

518. North, Sterling. *Little Rascal.* New York: Dutton, 1965, $5.50.

519. North, Sterling. *Rascal: A Memoir of a Better Era.* New York: Dutton, 1963, $5.95.

520. Olson, Sigurd F., and Les Blacklock. *The Hidden Forest.* New York: Viking, 1969, $17.95.

521. Olson, Sigurd F. *The Singing Wilderness.* New York: Knopf, 1956, $6.95.

522. Pierre, W.H., et al., eds. *Plant Environment and Efficient Water Use.* Madison: American Society of Agronomy and Soil Science Society of America, 1966, $6.00.

523. Pinney, Roy. *Wildlife in Danger.* New York: Hawthorn, 1966, $4.50.

524. Pringle, Laurence. *Into the Woods: Exploring the Forest Ecosystem.* New York: Macmillan, 1973, $4.95.

525. Pringle, Laurence. *The Only Earth We Have.* New York: Macmillan, 1969, $5.95; 1971, $0.95, paper.

526. Randall, Janet. *To Save a Tree: The Story of the Coast Redwoods.* New York: McKay, 1971, $4.97.

527. Richter, Conrad. *Light in the Forest.* New York: Knopf, 1953, $6.95; 1966, $4.95; AMSCO, 1970, $1.90, paper; Bantam Books, $1.25, paper.

528. Russell, Helen R. *The True Book of Buds: Surprise Packages.* Chicago: Childrens Press, 1970, $5.25.

Seuss, Dr. See Geisel.

529. Silverberg, Robert. *The Auk, the Dodo and the Oryx: Vanished and Vanishing Creatures.* New York: Crowell, 1967, $4.95; Apollo, 1970, $0.95, paper.

530. Silverberg, Robert. *John Muir: Prophet*

Among the Glaciers. New York: Putnam, 1972, $4.97.

531. Silverberg, Robert. *Vanishing Giants: The Story of the Sequoias*. New York: Simon and Schuster, 1969, $4.50.

532. Stephens, Alan A. *Tree Meditation and Other Poems*. Chicago: Swallow, 1971, $5.00; paper, $2.75.

533. Stern, Phil Van Doren, ed. *The Annotated Walden*. New York: Crown (Bonanza), 1971, $7.98.

534. Sunset Books. *Garden Trees*. Menlo Park: Lane, 1976, $2.45.

535. Sunset Books. *Cabins & Vacation Houses*. Menlo Park: Lane, 1975, $2.45.

536. Swift, Ernest F. *A Conservation Saga*. Washington: National Wildlife Federation, 1967, $3.00.

537. Swift, Hildegarde H. *The Edge of April: A Biography of John Burroughs*. New York: Morrow, 1957, $6.50.

538. Teale, Edwin Way. *The American Seasons*. New York: Dodd, Mead, 1976, $17.50.

539. Teale, Edwin Way. *Wandering Through Winter*. New York: Dodd, Mead, 1965, $10.00; Apollo, 1969, $2.50, paper.

540. Teale, Edwin Way, ed. *The Wilderness World of John Muir*. Boston: Houghton Mifflin, 1954, $8.95.

541. Thoreau, Henry David. *Walden: or Life in the Woods*. Garden City: Doubleday (Anchor), 1955, $1.45, paper.

542. Whitman, Walt. *The Collected Poetry and Selected Prose and Letters of Walt Whitman*, edited by Emory Holloway. New York: Random, 1961, $15.00.

543. *Woodcarving: Yesterday and Today in America*. Washington: Photo Lab, $2.25.

544. Zimmerman, Fred W. *Exploring Woodworking*. South Holland: Goodheart-Willcox, 1976, $6.64; school price $4.98. Workbook, $1.96; school price, $1.47.

SIXTEEN MM FILMS

* Indicates plus shipping and handling.
** Indicates that the film may be available from a university distributor.

545. *The American Wilderness*. Films Inc. $40 rental; $550 purchase. Grade 7-adult.

546. *America's Endangered Species*. Films Inc. (Wolper Organization). 1973. Color, 20 min. $20 rental; $275 purchase. Grade 7-adult.

547. *Analyzing Advertising*. Centron. 1973. Color, 13 min. $195 purchase. Primary-junior high.

548. *Balancing the Benefits*. American Forest Institute, New England Regional Office.

Twelve minutes. Free loan. General audience.

549. *Baobab: Portrait of a Tree*. University of Michigan (McGraw-Hill). 1973. Color, 53 min. $22.75 rental. Grade 7-adult.

550. *Before the Mountain Was Moved*. McGraw-Hill. $35 rental. Grade 9-adult.

551. *Bird of Prey (The Red-Tailed Hawk)*. University of Michigan (Britannica). 1972. Color, 14 min. $6.95 rental. Grade 7-adult.

552. *Bulldozed America*. Carousel. 1965. B&W. $135 purchase.

553. *Chaparral — The Elfin Forest*. University of Arizona. 1964. $5.25 rental; $125 purchase. Grade 7-adult.

554. *Clearcutting*. Oregon State University. 1971. Color, sound, 29 min. $6.20 rental from Audio-Visual Center, Washington State University. College.

555. *The Community*. Britannica. B&W: $6 rental, $75 purchase; color: $9 rental, $150 purchase. Grade 9-adult.

556. *The Coniferous Forest Biome*. Britannica. B&W: $7 rental, $115 purchase; color: $11 rental, $220 purchase. Grade 8-adult.

557. *Cottonwood*. West Wind Productions. Color, 15 min. Music effects, non-narrative. $20 rental; $225 purchase.

558. *Craftsmen*. Audio-Visual Center, Washington State University. A Barr Production. 1972. Color, 19 min. $8.10 rental; $275 purchase. Grade 7-college. Also available for rental and purchase from Division of Continuing Education, Audiovisual Instruction, 1633 S.W. Park Avenue, Portland, Oregon. $10.50 rental; $275 purchase. May also be purchased from Barr Films, $275.

559. *Death of an Old Tree*. Journal Films. 1975. Color, 9 min. $135 purchase.**

560. *Distribution of Plants and Animals*. Britannica. B&W: $7 rental, $115 purchase; color: $11 rental, $220 purchase. Grade 9-adult.

561. *Ecology of Olympic Rain Forest*. International. 20 min. $12.50 rental; $250 purchase. Grade 5-adult.

562. *Ecology Primer*. American Educational Films. Color, 20 min. $30 rental; $285 purchase. Also available in Spanish.

563. *Ecosystems: Mountain Forest and Meadows*. AIMS. 1972. Color, 11 min. $20 rental; $155 purchase. Grade 9-adult. Also available in Spanish.

564. *Environmental Enrichment — What You Can Do About It*. Centron. 1972. Color, 21 min. $290 purchase. Primary-adult.

565. *The Eternal Forest*. GSA. 1970. 20 min.

Free loan. Grade 5-adult.

566. *The Everglades*. Films Inc. Color, 28 min. $25 rental; $355 purchase. Grades 5-8.

567. *The Everlasting Forest*. St. Regis Paper Co. Free loan. Grade 6-adult.

568. *Food for a Small Planet*. Pictura (Richter McBride). Color, 10 min. $20 rental, $165 purchase.

569. *For All to Enjoy*. Conservation Foundation. $10.00 rental; $140 purchase for either, plus $2.50 postage and handling. Grade 7-adult.

570. *Forest of Trees and Logs*. American Educational Films. Color, 15 min. $25 rental; $230 purchase. Grade 4-adult.

571. *Forests and the Insect Factor*. American Forest Institute, New England Office. Twenty-eight minutes. Free loan. $100 purchase. General audience.

572. *The Foresters*. Modern Talking Pictures. Color, 26 min. Free loan. Grade 7-adult.

573. *Forests Are for People*. Modern Talking Pictures. (American Forest Institute) Free loan; $125 purchase. Grade 7-adult.

574. *Forests U.S.A.: Insects and Management*. Oregon Department of Forestry. Free loan. Grade 7-adult.

575. *The Friendly Flame*. University of Michigan (Film Communicators). Color, 27 min. $11.55 rental. Grade 7-adult.

576. *From Yellowstone to Tomorrow*. Films Inc. (National Broadcasting Company). 1972. Color, 51 min. $40 rental; $550 purchase. Grade 5-adult.

577. *Golden Eagle — No Natural Enemy*. Films Inc. (Shosoni). Color, 22 min. $22 rental; $305 purchase. Grades 5-12.

578. *Have Our Planet and Eat It Too?* Churchill. Color, 24 min. $25 rental; $335 purchase. Junior-senior high.

579. *Home*. Southern Baptist. $7.50 rental (service); $300 purchase. Grade 7-adult.

580. *House of Man, Part I: Our Changing Environment*. Britannica. B&W: $7 rental, $115 purchase; color: $11 rental, $220 purchase. Grades 4-12.

581. *In Search of the Last Redwood*. California Redwood Association. Color, 25 min. Free loan.

582. *Ishi in Two Worlds*. McGraw-Hill. $20 rental; $285 purchase. Grade 7-adult.

583. *John Muir's High Sierra*. Pyramid. Color, 27 min. $25 rental.

584. *The Last Stand*. Kitty Morgan. Color, 21 min. $25 rental; $125 purchase. Grade 7-adult.

585. *Let's Build a House*. Churchill. 1960.

Color, 11 min. $15 rental; $130 purchase. Primary.

586. *Life in a Vacant Lot*. Britannica. B&W: $6 rental, $75 purchase; color: $9 rental, $150 purchase. Grade 5-adult.

587. *Life in the Forest*. Britannica. B&W: $6 rental, $75 purchase; color: rental, $150 purchase. Grades 5-12.

588. *The Light in the Forest*. Walt Disney. Color, 93 min. $50 rental.

589. *Limits to Growth*. Audio-Visual Center, Washington State University. 28 min, color, sound. $8.60. College.

590. *The Limits to Growth*. Lane County Council of Governments. See Lane County IED. B&W, 30 min. Free loan only to public schools in Lane County, Oregon. Purchase, $300.

591. *Living Filter*. Audio-Visual Center, Washington State University. 1972. Color, sound, 17 min. $7.60 rental. Grade 10-college.

592. *Man and the Environment: Primitives to Present*. University of Michigan. B&W. $10 rental; $130 purchase. Grades 7-12.

593. *Mineral King*. University of Southern California. 1972. $8.50 rental; $364 purchase. Grade 7-adult.

594. *Miner's Ridge*. Sierra Club (distributed by Association). Color, 22 min. $7.50 rental; $285 purchase. Junior high-adult.

595. *Multiply and Subdue the Earth*. (CSC-1979). Indiana University. $23 rental. Grade 9-adult.

596. *My World . . . Earth*. Churchill. 1974. Color, 11 min. $15 rental; $155 purchase. Primary.

597. *Natural Selection*. Britannica. B&W: $7 rental, $115 purchase; color: $11 rental, $220 purchase. High school-adult.

598. *Natural Timber County*. Ron Finne. 53½ min. $50 rental; $600 purchase. Grade 4-adult.

599. *Nature in the City*. Journal Films. 1971. Color, 13 min. $175 purchase.

600. *Nature Is for People*. AIMS. 1969. Color, 9 min., no narration. $20 rental; $130 purchase. Primary-adult.

601. *New Man in the Forest*. International Film Bureau. 1971. Color, 26 min. $20 rental; $335 purchase.

602. *No Room for Wilderness*. Association. $7 rental.* Grade 7-adult.

603. *NOVA* programs from Public Broadcasting Service. Write to Public Television Library for information about availability of the programs.

604. *Off Road Controversy*. Association. $7.50

rental*; $350 purchase. Grade 7-adult.

605. *One Spring Day.* American Educational Films. No narration. Color, 10 min. $20 rental; $130 purchase.

606. *1000 Suns.* Barr. Color, 9 min. $150 purchase. Rental from Essentia, $25.

607. *Open Space.* ACI Media. $170 purchase. Grade 7-adult.

608. *Our Endangered Wildlife.* McGraw-Hill. $30 rental; $695 purchase. Grade 7-adult.

609. *Our Environment: Everybody's Business.* Cornell University. Color, 13:30 min. $5 rental; $110 purchase.

610. *Paper in Art.* Churchill. 1967. Color, 17 min. $21 rental; $215 purchase. Elementary-junior high.

611. *Pave It and Paint It Green.* University of California. Color, 27 min. $24 rental; $330 purchase. Grade 7-adult.

612. *The People's Heritage.* Pictura. $20 rental. Grade 7-adult.

613. *Pest Control and the Environment.* Cornell University. $5 rental; $135 purchase. Grade 9-adult.

614. *Planning the Land* (Land Conservation series). ACI Films. 1975. Color, 14 min. $210 purchase.

615. *The Poisoned Planet.* McGraw-Hill. $20 rental; $305 purchase. Grade 7-adult.

616. *The Pond and the City.* Britannica. Color. $11 rental; $220 purchase. Grades 6-12.

617. *Preserving Our American Wilderness.* Films Inc. (National Broadcasting Company). 1971. Color, 10 min. $20 rental; $145 purchase. Grades 5-12.

618. *Problems of Conservation: Forest and Range.* Britannica. 14 min. B&W: $6 rental, $95 purchase; color: $9 rental, $185 purchase. Grade 7-adult.

619. *The Realities of Recycling.* Stuart Finley. $30 rental; $300 purchase. Grade 7-adult.

620. *Recycling.* Stuart Finley. $20 rental; $200 purchase. Grade 7-adult.

621. *Recycling Waste.* Journal Films. 1972. Color, 12 min. $165 purchase.** Grades 7-12.

622. *The Redwoods.* Association. $7.50 rental.* Grade 7-adult.

623. *The Redwood Trees.* University of Arizona. 1960. $7.25 rental. Grade 4-adult.

624. *The River.* Washington State University. 1937. B&W, 32 min. $4.70 rental. Grade 7-adult.

625. *The River That Came Back.* Perennial Education. $13 rental; $130 purchase. Elementary-adult.

626. *Satan's Choice.* Consulate General of Canada, free loan to groups in North Central States. (Write for catalog and lending information.)

627. *Say Goodbye.* Films Inc. (Wolper Organization). 1973. Color, 50 min. $40 rental; $575 purchase. Grade 7-adult.

628. *Seed Dispersal,* 3rd ed. Britannia. Color. $9 rental; $150 purchase. Grades 2-6.

629. *A Sense of Privilege* (Alaska — threatened wilderness). Carousel. Color, 28 min. $375 purchase. Grade 5-adult.

630. *Sharing the Land.* ACI Films. 1974. Color, 24 min. $325 purchase. Grade 7-adult. University of Michigan. $12.55 rental.

631. *Sodbusters.* (CSC-2418) Indiana University. $12.50 rental. Grade 5-adult.

632. *Something for the Trees . . . Something for the City.* Environmental Action Coalition. 1976. Color, 14 min. $185 purchase. Elementary school to adult.

633. *Succession: From Sand Dune to Forest.* Britannica. B&W: $7 rental, $115 purchase; color: $11 rental, $220 purchase. High school-adult.

634. *Strip Mine Trip.* Churchill. 1972. Color, 11 min. $15 rental; $155 purchase. Junior high-adult.

635. *The Temperate Deciduous Forest.* Britannica. B&W: $7 rental, $115 purchase; color: $11 rental, $220 purchase. High school-adult.

636. *Time-Lapse Studies of Growing Trees.* Audio-Visual Center, Washington State University (Syracuse University.) 1953. Color, sound, 10 min. $4.50 rental.

637. *To Touch the Sky.* Modern Talking Pictures. Color, 28½ min. Free loan. Grade 5-adult.

638. *The Tragedy of the Commons.* University of Southern California. (Produced by King Screen Productions). Color, 23 min. $12 rental. High school.

639. *Tree and Shrub Planting.* Perennial Education. Color, 11½ min. $13 rental; $130 purchase. Elementary-adult.

640. *A Tree Is a Living Thing.* Britannica. (Produced by the National Film Board of Canada). 11 min. B&W: $6 rental, $75 purchase; color: $9 rental, $150 purchase. Primary grades.

641. *A Tree Grows for Christmas* or *The Christmas Tree.* Forest Service, USDA. Free loan. Grade 5-adult.

642. *Trees.* Grove. 15 min. $35 rental; $175 purchase. Grade 7-adult.

643. *Trees and People.* Association. Color, 29 min. Available to junior high school level

and up in California, Washington, Oregon. Free loan, user pays one-way postage.

644. *The Tropical Rain Forest*. Britannica. B&W: $7 rental, $115 purchase; color, $11 rental, $220 purchase. Grade 9-adult.

645. *Two Yosemites*. Association. Color, 10 min. $7.50 rental.

646. *Urban Sprawl vs. Planned Growth*. Stuart Finley. $20 rental; $200 purchase. Grade 7-adult.

647. *Use It, Use It Up*. University of California Extension Media Center. 1975. Color, 26 min. $23 rental; $320 purchase.

648. *A Walk in the Woods*. Pyramid. Color, 28 min. $35 rental.

649. *The Wasted Woods*. Associated—Sterling Films. $7.50 rental. * Grade 6-adult.

650. *Water Is So Clear That a Blind Man Could See*. (NCS-1228). Indiana University. $12.50 rental. Grade 7-adult.

651. *West Chichagof*. Association. $7.50 rental.* Grade 7-adult.

652. *What Is Ecology?* Britannica. B&W: $6 rental, $75 purchase; color: $9 rental, $150 purchase. Grade 9-adult.

653. *Where All Things Belong*. Essentia. Color, 28 min. $40 rental; $400 purchase.

654. *Where Do We Go from Here?* University of Michigan (Ealing). 1974. Color, 15 min. $7.90 rental. Grade 10-adult.

655. *Whole Earth's Invisible Colors* (use of multispectral sensing). University of Michigan (Cybern Films). 1972. Color, 20 min. $10.95 rental. Grade 7-adult.

656. *Wild Green Things in the City*. ACI Films. 1974. Color, 11 min. $185 purchase. Grades 1-8.

657. *Wilderness at Bay — Yellowstone National Park*. Pictura (Survival Anglia). Color, 26 min. $40 rental; $350 purchase.

658. *Wildfire*. Films Incorporated. 1972. $25 rental; $575 purchase. Grade 5-adult.

659. *The Woods and Things*. Churchill. 1971. Color, 11 min. $15 rental; $155 purchase. All Ages.

660. *Yankee Craftsman*. Journal Films. 1972. Color, 18 min. $225 purchase.** Grade 7-adult.

MULTI-MEDIA

661. *The American Forest: Not to Conquer, but to Continue*. American Plywood Association. Seventy-six slides with sound. $20.00. Grade 9-adult.

662. *Backyard Ecology Series: Log*. BFA Educational Media. Super 8mm loop. $124.75.

663. *The Birds, the Bees and the Trees*. Southern Forest Institute. Seventy-eight slides with sound. Free loan. Purchase $25.00. Also available on loan from American Forest Institute New England Office.

664. *Careers in Environmental Protection*. Vocational Education Productions. Filmstrip with cassette, script. $13.50. Grades 9-12.

665. *Careers in Forestry*. Vocational Education Productions. Filmstrip with cassette, script. $13.50. Grades 9-12.

666. *Careers in Resource Conservation*. Soil Conservation Society of America. Fifty-eight slides with printed script. $10.50; $13 with 1-min cassette tape. Junior and senior high schools.

667. *Changing Seasons: The Story of a Year*. Troll. Four super 8mm film loops, color, 4 min each. $99.80; individual loops $24.95. Grades 1-8.

668. *Echoes of Michigan*. University of Michigan. 1966. Filmstrip, 192 frames, 22 min, color, tape, manual. $12.50. Grades 5-12.

669. *Ecology and Agriculture*. Vocational Education Productions. Five filmstrips with sound, scripts, transparencies, reference guides, and resource materials. $65.00. Grades 9-12.

670. *Ecology* and *Botany* series. Outdoor Pictures. All of the following titles are available as slides or filmstrips and priced as follows: Slide sets, 35 to 75 slides, $24.50, narration script included; filmstrips, 35 to 75 frames, narration script included, $10.95; cassettes for either slide sets or filmstrips, $5.00 each. Junior high to adult.

Ecology at Timberline. Fifty-one frames.
Ecology of the Boreal Forest. Fifty-one frames.
Let's Learn the Trees. Fifty-one frames.
Life History of a Gymnosperm. Forty-three frames.
Trees of California. Fifty-one frames.
Trees of Washington and Oregon. Fifty-one frames.
Trees of the West. Fifty-one frames.

671. *Ecology of Forest and Mountain Top Communities* (A-5022-G). Harvest Laboratories. Eight captioned color filmstrips, teachers guides and student activity worksheets. $64.95.

672. *The Ecology of a Temperate Rain Forest*. Imperial Educational Resources. 1973. Set of 2 filmstrips. $25.95 with records; $28.95 with cassettes. Intermediate.

673. *Ecology — Our Challenge. Ecology of Forest and Mountain Top Communities*. Harvest Laboratories. Captioned color filmstrip, with teacher's guide and study

activity worksheet masters. $9.00.

674. *Ecological Communities.* Coronet. 1971. Six filmstrips with sound. With cassettes, $85.00; with records, $77.00. Grades 7-12.

675. *Ecological Imbalance: Six Systems Disturbed.* Eye Gate. Six captioned filmstrips. $41.00 plus shipping and handling. Grades 7-12.

676. *Elementary Economics.* BFA Educational Media. 1973. Twelve filmstrips. With cassettes, $102.00; with records, $84.00. Grades K-9.

677. *Environment and Survival.* Inquiry Audiovisuals (Denoyer-Geppert). Four filmstrips: Life in a . . . Sand Dune Succession, Bog, Alpine Environment, Fallen Log Microcommunity. Color, with record or cassette, teacher's guide. $46.00.

678. *Erosion and Soil Formation* (33 frames) and *Fossils: What They Are and Where to Find Them* (53 frames). Creative Learning. Two sound color filmstrips with record. $18.00.

679. *Extinct, Endangered and Threatened.* Society for Visual Education. 1975. Set of 6 filmstrips, 6 records or cassettes. $95. Junior high.

680. *The Forest: A Stable Community* (from Plant and Animal Relationships series). Britannica. Captioned color filmstrip. $10.00. Grades 4-6.

681. *Forest and Forest Products.* BFA Educational Media. Five filmstrips, $40.00. Grades 4-9.

682. *The Forest Resource.* Western Wood Products Association. Fifty-three color slides with script or sound. Free loan. Purchase: $40.00 with cassettes; $35 with script.

683. *Forest Resources and Ecology.* American Forest Institute. Slides with sound cassette. $25.00. Grade 9-adult.

684. *Forest Traumas.* American Forest Institute, New England Office. Slides with script, 10 min. Free loan.

685. *Forests of the Americas.* Britannica. Color. Four filmstrips: Tropical Forests of the Americas, The North Conifer Forest, The Eastern Deciduous Forest, The Western Conifer Forest. Each filmstrip $10; set of the four $32.90. Intermediate grades.

686. *Furor Over Forest.* Southern Forest Products Association. Slides with sound. $30.00.

687. *The Gods Were Tall and Green.* Lyceum. Two filmstrips with sound. With cassettes, $45.00; with records, $36.00. Grade 4 and above.

688. *Haiku: The Hidden Glimmering.* Lyceum. Filmstrip, 60 frames, 14½ min, teacher's guide. $22.50 with cassette; $18 with record.

689. *Haiku: The Mood of the Earth.* Lyceum. Two filmstrips with sound. With cassettes, $45.00; with records, $36.00. Grade 7-adult.

690. *Investigations in Biology: A Biological Approach* (68958). Denoyer-Geppert. Slides with teacher's guide. $40.00 per unit; $180.00 for 6-unit set. Grades 9-12.

691. *The Journal of Henry David Thoreau: The Seasons.* Educational Development Corporation. Two filmstrips with sound. With cassettes, $57.95; with records, $51.95. Grade 7-adult.

692. *Leaves and Trees.* Gull Lake Environmental Education Project. Flash card set, 25 cards. $3.25.

693. *Let Forests Free the Environment.* Southern Forest Products Association. Slides with sound. $30.00.

694. *Life in the Forests.* Society for Visual Education. Filmstrip, 59 frames, 16 min. $9.00 with guide; $6.50 with cassette or record. Junior high.

695. *Lumbering Era in Michigan History* (*1860-1900*). University of Michigan. 1956. Filmstrip, 66 frames, manual. $3.00. Grades 5-12.

696. *Maple Tree.* Society for Visual Education. 1973. Twenty color, 2 x 2-inch slides and guide. $14.00. Intermediate.

697. *Man and His Environment: In Harmony and in Conflict.* Center for the Humanities. Two carousels with cassettes, high school edition. $119.44.

698. *Northern Forest Lands* (*The Boreal Forest*). Eye Gate. Five color filmstrips. $36.25. Elementary grades.

699. *Northwest Forest Vegetation.* Hubbard. Set of 20 color slides (35mm) with descriptions. $20.00.

700. *Operation Salvage: Paper as a Reusable Resource.* American Forest Institute. Color filmstrip, 17 min. $26.00 with record; $15.00 slide set. (Also available on free loan from AFI New England Office.)

701. *Our Diminishing Natural Resources* (in Current Issues in American Society series). Teaching Resources (New York *Times*). Filmstrip, 55 frames, color. $15.50 with 12-inch LP record; $16.50 with cassette.

702. *People of the Forest: A Study in Human Values Learning Module.* Society for Visual Education. 1975. Includes filmstrips, cassettes, activity cards, games, murals, teacher's guides. $175.00. Components may be purchased separately. Primary-intermediate.

703. *Pollution: Is the gunk here for good?* Coronet. Documentary photos, 6 filmstrips. $80.00 with records; $88.00 with cassettes. Grades 7-12.

704. *The Role of Trees in the Environment.* Educational Development Corporation. Four filmstrips with sound. With cassettes, $57.95; with records, $51.95. Grades 9-12.

705. *Solid Waste and Recycling.* Educational Modules. Teacher's manual, ten transparencies, twenty 35mm slides. $58.00. Grades 7-12.

706. *Songs of the Forest.* Droll Yankees. Recording, 12-inch. $6.00. All grades.

707. *The Story of Soil.* Creative Learning. Captioned color filmstrip, 35 frames. $5.75. Grades 1-6.

708. *This Unique Bit of Life . . . How Trees Affect the Environment.* Guidance Associates. Filmstrip with sound, record or cassette, $26.00. Grade 7-adult.

709. *Timber: Washington's Most Valuable Crop.* Society for Visual Education. Sound filmstrip. $10.00 with guide; $6.50 with record or cassette.

710. *Trees and Environment* cassette series. American Forest Institute. Seven cassettes with a different 15-min program on each side.
1. *Trees and Water* and *When and Why Foresters Clearcut.*
2. *Care and Propagation of Redwoods* and *Trees and Insects.*
3. *Trees and Wildlife* and *Trees and Housing.*
4. *Making the Most of the Tree* and *Trees and Air.*
5. *Navajo Forest Resource* and *Stretching the Forest Resource.*
6. *Wood and the Home Environment* and *The U.S. Forest Service: Its Public Image.*
7. *Progress in Industrial Forestry* and *Careers in Forestry.*
Each Cassette $2.00; scripts available 1-10 copies free. Single cassettes free.

711. *Trees for 2001: Today's Foresters in Action.* American Forest Institute. Color filmstrip with sound, record. $26.00. Grade 7-adult.

712. *The Tropical Rain Forest.* Eye Gate. Six color filmstrips. $43.50. Elementary grades.

713. *Weathering and Erosion* (39 frames) and *Glaciation: Ice Shapes the Land* (41 frames). Creative Learning. Two sound color filmstrips with record and guide. $20.00.

714. *The Wilderness Resource.* Revised 1976. Western Wood Products Association. Eighty color slides with script or sound. Free loan. Purchase: $35.00 with script; $40.00 with cassette.

715. *Willa Cather: The Pioneer West* (in Women Writers: Voices of Dissent series). Teaching Resources Films (New York *Times*). Filmstrip, 62 frames. $15.50 with 12-inch LP record; $16.50 with cassette.

716. *When the Legends Die.* Films Inc. (Movie Strip Department). Adaptation of movie to filmstrip. Two color filmstrips, 2 cassettes, and teacher's guide. $49.50.

PAMPHLETS

American Forest Institute:

717. *The Effects of Clearcutting on Forest Soils.*

718. *Forest Facts and Figures.* One to ten copies free. Additional copies, 20 cents each.

719. *Forests and Trees of the United States.* Single copy free. Additional copies 20 cents each.

720. *Growth of a Tree.* Single copy free. Additional copies 20 cents each.

721. *Multiple Use of Our Forests.*

722. *Recycling Questions and Answers.* One to ten copies free; additional copies 5 cents each.

American Forest Institute, New England Office:

723. *A Brief New England Forest History.*

724. *Natural Forest Vegetation Zones of New England.* 1955. Published by the New England Section, Society of American Foresters.

725. *New England Forest Facts.*

American Paper Institute:

726. *Community Paper Recycling.* Single copy free; additional copies 50 cents each.

727. *Household Paper Products and the Environment.* Free.

728. *Paper and Paper Manufacture.* Single copy free; additional copies $9 per 100 copies.

729. *What's So Special About Paper?* Single copy free; additional copies $6 per 100 copies.

American Wood Council:

730. *Reader's Guide to Wood Products.*

731. *Some Little-Known Facts About Wood.* Free.

732. Clark, Fred G., and Richard S. Romanoczy. *How We Live.* New York: American Economic Foundation. 1976 (first published 1944). $1.00 plus $0.24 postage.

733. Conservation Foundation. *Off-Road Vehicle and Environmental Quality.* Second edition. $4.00.

734. Crown Zellerbach, Northwest Timber Operations. *Logger Lingo.*

Eastman Kodak Company:

735. *Basic Art Techniques for Slide Production.* V1-27. 45 cents.

736. *Planning and Producing Slide Programs.* S30. $3.25.

Georgia-Pacific Corporation:

737. *Forestry Products Industry Museums: Displays and Exhibits in the United States and Canada.* Revised edition. First copy free; additional copies 25 cents while quantities last.

738. *Kraft Pulp and Paper Production at Toledo Oregon Mill.* Teaching chart. First copy free; additional copies 25 cents each while quantities last.

739. *Progress in Matters of Public Concern.* First copy free; additional copies 25 cents while quantities last.

740. *Pulp, Paper and Chemical Production, Bellingham, Washington.* Teaching chart. First copy free; additional copies 25 cents while quantities last.

741. *To Grow a Tree.* Management of timberlands; species of trees. First copy free; additional copies 25 cents each while quantities last.

Keep America Beautiful, Inc.:

742. *71 Things You Can Do to Stop Pollution.* 5 cents.

743. *Your Environmental Action Starts Here.* 50 cents.

League of Women Voters:

744. *Getting a National Perspective on Land Use.* 35 cents.

745. *Our National Forests: Can They Meet Future Needs?* (Land Use Letter, April 1975) 25 cents.

746. *Recycle: In Search of New Policies for Resource Recovery.* 75 cents.

747. *Reduce: Targets, Means and Impacts of Source Reduction.* 1975. $1.00.

748. Martinelli, M., Jr. *Water Yield Improvement from Alpine Areas: The Status of Our Knowledge* (on snow management). USDA Forest Service Research Paper RM-138. 1975. Fort Collins: Rocky Mountain Forest and Range Experiment Station.

Massachusetts Audubon Society:

749.
a. *Going to Seed — A Manual of Winter Feeding.* 15 cents.
b. *How to Be a Twig Detective.* 5 cents.
c. *How to Make a Terrarium.* 5 cents.
d. *Leaves.* 5 cents.
e. *Nest Boxes for Birds.* 15 cents.

f. *Simple Feeders.* 5 cents.
g. *Trees — An Aid to Identification.* 5 cents.

750. Muench, John Jr. *Taking the Pins Out of Forest Policy:* The S. J. Hall Lectureship in Industrial Forestry. Berkeley: University of California, Department of Forestry and Conservation. 1975. 8 pp. Free on request from College of Natural Resources, University of California.

National Audubon Society:

751. *Audubon Nature Bulletins.* NB1. Seventy-three different bulletins in set. $22.50. Individual bulletins available in quantities of 30 or more (same title) for 35 cents apiece, $10.50 minimum.

752. *Good Teaching Aids.* NB2-13. $4.55 per set.

753. *Bulletins on Plant Identification.* NB5-14. $4.90.

National Forest Products Association:

754.
a. *Clearcutting — Environmental and Economic Benefits*
b. *Housing and Timber: You Can't Have One Without the Other*
c. *Wilderness Preservation: Do Americans Receive Full Benefits?*
d. *Wildlife Management Requires Forest Management.*

755. *The Clearcutting Issue.*

756. *Colleges and Universities.* Free in limited quantities.

757. *The Energy Conservation Issue: How Wood Helps Reduce Power Consumption and Home Operating Cost.*

758. *The Forest Management Issue.*

759. *The Housing Issue.*

760. *Opportunities Unlimited — In the Forest Products Industries.* Free in limited quantities.

761. *The Timber Supply Issue.*

762. *Timber: World Resources and Reserves and United States Policy.*

763. *Where Will the Wood Come From?*

764. *The Wilderness Issue.*

765. *The Wilderness Issue: How Much Can America Afford?*

766. *Wood — Nature's Best Energy Saver.*

767. *Wood — The Renewable Resource.*

768. National Science Teachers Association. *How to Present Audible Multi-Imagery in Environmental Education.* Washington: The Association. 50 cents.

National Wildlife Federation:

769. *Endangered Species of the United States.*

Single copy free; additional copies 15 cents each.

770. *Invite Wildlife to Your Backyard*. Single copy free; additional copies 25 cents each.

771. *Recycling*. Single copy free; additional copies 15 cents each.

772. *Wildlife of Forests and Rangelands*. Single copy free; additional copies 10 cents each.

773. *Wildlife Notes*. Single copy free; additional copies 25 cents each.

774. Nichols, James O. *The Gypsy Moth*. Pennsylvania Department of Environmental Resources. 1973. Free.

775. Northwest Pulp and Paper Association. *Meeting the Challenge: A Progress Report on Pollution Control by the Northwest Pulp and Paper Industry*.

Soil Conservation Society of America:

776. *Better Environment*. Cartoon Booklet Series. 1-9 copies, $0.35 each; all 10, $2.00; Teacher's Guides for each, $0.25 each; for the series, $2.00.

1. *The Story of Land*.
2. *The Wonder of Water*.
3. *Keep Our Land Beautiful*.
4. *Making a Home for Wildlife on the Land*.
5. *Food and the Land*.
6. *Working Together for a Livable Land*.
7. *Plants, How They Improve Our Environment*.
8. *The Earth, Our Home in Space*.
9. *Plants, Animals & Man — Sharing the Earth*.
10. *Pioneers of Conservation in America*.

777. *Making Urban and Rural Land Use Decisions*. 75 cents.

Southern Forest Institute:

778. *How Paper Comes from Trees*. 1-10 copies free; additional copies 15 cents each.

779. *Your Fabulous Friend*. 1-10 copies free; additional copies 15 cents each.

Southern Forest Products Association:

780. *Managing Your Family Forest*. Single copy free; additional copies 10 cents each.

781. *Our Forests*. Single copy free; additional copies 25 cents each. *Our Forests Teacher's Manual* available to teachers on request.

782. *Questions & Answers About Forests*. Single copies free; additional copies 15 cents each.

783. *The South's Third Forest*. Single copies free; additional copies 15 cents each.

784. St. Regis Paper Company. *The Life of the Forest*. Available in limited quantities.

785. *Tree Watching*. Minnesota Environmental Sciences Foundation. $1.50.

U.S. Forest Service (order from Government Printing Office):

786. *An Annotated Bibliography of the Effects of Logging on Fish of the Western United States and Canada*.

787. *Energy and Raw Materials Potential of Wood in the Pacific Coast States, U.S. Forest Service Pacific Northwest Forest and Range Experiment Station Report No. 18*.

788. *Forestry Schools in the United States*. FS-9.

789. *Gypsy Moth-Its Natural Enemies*. AIB 381. $0.70.

790. *Highlights in the History of Forest Conservation*. AIB-83, $1.55.

791. *How a Tree Grows*. FS-32. $0.25.

792. *In Your Service*. AIB-136. $0.50.

793. *People, Cities, and Trees*. PA-958.

794. *Products of American Forests*. MP-861. $0.70.

795. *Rx for Wounded Trees*. AIB-387. $1.35.

796. *Search for Solitude — Our Wilderness Heritage*. PA-942. $0.85.

797. *Silviculture Is Growing Trees*. 1975. 001-001-00402-2. 55 cents.

798. *Some Observations on Campground Trampling and Ground Cover Response*.

799. *Sulfur Damage to Douglas Fir Near a Pulp and Paper Mill in Western Montana*.

800. *A Tree Hurts, Too*. AIB-396. $1.30.

801. *Trees for Polluted Air*. MP-1230. $0.25.

802. *Trees of Our National Forests, Their Beauty and Use*. PA-1124. $0.70.

803. *What the Forest Service Does*. FS-20.

804. *What We Get from Trees*. Poster. FS-279.

805. *Why Leaves Change Color*. FS-12. Free.

806. *Wilderness Users in the Pacific Northwest — Their Characteristics, Values, and Management Preferences*.

807. *Wildlife for Tomorrow*. PA-989. $1.00.

808. *Your Tree's Troubles May Be You*. AIB 372. $0.70.

809. *Your Water Supply and Forests*. AIB-305.

U.S. Department of the Interior (order from Government Printing Office):

810. *Homes for Birds*. 2400-0050. 35 cents.

811. Indian Series.

Indians of the Eastern Seaboard. S/N 2402-00014. 40 cents.

Indians of Arizona. S/N 2402-00010. 40 cents.

Indians of California. S/N 2402-00011. 35 cents.

Indians of Lower Plateau. S/N 2402-00017. 40 cents.

Indians of New Mexico. S/N 2402-00019. 35 cents.

Indians of Northwest. S/N 2404-00020.

812. *United States Wall Map* showing distribution of federal lands in National

Parks and Monuments, Forests, Recreation Areas, and Wilderness Areas. 024011-00019-4. $3.00.

U. S. Government Printing Office:

813. *Action for Environmental Quality — Standards and Enforcement for Air and Water Pollution Control.* 5500-00087. 65 cents.

814. *American Wood Series.* Individual pamphlets on 30 trees. Listed in *Trees and Forest Management* subject bibliography (see that entry).

815. *The Challenge of the Environment — A Primer on EPA's Statutory Authority.* 5500-0078, 40 cents.

816. *Color It Green with Trees: A Calendar of Activities for Home Arborists.* Revised 1972. 001-000-01557. 40 cents.

817. *Conservation Publications and Related Subjects.* Subject bibliography. Free.

818. *National Parks of the United States Map and Guide.* Includes all areas in the National Park System. 2405-00546. 35 cents.

819. *Noise Pollution — Now Hear This.* 5500-0072. 35 cents.

820. *Teaching Materials for Environmental Education.* 0101-0234. 95 cents.

821. *Trees and Forest Management.* Subject Bibliography SB-086. Free.

822. *Trees for Shade and Beauty, Their Selection and Care.* Revised 1972. 001-000-01606-7.

Western Wood Products Association:

823. *Federal Timber Sales* (bidding process for federal timber). Two copies free; additional copies 5 cents each.

824. *The Forester in the Plaid Shirt.* Limited number free.

825. *Great Trees of the West.* Poster. Single copy free; additional copies 15 cents each.

826. *Lumber — How It Is Manufactured.* Wall chart 23 X 38 inches. Picture story.

827. *Our Forest Bank Account.*

828. *A Vital Aspect of Forest Ecology — Clearcutting.*

829. *Western Forests — A Regrowth Record.*

830. *Western Sawlog Lumber Products.* Three ways of sawing logs.

831. *Wilderness: Just How Wild Should It Be?*

832. *The Wilderness Resource.*

Weyerhaeuser Company

833. *Forestry to Fit the Future.* Free.

834. *Soil.* Free.

835. Zobel, Bruce. *Increasing Productivity of*

Forest Lands Through Better Trees. The S. J. Hall Lectureship in Industrial Forestry. Berkeley: University of California, Department of Forestry and Conservation. 1974. 19pp. Free on request from College of Natural Resources, University of California.

RELATED CURRICULUM MATERIALS

836. Air Pollution Control Association. *Air Pollution Experiments for Junior and Senior High School Science Classes.* Pittsburgh: The Association, $1.50. Grades 7-12.

837. Biological Sciences Curriculum Study. *Biological Science: An Ecological Approach* (BSCS Green Version). Chicago: Rand McNally, student text $9.90; teacher's edition, $9.90.

838. Bureau of Land Management, U.S. Department of the Interior. *All Around You — An Environmental Study Guide.* Stock no. 2411-00043. Washington: Government Printing Office, $2.35.

839. Charles, Cheryl, and Jan Rensel. *I Thought That I Would Never Be.* Branch 3. Tiburon: Project Learning Tree, 1977.

840. *Contours: Studies of the Environment.* Edited by W. A. Andres. Englewood Cliffs: Prentice-Hall. Titles are *A Guide to the Study of . . . Freshwater Ecology*, 1972; *Environmental Pollution*, 1972; *Soil Ecology*, 1973; *Terrestrial Ecology*, 1974. Each guide, $6.57 cloth; $3.66 paper. Teacher's guide, $3.39.

841. Cooper, Elizabeth K. *Science In Your Own Backyard.* New York, Harcourt Brace Jovanovich, 1958, $5.50. Grades 7-9.

842. Dickey, Miriam E., and Charles E. Roth. *Beyond the Classroom: Using the Urban Environment As An Instructional Medium.* Lincoln: Massachusetts Audubon Society, 1972, $2.50.

843. Dickey, Miriam E., and Charles E. Roth. *A Who's Who of Urban America.* Book and booklet with activity cards. Lincoln: Massachusetts Audubon Society, 1972, $2.50.

844. Energy-Environment Materials Project of the National Science Teachers Association. *Energy-Environment Source Book* by John M. Fowler. 1975. $4.00. *Energy-Environment Mini-Unit Guide*, Stephen M. Smith et al., eds. 1975. $3.00. Washington: The Association.

845. *Energy, People, and the Environment: Coal Mining.* Education Development Center. 4-week course. 1976.

846. Environmental Protection Agency. *A*

Curriculum Activities Guide to Water Pollution and Environmental Studies. Books. Volume I, Stock no. 5501-00414; Volume II, Stock no. 5501-00415. $2.25 each. Washington: Government Printing Office.

847. *Essence I.* Environmental Study cards. Stock no. 6756. 1974, $21.98. *Essence II.* Stock no. 6757, $36.63. Reading: Addison-Wesley.

848. Fegeley, Thomas, Rita Reemer, and Lynn Rinehart. *Recycling.* Emmaus: Rodale, $1.50. Grades K-8.

849. *Games for the Science Classroom: An Annotated Bibliography,* Paul B. Hounshell and Ira R. Trollinger, eds. Washington: National Science Teachers Association. 1977. $3.75.

850. Goldstein, Jerome. *Garbage As You Like It.* Emmaus: Rodale, 1969, $5.95.

851. Group for Environmental Education. *Yellow Pages of Learning Resources.* Philadelphia: Group for Environmental Education, 1972, $1.95.

852. Hawkinson, John, and Martha Faulhaber. *Music and Instruments for Children to Make.* Chicago: Whitman, 1969, $4.75.

853. *Investigating Your Environment: Teaching Materials for Environmental Education.* Forest Service, U.S. Department of Agriculture. Includes investigations on animals, forest, soil, water, and a land-use simulation. 1976.

854. *Investigating Your Environment.* Biological Sciences Curriculum Study. 1975. Reading: Addison-Wesley. Student Handbook and Teacher Handbook, $3.99 each; 10 student resource booklets on various topics, including *Land Use,* $2.37.

855. IPS. *Introductory Physical Science.* Englewood Cliffs: Prentice-Hall. 1972. $6.49.

856. Keep America Beautiful, Inc. *Catalog of Environmental Films.* 15 cents.

857. Knapp, Clifford *Outdoor Activities for Environmental Studies.* Danville: Instructor Publications, 1971, $1.95.

858. Knapp, Clifford. "Teaching Environmental Education with a Focus on Values." *Journal of Environmental Education.* Summer 1972.

859. Metropolitan Life Insurance Company. *Exploring Your Environmental Choices: An Inquiry and Decision-Making Approach.* Teacher's Guide, cassette, spirit masters and overheads, family participation leaflets. New York: Metropolitan Life, $18.50. Grades 7-12.

860. *National Environmental Study Area: A Guide.* Stock no. 1972-0-469-326. 1972.

Washington: Government Printing Office.

861. National Wildlife Federation. *Environmental Discovery Units.* Self-contained guides for teachers; 24 titles include *Oaks, Acorns, Climate and Squirrels,* and *Plant Puzzles: Natural Structure.* Washington: The Federation, $1.50 (some titles, $1.00); complete set $25.00.

862. Nickelsburg, Janet. *Ecology: Habitats, Niches, and Food Chains.* Philadelphia: Lippincott, 1969, $5.50.

863. *Our Man-Made Environment Book 7.* Cambridge: Massachusetts Institute of Technology, 1971, $4.95. *Teacher's Guide* from Group for Environmental Education, $2.00.

864. Outdoor Biology Instructional Strategies (OBIS). *OBIS Activities Trial Edition.* Sets I and II. Twenty-four activities (including crafts, simulations, and investigation) in each set. Set I, $8.50; Set II, $9.50; Trial module $2.00.

865. Patterson, Frank G. *Forests: A Dichotomy Between Dollars and Dreams.* In *Sourcebook for Environmental Education,* V. Eugene Vivian, ed. Browns Mills: Conservation and Environmental Studies Center, 1969, $5.95. Grades 7-9.

866. Peck, Ruth. *Art Lessons That Teach Children About Their Natural Environment.* West Nyack: Parker, 1973, $10.95.

867. *Pollution.* Paul Klinge and Clarence Lange, eds. Reston: National Association of Biology Teachers, 1973, $2.00.

868. Pringle, Laurence P., ed. *Discovering the Outdoors: Investigations of Life in Field, Forests and Ponds.* Garden City: Doubleday, 1969, $4.95. Grade 4-adult.

869. Reemer, Rita. *Teaching Organic Gardening,* Emmaus: Rodale, $6.95. Grades 4-12.

870. Sibley, Hi. *One Hundred Two Bird Houses, Feeders You Can Make.* South Holland; Goodheart-Willcox, $4.00; school price, $3.00.

871. Sierra Club. *Teachers Packet* (includes "Handbook for Ecology Action," and "A Beginning"). San Francisco: Information Services, Sierra Club, $2.00.

872. Stapp, William B., and Dorothy A. Cox. *Environmental Education Activities Manual.* 6-volume set. 1974, $10.00. Order from Dorothy A. Cox.

873. Tanner, Thomas R. *Ecology, Environment and Education.* Lincoln: Professional Educators, 1974, $1.75. (Distributed by Cliffs.)

874. Terry Mark. *Teaching for Survival.* Perrysville: Reed & Sons, $0.95. (Originally published by Ballantine, 1971.)

875. Troost, Cornelius J., and Harold Altman, eds. *Environmental Education: A Sourcebook.* New York: Wiley, 1972, $9.95.

876. Van Matre, Steve. *Acclimatization,* 1972, $3.25; *Acclimatizing,* 1974, $3.75. Martinsville: American Camping Association.

877. *We Can Help!* Environmental Education Teaching Resources. Developed for U.S. Fish and Wildlife Service, Department of the Interior. User's Guide 24 Outdoor Classroom Guides. Available from Jenny Publishing Company, $14.50 plus $1 postage and handling.

878. Werling, Donn Paul *Environmental Education and Your School Site.* Chicago: Open Lands Project, $3.00.

SIMULATIONS/GAMES

879. *Adapt.* How societies adapt to environment. Interact. About 5 class periods. $12.00.

880. *Balance.* Simulation of four families caught in ecological dilemmas. Interact. $12.00. Grades 8-12.

881. *Baldicer.* John Knox. $25.00.

882. *Centerplace City.* Directions and rules for playing *Centerplace* appeared in an article by Dennis Asmussen and Richard Cole entitled "A Land-Use Alternative Model for Upper Elementary Environmental Education," in the May 1970 issue of *Journal of Geography*, pp. 267-272.

883. *Colorado*: Problems and Promises. Public Service Company of Colorado. Free loan.

884. *Conserv-O.* ED081 595, ERIC, Columbus. ERIC charge.

885. *Cope.* Interact. $12.00.

886. *Cycles and Balance.* Society for Visual Education. Board game with cassettes. $28.00. Primary-intermediate.

887. *Design.* Simulation of designing and furnishing a home. Interact. $20.00. Grades 5-12.

888. *Dirty Water.* Reed & Sons. $7.00.

889. *Eco: An Island Simulation Game.* Department of Public Instruction, Olympia, Washington.

890. *Ecology.* Damon/Education Division. $7.00.

891. *Ecology: The Game of Man and Nature.* Reed & Sons. $6.00. Grade 5 and up.

892. *Ecopolis.* Interact. $12.00.

893. *The Energy-Environment Game.* Edison Electric Institute. $26.00.

894. *Environmental Issues: A Courtroom Simulation.* Request from Environmental Education Coordinator, Bureau of Land Management (220), U.S. Department of the Interior. First Copy free.

895. *Food Chain.* Prentice-Hall, Inc. Contact publisher for price.

896. *Forest Adventure.* ED 081 595 ERIC, Columbus. ERIC charge.

897. *Graphigame: Environmental Attitudes.* Education Ventures, Inc. (Distributed by Cardinal Printers.) $5.00.

898. *Homestead*: Simulation of establishing a frontier farm and community. Interact. About 9 class periods. $20.00. Grades 5-12.

899. *Indian Valley.* American Forest Institute. Single copy free; additional copies $0.20 each. Grade 6 and up.

900. *Land Use* and book *Mike's World — Your World.* Education Ventures, Inc. (Distributed by Cardinal Printers.) Game, $4.00; book, $0.75.

901. *New Town.* Harwell Associates. 10-student kit, $16.00; 20-student kit, $28.00. Grades K-12.

902. *No Dam Action.* Instructional Simulations, Inc. $115.00.

903. *Open Space.* Education Ventures, Inc. (Distributed by Cardinal Printers.) $6.00.

904. *Outdoor Survival.* Stackpole, $10.00. Also available from Reed & Sons.

905. *Planet Management.* Houghton Mifflin. $16.98.

906. *Pleasantville.* Directions and rules for playing *Pleasantville* appeared in an article by James Kracht and Peter Martorella entitled, "Simulation and Inquiry Models Applied to the Study of Environmental Problems," in the May 1970 issue of *Journal of Geography*, pp. 273-278.

907. *Pollution.* Games Central. $30.00 plus $1.00 shipping and handling.

908. *Pollution Game.* An article by Lester Jay Gould in *The Science Teacher*, October 1972, p. 52.

909. *The Pollution Game.* Houghton Mifflin. $13.65.

910. *Population.* Reed & Sons. $7.00.

911. *Possum Creek Valley.* Southern Forest Institute. $1.50.

912. *Pressure.* Interact. $12.00.

913. *Propaganda.* WFF'N'Proof, Learning Games Associates. $10.00 plus $1.00 postage and handling.

914. *The Redwood Controversy.* Houghton Mifflin. $10.98.

915. *Sacrifice.* Education Ventures, Inc. (Distributed by Cardinal Printers.) $7.00.

916. *Smog.* Reed & Sons. $7.00.

917. *The Tree Ring Kit.* Telocote Press, Inc. $1.00.

PUBLISHERS

ABELARD-SCHUMAN LTD., 666 Fifth Avenue, New York, NY 10019

ABT (see GAMES CENTRAL)

ABINGDON PRESS, 201 Eighth Avenue South, Nashville, TN 37202

ACADEMIC, Subsidiary of Harcourt Brace Jovanovich, Inc., 111 Fifth Avenue, New York, NY 10003

ACE BOOKS, Division of Charter Communications, Inc., 1120 Avenue of the Americas, New York, NY 10036

ACROPOLIS BOOKS LTD., 2400 17th Street, NW, Washington, DC 20009

ACI FILMS, INC., ACI MEDIA, INC., 35 West 45th Street, New York, NY 10036

ADDISON-WESLEY PUBLISHING COMPANY, INC., Reading, MA 01867

AHM PUBLISHING COMPANY, 3110 North Arlington Heights Road, Northbrook, IL 60004

AIMS INSTRUCTIONAL MEDIA SERVICES, INC., 626 Justin Avenue, Glendale, CA 91201

AIR POLLUTION CONTROL ASSOCIATION, 4400 Fifth Avenue, Pittsburgh, PA 15213

ALASKA LOGGERS ASSOCIATION, INC., 1111 Stedman Street, Suite 200, Ketchikan, AK 99901

AMERICAN CAMPING ASSOCIATION, INC., Bradford Woods, Martinsville, IN 46151

THE AMERICAN ECONOMIC FOUNDATION, 51 East 42nd Street, New York, NY 10017

AMERICAN EDUCATIONAL FILMS, Box 5001, 132 Lasky Drive, Beverly Hills, CA 90212

AMERICAN FOREST INSTITUTE, 1619 Massachusetts Avenue, NW, Washington, DC 20036

AMERICAN FOREST INSTITUTE, New England Office, 96 Harlow Street, Bangor, ME 04401

AMERICAN FORESTRY ASSOCIATION, 1319 18th Street, NW, Washington, DC 20036

AMERICAN INSTITUTE OF ARCHITECTS, 1735 New York Avenue, NW, Washington, DC 20006

AMERICAN INSTITUTE OF LANDSCAPE ARCHITECTS, 6810 North Second Place, Phoenix, AZ 85012

AMERICAN PAPER INSTITUTE, 260 Madison Avenue, New York, NY 10016

AMERICAN PLYWOOD ASSOCIATION, 1119 A Street, Tacoma, WA 98401

AMERICAN SOCIETY OF AGRONOMY, 677 South Segoe Road, Madison, WI 53711

AMERICAN SOCIETY OF LANDSCAPE ARCHITECTS, 1750 Old Meadow Road, McLean, VA 22101

AMERICAN SOCIETY OF PLANNING OFFICIALS, 1313 East 60th Street, Chicago, IL 60637

AMERICAN WOOD COUNCIL, 1619 Massachusetts Avenue, NW, Washington, DC 20036

AMSCO SCHOOL PUBLICATIONS, INC., 315 Hudson Street, New York, NY 10013

ANCHOR BOOKS, Doubleday & Company, Inc., Garden City, NY 11530

APOLLO EDITIONS, 666 Fifth Avenue, New York, NY 10019

ARNO PRESS, 330 Madison Avenue, New York, NY 10017

ASSOCIATION FILMS, INC., 866 Third Avenue, New York, NY 10022

ATHENEUM PUBLISHERS, 122 East 42nd Street, New York, NY 10017

AVON BOOKS, 959 Eighth Avenue, New York, NY 10019

BALLANTINE BOOKS, Random House Distribution Center, Westminster, MD 21157

BANTAM BOOKS, INC., 666 Fifth Avenue, New York, NY 10019

A.S. BARNES & CO., INC., Forsgate Drive, Cranbury, NJ 08512

BARR FILMS, PO Box 5667, 3490 East Foothill Boulevard, Pasadena, CA 91107

BENEFIC PRESS, 10300 West Roosevelt Road, Westchester, IL 60153

BENNETT BOOKS, Chas. A. Bennett Co., Inc., 809 West Detweiller Drive, Peoria, IL 61614

BFA EDUCATIONAL MEDIA, 2211 Michigan Avenue, PO Box 1795, Santa Monica, CA 94046

THE BOBBS-MERRILL COMPANY, INC., 4300 West 62nd Street, Indianapolis, IN 46206

BONANZA (See CROWN)

BROWN UNIVERSITY PRESS, 71 George Street, Box 1881, Providence, RI 02912

BRITANNICA (see ENCYCLOPAEDIA BRITANNICA)

BUDEK FILMS (see HARVEST LABS)

BUREAU OF LAND MANAGEMENT, US Department of the Interior, Washington, DC 20240

BURGESS PUBLISHING CO., 7108 Ohms Lane, Minneapolis, MN 55435

CALIFORNIA REDWOOD ASSOCIATION, 617 Montgomery Street, San Francisco, CA 94111

CALIFORNIA STATE POLYTECHNIC UNIVERSITY, 3801 West Temple Avenue, Pomona, CA 91768

CALIFORNIA TOMORROW, Monadnock Building, 681 Market Street, San Francisco, CA 94105

CANADIAN CONSULATE GENERAL, Film Library, 310 South Michigan Avenue, Chicago, IL 60604

CARDINAL PRINTERS, INC., Teaching Aids/Games Division, Wesleyan University, Middletown, CT 06457

CAROUSEL FILMS, INC., 1501 Broadway, New York, NY 10036

CAXTON PRINTERS, LTD., Caldwell, ID 83605

CENTER FOR ADVANCED COMPUTATION, University of Illinois, Urbana, IL 61801

THE CENTER FOR HUMANITIES, INC., Two Holland Avenue, White Plains, NY 10603

CENTER FOR SCIENCE IN THE PUBLIC INTEREST, 1779 Church Street, NW, Washington, DC 20036

CENTRON EDUCATIONAL FILMS, 1621 West Ninth Street, Lawrence, KS 66044

CHILDRENS PRESS, 1224 West Van Buren Street, Chicago, IL 60607

CHURCHILL FILMS, 662 North Robertson Boulevard, Los Angeles, CA 90069

CLIFFS NOTES, INC., PO Box 80728, Lincoln, NB 68501

COLLIER (see MACMILLAN)

COLLINS WORLD, 2080 West 117th Street, Cleveland, OH 44111

COLOPHON (see HARPER & ROW)

COMSTOCK EDITIONS, INC., 3030 Bridgeway Boulevard, Sausalito, CA 94965

CONSERVATION & ENVIRONMENTAL STUDIES CENTER, INC., Box 2230, RD7, Browns Mills, NJ 08015

THE CONSERVATION FOUNDATION, 1717 Massachusetts Avenue, NW, Washington, DC 20036

CONTEMPORARY/MCGRAW-HILL FILMS, Princeton Road, Hightstown, NJ 08520

CORNELL UNIVERSITY FILM LIBRARY, 31 Roberts Hall, Cornell University, Ithaca, NY 14853

CORONET INSTRUCTIONAL MEDIA, 65 East South Water Street, Chicago, IL 60601

COWARD, MCCANN & GEOGHEGAN, INC., PO Box 50, East Rutherford, NJ 07073

DOROTHY A. COX, 30808 Lamar, Farmington Hills, MI 48024

CREATIVE EDUCATIONAL SOCIETY, 123 South Broad Street, Mankato, MN 56001

CREATIVE LEARNING, 19 Market Street, Warren, RI 02885

CROWELL (Apollo Editions), 666 Fifth Avenue, New York, NY 10019

CROWELL-COLLIER (see MACMILLAN)

THOMAS Y. CROWELL COMPANY, INC., 666 Fifth Avenue, New York, NY 10019

CROWN (Bonanza), Crown Publishers, Inc., 1 Park Avenue, New York, NY 10016

CROWN ZELLERBACH, 1500 SW First Avenue, Portland, OR 97201

DAMON/EDUCATION DIVISION, 80 Wilson Way, Westwood, MA 02090

JOHN DAY, Division of Thomas Y. Crowell, 666 Fifth Avenue, New York, NY 10019

DELL PUBLISHING CO., INC., 1 Dag Hammarskjold Plaza, 245 East 47th Street, New York, NY 10017

DENOYER-GEPPERT, 5235 Ravenswood Avenue, Chicago, IL 60640

DEVIN-ADAIR COMPANY, INC., 143 Sound Beach Avenue, Old Greenwich, CT 06870

THE DIAL PRESS, 1 Dag Hammarskjold Plaza, 245 East 47th Street, New York, NY 10017

DODD, MEAD & COMPANY, INC., 79 Madison Avenue, New York, NY 10016

DOUBLEDAY & COMPANY, INC., Garden City, NY 11530

DOVER PUBLICATIONS, INC., 180 Varick Street, New York, NY 10014

DROLL YANKEES INC., Mill Road, Foster, RI 02825

E.P. DUTTON & CO., INC., 201 Park Avenue South, New York, NY 10003

EASTMAN KODAK COMPANY, 343 State Street, Rochester, NY 14650

ERIC Information Analysis Center for Science, Mathematics, and Environmental Education, The Ohio State University, 1200 Chambers Road, Columbus, OH 43210

EDISON ELECTRIC INSTITUTE, 90 Park Avenue, New York, NY 10016

EDUCATION DEVELOPMENT CENTER, 15 Mifflin Place, Cambridge, MA 02138

EDUCATION VENTURES (see CARDINAL PRINTERS)

EDUCATIONAL DEVELOPMENT CORPORATION (see IMPERIAL EDUCATIONAL RESOURCES)

EDUCATIONAL MODULES, INC., Merrell Scientific Division, 1665 Buffalo Road, Rochester, NY 14624

ENCYCLOPAEDIA BRITANNICA Educational Corporation, 425 North Michigan Avenue, Chicago, IL 60611

ENERGY & MAN'S ENVIRONMENT, 0224 SW Hamilton, Portland, OR 97201

ENVIRONMENTAL ACTION COALITION, 235 East 49th Street, New York, NY 10017

ESSENTIA, PO Box 129, Tiburon, CA 94920

M. EVANS & CO., INC., 216 East 49th Street, New York, NY 10017

EXPOSITION PRESS, INC., 800 Oyster Bay Road, Hicksville, NY 11801

EYE GATE MEDIA, 146-01 Archer Avenue, Jamaica, NY 11435

FARRAR, STRAUS & GIROUX, INC., 19 Union Square, New York, NY 10003

FAWCETT WORLD LIBRARY, 1515 Broadway, New York, NY 10036

J.G. FERGUSON PUBLISHING COMPANY, 111 East Wacker Drive, Chicago, IL 60601

FILMS INCORPORATED, 1144 Wilmette Avenue, Wilmette, IL 60091

STUART FINLEY, 3428 Mansfield Road, Falls Church, VA 22041

RON FINNE, Filmmaker, 36526 Jasper Road, Springfield, OR 97477

FOLLETT PUBLISHING CO., 1010 West Washington Boulevard, Chicago, IL 60607

FOREST HISTORY SOCIETY, INC., PO Box 1581, Santa Cruz, CA 95061

FOREST SERVICE, USDA, Films, National Audio-Visual Center, Sales Branch (GSA), Washington, DC 20409, or regional film libraries of the Forest Service

FORUM PRESS, PO Box 915, St. Charles, MO 63301

W.H. FREEMAN & CO., 660 Market Street, San Francisco, CA 94104

FRIENDS OF THE EARTH, 529 Commercial Street, San Francisco, CA 94111

FRIENDSHIP PRESS, 475 Riverside Drive, New York, NY 10027

FUNK & WAGNALLS CO., THOMAS Y. CROWELL, 666 Fifth Avenue, New York, NY 10019

GAMES CENTRAL-ABT ASSOCIATES INC., 55 Wheeler Street, Cambridge, MA 02138

GEORGIA-PACIFIC CORPORATION, 900 SW Fifth Avenue, Portland, OR 97204

GARRARD PUBLISHING COMPANY, 1607 North Market Street, Champaign, IL 61820

GOLDEN BOOKS, Western Publishing Company, Inc., 1220 Mound Avenue, Racine, WI 53404

GOLDEN GATE, Division of Childrens Press, 1247½ North Vista Street, Los Angeles, CA 90046

GOLDEN PRESS (see WESTERN PUBLISHING COMPANY)

GOODHEART-WILLCOX, 123 West Taft Drive, South Holland, IL 60473

STEPHEN GREENE PRESS, PO Box 1000, Fessenden Road, Indian Flat, Brattleboro, VT 05301

GROSSET & DUNLAP, INC. Publishers, 51 Madison Avenue, New York, NY 10010

GROSSMAN PUBLISHERS, Division of Viking Press, 625 Madison Avenue, New NY 10022

GROUP FOR ENVIRONMENTAL EDUCATION INC., 1214 Arch Street, Philadelphia, PA 19107

GROVE PRESS, INC., 196 West Houston Street, New York, NY 10014

GSA, General Services Administration, National Audio-Visual Center, Washington, DC 20409

GUIDANCE ASSOCIATES, 757 Third Avenue, New York, NY 10017

GULL LAKE ENVIRONMENTAL EDUCATION PROJECT, Kellogg Bird Sanctuary, 12685 East C Avenue, Augusta, MI 49012

HAFNER (see MACMILLAN)

HARCOURT BRACE JOVANOVICH, INC., 757 Third Avenue, New York, NY 10017

HARPER & ROW, PUBLISHERS, INC., Keystone Industrial Park, Scranton, PA 18512

HASTINGS HOUSE PUBLISHERS, INC., 10 East 40th Street, New York, NY 10016

HARVARD UNIVERSITY PRESS, Cambridge, MA 02138

HARVEST LABORATORIES, Pelham Street, Newport, RI 02840

HARWELL ASSOCIATES, Box 95, Convent Station, NJ 07961

HAWTHORN BOOKS, 260 Madison Avenue, New York, NY 10016

HEARTHSIDE PRESS INC., 445 Northern Boulevard, Great Neck, NY 10021

D.C. HEATH AND COMPANY, 125 Spring Street, Lexington, MA 02173; Distribution Center, 2700 North Richardt Avenue, Indianapolis, IN 46219

EDWARD HINES LUMBER CO., Post Office Box 191, Laramie, WY 82070

HOLIDAY HOUSE, 18 East 53rd Street, New York, NY 10022

HOLT, RINEHART AND WINSTON, INC., 383 Madison Avenue, New York, NY 10017

HOUGHTON MIFFLIN COMPANY, (for games, Department M), 1 Beacon Street, Boston, MA 02107

HUBBARD SCIENTIFIC CO., Box 104, Northbrook, IL 60062

IMPERIAL EDUCATIONAL RESOURCES (Division of Educational Development Corporation), PO Box 5500, 202 Lake Miriam Drive, Lakeland, FL 33803

INDIANA UNIVERSITY, Audio-Visual Center, Bloomington, IN 47401

INQUIRY AUDIO VISUALS, 1754 West Farragut Avenue, Chicago, IL 60640

INSTRUCTIONAL AIDS, INC., PO Box 191, Mankato, MN 56001

INSTRUCTIONAL SIMULATIONS, INC., 2147 University Avenue, St. Paul, MN 55114

THE INSTRUCTOR PUBLICATIONS, INC., Dansville, New York, NY 14437

INTERACT, PO Box 262, Lakeside, CA 92040

INTERNATIONAL FILM BUREAU INC., 332 South Michigan Avenue, Chicago, IL 60604

INTERNATIONAL UNION for Conservation of Nature and Natural Resources, 1110 Morges, Switzerland

IOWA DEPARTMENT OF PUBLIC INSTRUCTION, Curriculum Division, Grimes State Office Building, Des Moines, IA 50319

JENNY PUBLISHING COMPANY, INC., 57 Queen Avenue South, Minneapolis, MN 55405

JOHNNY HORIZON NEWS BUREAU, Johnny Horizon Program, Washington, DC 20240

THE JOHNS HOPKINS UNIVERSITY PRESS, Baltimore, MD 21218

JOURNAL FILMS, INCORPORATED, 930 Pitner Avenue, Evanston, IL 60202

JURSNICK PRINTING CO., Great Falls, MT 59401

WILLIAM KAUFMAN, INC., 1 First Street, Los Altos, CA 94022

KEEP AMERICA BEAUTIFUL, INC., 99 Park Avenue, New York, NY 10016

ALFRED A. KNOPF, INC., Subsidiary of Random House, Inc., 201 East 50th Street, New York, NY 10022

JOHN KNOX PRESS, 341 Ponce de Leon Avenue, NE, Atlanta, GA 30308

LANE COUNTY IED, Environmental Management Services, 135 East Sixth Avenue, Eugene, OR 97401

LANE PUBLISHING CO., Willow & Middlefield Roads, Menlo Park, CA 94025

LEAGUE OF WOMEN VOTERS of the United States, 1730 M Street, NW, Washington, DC 20036

LEARNING GAMES ASSOCIATES, 1490 South Boulevard, Ann Arbor, MI 48014

J.B. LIPPINCOTT COMPANY, East Washington Square, Philadelphia, PA 19105

LITTLE, BROWN AND COMPANY, 34 Beacon Street, Boston, MA 02106

LITTON EDUCATIONAL PUBLISHING, INC., 300 Pike Street, Cincinnati, OH 45202

LOTHROP (see MORROW)

LYCEUM PRODUCTIONS, INC., PO Box 1018, Laguna Beach, CA 92652

MACMILLAN PUBLISHING CO., INC., Front and Brown Streets, Riverside, NJ 08075

MASSACHUSETTS AUDUBON SOCIETY, Hatheway Environmental Education Institute, Lincoln, MA 01773

MCCLAIN PRINTING COMPANY, 212 Main Street, Parsons, WV 26287

MCGRAW-HILL BOOK COMPANY, 8171 Redwood Highway, Novato, CA 94947

MCGRAW-HILL BOOK COMPANY, 1221 Avenue of the Americas, New York, NY 10020

MCGRAW-HILL FILMS (see CONTEMPORARY/MCGRAW-HILL)

DAVID MCKAY CO., INC., 750 Third Avenue, New York, NY 10017

JULIAN MESSNER, Division of Simon & Schuster, Inc., 1 West 39th Street, New York, NY 10018

METROPOLITAN LIFE, 1 Madison Avenue, New York, NY 10010

MINNESOTA ENVIRONMENTAL SCIENCES FOUNDATION, INC., 5400 Glenwood Avenue, Minneapolis, MN 55422

THE MIT PRESS, Massachusetts Institute of Technology, 28 Carleton Street, Cambridge, MA 02142

MODERN LIBRARY (see RANDOM HOUSE)

MODERN TALKING PICTURE SERVICE, 2323 New Hyde Park Road, New Hyde Park, NY 11040

KITTY MORGAN, NO. 9, 37 Spring Street, New York, NY 10012

WILLIAM MORROW & COMPANY, INC., 105 Madison Avenue, New York, NY 10010

NATIONAL ACADEMY OF SCIENCES, 2101 Constitution Avenue, NW, Washington, DC 20418

NATIONAL ARCHIVES AND RECORDS, General Services Administration, Washington, DC 20408

NATIONAL ASSOCIATION OF BIOLOGY TEACHERS, 11250 Roger Bacon Drive, Reston, VA 22090

NATIONAL ASSOCIATION OF STATE FORESTERS, Department of Natural and Economic Resources, PO Box 27687, Raleigh, NC 27611

NATIONAL AUDIO-VISUAL CENTER, Sales Branch GSA, Washington, DC 20409

NATIONAL AUDUBON SOCIETY, 950 Third Avenue, New York, NY 10022

NATIONAL FOREST PRODUCTS ASSOCIATION, 1619 Massachusetts Avenue, NW, Washington, DC 20036

NATIONAL PARK SERVICE, U.S. Department of the Interior, Washington, DC 20240

NATIONAL PARKS & CONSERVATION ASSOCIATION, 1701 18th Street, NW, Washington, DC 20009

NATIONAL SCIENCE TEACHERS ASSOCIATION, 1742 Connecticut Avenue, NW, Washington, DC 20009

NATIONAL WILDLIFE FEDERATION, 1412 16th Street, NW, Washington, DC 20036

NATURAL HISTORY PRESS (see DOUBLEDAY)

NEW AMERICAN LIBRARY, 1301 Avenue of the Americas, New York, NY 10019

NORTH CAROLINA STATE UNIVERSITY, School of Forest Resources, Raleigh, NC 27607

NORTHWEST PULP AND PAPER ASSOCIATION, 555 116th Avenue, NE, Bellevue, WA 98004

W.W. NORTON & COMPANY, INC., 500 Fifth Avenue, New York, NY 10036

NOVA, Public TV Library, Videoprogram Service, 475 L'Enfant Plaza West, SW, Washington, DC 20027

F.M. O'BRIEN BOOKSELLER, 34 & 36 High Street, Portland, ME 04101

OPEN LANDS PROJECT, 53 West Jackson Boulevard, Chicago, IL 60604

DIVISION OF CONTINUING EDUCATION, Audiovisual Instruction, 1633 Southwest Park Avenue, Portland, OR 97201

OREGON HISTORICAL SOCIETY, 1230 Southwest Park Avenue, Portland, OR 97205

DEPARTMENT OF FORESTRY, State of Oregon, 2600 State Street, Salem, OR 97310

OREGON STATE UNIVERSITY, School of Forestry, Corvallis, OR 97331

OUTDOOR BIOLOGY INSTRUCTIONAL STRATEGIES (OBIS), Lawrence Hall of Science, University of California, Berkeley, CA 94720

OUTDOOR PICTURES, PO Box 277, Anacortes, WA 98221

OXFORD UNIVERSITY PRESS, INC., 200 Madison Avenue, New York, NY 10016

PANTHEON BOOKS DIVISION, Random House, Inc., 201 East 50th Street, New York, NY 10022

PARENTS' MAGAZINE PRESS, 52 Vanderbilt Avenue, New York, NY 10017

PARKER PUBLISHING COMPANY, INC., West Nyack, NY 10994

PEGASUS (see BOBBS-MERRILL)

PELICAN PUBLISHING CO., INC., 630 Burmaster Street, Gretna, LA 70053

PENGUIN BOOKS, INC., 625 Madison Avenue, New York, NY 10022

PENNSYLVANIA DEPARTMENT OF ENVIRONMENTAL RESOURCES, DIVISION OF FOREST PEST MANAGEMENT, 34 Airport Drive, Harrisburg International Airport, Middletown, PA 17057

PERENNIAL EDUCATION, INC., PO Box 236, 1825 Willow Road, Northfield, IL 60093

PERGAMON PRESS, INC., Maxwell House, Fairview Park, Elmsford, NY 10523

PHOTO LAB, INC., 3825 Georgia Avenue, Washington, DC 20011

PICTURA FILMS DISTRIBUTION CORPORATION, 43 West 16th Street, New York, NY 10011

PRAEGER PUBLISHERS, INC., 111 Fourth Avenue, New York, NY 10003

PRENTICE-HALL, INC., Englewood Cliffs, NJ 07632

PROFESSIONAL EDUCATORS PUBLISHERS INC., PO Box 80728, Lincoln, NB 68501

PROJECT LEARNING TREE, PO Box 129, Tiburon, CA 94920

PUBLIC SERVICE COMPANY OF COLORADO, 550 15th Street, Denver, CO 80201

PUBLIC TELEVISION LIBRARY, Videoprogram Service, 475 L'Enfant Plaza West, SW, Washington, DC 20027

G.P. PUTNAM'S SONS, Coward, McCann & Geoghegan, 200 Madison Avenue, New York, NY 10016

PYRAMID (see HARCOURT BRACE JOVANOVICH)

RAND MCNALLY & COMPANY, PO Box 7600, Chicago, IL 60680

RANDOM HOUSE, INC., 400 Hahn Road, Westminster, MD 21157

REED & SONS, Box 250, Route 2, Perrysville, OH 44864

HENRY REGNERY CO., 180 North Michigan Avenue, Chicago, IL 60601

RESTON (see PRENTICE-HALL)

RIO GRANDE PRESS, INC., Glorietta, NM 87535

ROCKY MOUNTAIN FOREST AND RANGE EXPERIMENT STATION, Forest Service, USDA, Fort Collins, CO 80521

RODALE PRESS, INC., Emmaus, PA 18049

THE RONALD PRESS COMPANY, 79 Madison Avenue, New York, NY 10016

ST. MARTIN'S PRESS, INC., 175 Fifth Avenue, New York, NY 10010

ST. REGIS PAPER COMPANY, 150 East 42nd Street, New York, NY 10017

SCHOCKEN BOOKS, INC., 200 Madison Avenue, New York, NY 10016

SCHOLASTIC BOOK SERVICES, 50 West 44th Street, New York, NY 10036
CHARLES SCRIBNER'S SONS, 597-599 Fifth Avenue, New York, NY 10017
THE SEABURY PRESS, INC., 815 Second Avenue, New York, NY 10017
SENTRY (see HOUGHTON MIFFLIN)
SHELTER PUBLICATIONS (see RANDOM HOUSE)
SHOREY PUBLICATIONS, 110 Union Street, Seattle, WN 98111
SIERRA CLUB, 530 Bush Street, San Francisco, CA 94108
SILVER BURDETT COMPANY, 250 James Street, Morristown, NJ 07960
SIMON & SCHUSTER, INC., 630 Fifth Avenue, New York, NY 10020
SINAUER ASSOCIATES, INC., Sunderland, MA 01375
SINGER EDUCATION DIVISION, 1345 Diversey Parkway, Chicago, IL 60614
PETER SMITH, 6 Lexington Avenue, Gloucester, MA 01930
SOCIETY FOR VISUAL EDUCATION INC., 1345 Diversey Parkway, Chicago, IL 60614
SOCIETY OF AMERICAN FORESTERS, 5400 Grosvenor Lane, Bethesda, MD 20014
SOIL CONSERVATION SOCIETY OF AMERICA, 7515 NE Ankeny Road, Ankeny, IA 50021
SOIL SCIENCE SOCIETY OF AMERICA, American Society of Agronomy, 677 South Segoe Road, Madison, WI 53711
SOUTHERN BAPTIST RADIO-TELEVISION COMMISSION, Box 12157, Fort Worth, TX 76116
SOUTHERN FOREST INSTITUTE, 3395 NE Expwy, #380, Atlanta, GA 30341
SOUTHERN FOREST PRODUCTS ASSOCIATION, PO Box 52468, New Orleans, LA 70152
STACKPOLE BOOKS, PO Box 1831, Harrisburg, PA 17105
STAY AWAY JOE, Publishers, PO Box 2054, Great Falls, MT 59401
STERLING PUBLISHING CO., INC., 419 Park Avenue South, New York, NY 10016
SUPERINTENDENT OF DOCUMENTS, U.S. Government Printing Office, Washington, DC 20240
THE SWALLOW PRESS, INC., 811 West Junior Terrace, Chicago, IL 60613
TEACHING RESOURCES FILMS, An Educational Service of the New York Times, 2 Kisco Plaza, Mt. Kisco, NY 10549
TECOLOTE PRESS, INC., PO Box 217, Glenwood, NM 88039
TERRA SOCIETY, PO Box 110, Mount Prospect, IL 60056
THRESHOLD BOOKS, 365 Martha Street, Susanville, CA 96130
TROLL ASSOCIATES, 320 Route 17, Mahwah, NJ 07430
TROUBADOR PRESS, 385 Fremont Street, San Francisco, CA 94105
U.S. DEPARTMENT OF THE INTERIOR, Washington, DC 20240
U.S. FOREST SERVICE, Department of Agriculture, Washington, DC 20250
U.S. GOVERNMENT PRINTING OFFICE, Washington, DC 20240
UNIVERSITY OF ARIZONA, Bureau of Audiovisual Services, University of Arizona, Tucson, AZ 85721
COOPERATIVE EXTENSION, U.S. Department of Agriculture, University of California, Berkeley, CA 94720
UNIVERSITY OF CALIFORNIA, College of Natural Resources, Department of Forestry and Conservation; and Division of Agricultural Sciences, Berkeley, CA 94720
UNIVERSITY OF CALIFORNIA, Extension Media Center, Berkeley, CA 94720
UNIVERSITY OF CALIFORNIA PRESS, 2223 Fulton Street, Berkeley, CA 94720
FORESTRY LIBRARY, University of California, Berkeley, CA 94720
THE UNIVERSITY OF CHICAGO PRESS, 11030 South Langley Avenue, Chicago, IL 60628

UNIVERSITY OF ILLINOIS PRESS, Urbana, IL 61801

UNIVERSITY OF MICHIGAN, Audio-Visual Education Center, 416 Fourth Street, Ann Arbor, MI 48109

THE UNIVERSITY OF MICHIGAN, Television Center, 400 Fourth Street, Ann Arbor, MI 48103

UNIVERSITY OF MISSOURI PRESS, 107 Swallow Hall, Columbia, MO 65201

UNIVERSITY OF NEBRASKA PRESS, 901 North 17th Street, Lincoln, NB 68588

UNIVERSITY OF OKLAHOMA PRESS, 1005 Asp Avenue, Norman, OK 73069

UNIVERSITY OF SOUTHERN CALIFORNIA, Film Distribution Center, Division of Cinema, University Park, Los Angeles, CA 90007

UNIVERSITY OF TEXAS PRESS, Box 7819, University Station, Austin, TX 78712

UNIVERSITY OF WASHINGTON PRESS, Seattle, WA 98105

UNIVERSITY OF WISCONSIN PRESS, Box 1379, Madison, WI 53701

VAN NOSTRAND REINHOLD CO., Division of Litton Educational Publishing Inc., 300 Pike Street, Cincinnati, OH 45202

THE VIKING PRESS, INC., 625 Madison Avenue, New York, NY 10022

VISUAL EDUCATION, INC., PO Box 6039, Santa Barbara, CA 93111

VOCATIONAL EDUCATION PRODUCTIONS, California State Polytechnic University, San Luis Obispo, CA 93401

VOCATIONAL GUIDANCE MANUALS, 620 South Fifth Street, Louisville, KY 40202

WADSWORTH PUBLISHERS, INC., 10 Davis Drive, Belmont, CA 94002

HENRY Z. WALCK, INC., Division of David McKay, 750 Third Avenue, New York, NY 10017

WALKER & CO., 720 Fifth Avenue, New York, NY 10019

WALT DISNEY FILMS, distributed by Association Films, Inc.

FREDERICK WARNE AND CO., INC., 101 Fifth Avenue, New York, NY 10003

WASHINGTON STATE DEPARTMENT OF PUBLIC INSTRUCTION, Old Capitol Building, Olympia, WA 98504

WASHINGTON STATE UNIVERSITY, Audio-Visual Center, Pullman, WA 99163

WATSON-GUPTILL PUBLICATIONS, INC., 1 Astor Plaza, New York, NY 10036

FRANKLIN WATTS, INC., 730 Fifth Avenue, New York, NY 10019

WEBSTER/MCGRAW-HILL (see MCGRAW-HILL)

WEST WIND PUBLICATIONS, INC., PO Box 3532, Boulder, CO 80303

WESTERN PUBLISHING COMPANY, INC., 1220 Mound Avenue, Racine, WI 53404

WESTERN WOOD PRODUCTS ASSOCIATION, 1500 Yeon Building, Portland, OR 97204

WESTMINSTER, Room 905, Witherspoon Building, Philadelphia, PA 19107

WEYERHAEUSER COMPANY, Box A, Tacoma, WA 98401

ALBERT WHITMAN AND CO., 560 West Lake Street, Chicago, IL 60606

WIFF'N PROOF (see LEARNING GAMES ASSOCIATES)

WILDLIFE MANAGEMENT INSTITUTE, 709 Wire Building, 1000 Vermont Avenue, NW, Washington, DC 20005

JOHN WILEY & SONS, INC., 605 Third Avenue, New York, NY 10016

WINSTON PRESS, 25 Groveland Terrace, Minneapolis, MN 55403

WORLD (see COLLINS WORLD)

WORLDWATCH INSTITUTE, 1776 Massachusetts Avenue, NW, Washington, DC 20036

YALE UNIVERSITY PRESS, 302 Temple Street, New Haven, CT 06511

GUIDELINES FOR REQUESTING INFORMATION AND ASSISTANCE

BE SPECIFIC
Your chances of obtaining useful information will be greatly increased if you state exactly which materials you need, which issues interest you, or what questions you want answered. The accompanying bibliography was developed to help you be specific in your requests. The "send everything you have" approach is uneconomical and unecological.

AVOID CLASS-WIDE REQUESTS
Limit requests for information from any single source to one or two students and pool the collected data. If you cannot avoid a situation where many students ask for similar information, send all the requests in one envelope and ask that materials returned be mailed in one package to one address.

REQUEST ONLY WHAT YOU NEED
. . . and use what you get.

TRY LOCAL SOURCES FIRST
Many community and regional agencies, organizations, and industrial associations can provide valuable information and assistance, particularly on local issues and conditions. Your school librarian or your public library can also help locate information available.

SEND A SELF-ADDRESSED, STAMPED ENVELOPE
If you request material or information from volunteer organizations, include a self-addressed, stamped envelope. This will bring a quicker response because these organizations have very limited budgets and secretarial staffs.

PLAN ON TWO TO THREE WEEKS OF LEAD TIME
If you plan to use the material, such as a pamphlet or film, in conjunction with an activity, send your request *at least* two or three weeks ahead of time.

MAKE SPEAKER REQUESTS WELL IN ADVANCE
Most state agencies and volunteer organizations cannot afford to send their staff or members great distances to speak to one class. However, many resource agencies will assign personnel to meet with students on field trips near their field stations or offices. Most often, the educational experience provided by the presentation in the field is superior to a formal speech in the classroom.

ADDRESSES FOR ADDITIONAL INFORMATION AND MATERIAL

Citizen Conservation Organizations

AMERICAN FORESTRY ASSOCIATION, 1319 - 18th Street, N.W., Washington DC 20036, publishes *American Forests* (monthly periodical)

BOONE AND CROCKETT CLUB, C/O Carnegie Museum, 4400 Forbes Avenue, Pittsburgh, PA 15213

THE CONSERVATION FOUNDATION, 1717 Massachusetts Avenue, N.W., Washington DC 20036, publishes the *C F Letter* (monthly newsletter)

COUNCIL ON ECONOMIC PRIORITIES, 456 Greenwich Street, New York, NY 10013

DEFENDERS OF WILDLIFE, 2000 N Street N.W., Washington DC 20036, publishes *Defenders of Wildlife News* (newsletter)

DUCKS UNLIMITED, P.O. Box 66300, Chicago, IL 60666, publishes *Ducks Unlimited Magazine*

ENVIRONMENTAL ACTION, INC., Room 731, 1346 Connecticut Avenue N.W., Washington DC 20036, publishes *Environmental Action* (bi-monthly newsletter)

ENVIRONMENTAL DEFENSE FUND, INC., 162 Old Town Road, East Setauket, NY 11733

FOREST HISTORY SOCIETY, INC., P.O. Box 1531, Santa Cruz, CA 95060, publishes *Forest History* (quarterly)

FRIENDS OF THE EARTH, 529 Commercial Street, San Francisco, CA 94111, publishes *Not Man Apart* (bi-monthly newspaper)

IZAAK WALTON LEAGUE OF AMERICA, 1800 North Kent Street, Arlington, VA 22209, publishes *Outdoor America*

LEAGUE OF CONSERVATION VOTERS, 620 C Street, S.E., Washington DC 20003

LEAGUE OF WOMEN VOTERS OF THE U.S., 1730 M Street N.W., Washington DC 20036, publishes *The National Voter*

NATIONAL AUDUBON SOCIETY, 950 Third Avenue, New York, NY 10022, publishes *Audubon* (monthly periodical)

NATIONAL PARKS AND CONSERVATION ASSOCIATION, 1701 - 18th Street, N.W., Washington DC 20009, publishes *National Parks & Conservation Magazine* (monthly periodical)

NATIONAL WILDLIFE FEDERATION, 1412 - 16th Street N.W., Washington DC 20036, publishes *National Wildlife, Ranger Rick,* (magazines) and *Conservation News* and *Conservation Report* (newsletters)

NATURAL RESOURCES COUNCIL OF AMERICA, Suite 911, 1025 Connecticut Avenue N.W., Washington DC 20036

THE NATURE CONSERVANCY, Suite 800, North Kent Street, Arlington, VA 22209

SCIENTISTS' INSTITUTE FOR PUBLIC INFORMATION, 438 North Skinker, St. Louis, MO 63130, publishes *Environment* (monthly periodical)

SIERRA CLUB, 1050 Mills Tower, San Francisco, CA 94104, publishes *Sierra Club Bulletin* (monthly periodical) and *National News Report* (weekly newsletter)

SOIL CONSERVATION SOCIETY OF AMERICA, 7515 N.E. Ankeny Road, Ankeny, IA 50021, publishes the *Journal of Soil and Water Conservation* (monthly)

SPORT FISHING INSTITUTE, Suite 503, 719 - 13th Street N.W., Washington DC 20005, publishes the *S F I Bulletin* (monthly newsletter)

TROUT UNLIMITED, 4260 East Evans Avenue, Denver, CO 80222, publishes *Trout Magazine*

WESTERN FORESTRY AND CONSERVATION ASSOCIATION, 1326 American Bank Building, Portland, OR 97205

THE WILDERNESS SOCIETY, 729 - 15th Street N.W., Washington DC 20005, publishes *The Living Wilderness* (monthly periodical)

WILDERNESS WATCH, P.O. Box 3184, Green Bay, WI 54303

WILDLIFE MANAGEMENT INSTITUTE, 709 Wire Building, Washington DC 20005, publishes *Outdoor News Bulletin*

WORLD WILDLIFE FUND, Suite 619, 910 - 17th Street N.W., Washington DC 20006

ZERO POPULATION GROWTH, INC., 343 Second Street, Los Angeles, CA 94022, publishes *Equilibrium* (periodical) and *National Reporter* (newsletter)

For a more extensive listing of conservation organizations, see *The Conservation Directory:* (Washington D.C.: National Wildlife Federation)

Forest Industry Associations

AMERICAN FOREST INSTITUTE, 1619 Massachusetts N.W., Washington DC 20036, publishes *Green America*

AMERICAN PAPER INSTITUTE, 260 Madison Avenue, New York, NY 10016

AMERICAN PLYWOOD ASSOCIATION, 1119 A Street, Tacoma, WA 98401

AMERICAN PULPWOOD ASSOCIATION, 605 Third Avenue, New York, NY 10006

AMERICAN WOOD COUNCIL, 1619 Massachusetts N.W., Washington DC 20036

CALIFORNIA FOREST PROTECTIVE ASSOCIATION, 1127 - 11th Street, Suite 534, Sacramento, CA 95814

CALIFORNIA REDWOOD ASSOCIATION, 617 Montgomery Street, San Francisco, CA 94111

INDUSTRIAL FORESTRY ASSOCIATION, 1220 S.W. Columbia Street, Portland, OR 97201

NATIONAL FOREST PRODUCTS ASSOCIATION, 1619 Massachusetts N.W., Washington DC 20036

REDWOOD REGION CONSERVATION COUNCIL, 224 Roseburg Building, Santa Rosa, CA 95404

SOUTHERN FOREST INSTITUTE, 3395 Northeast Expressway, Suite 380, Atlanta, GA 30341

WESTERN WOOD PRODUCTS ASSOCIATION, 1500 Yeon Building, Portland, OR 97204

Forest Industry Companies

BOISE CASCADE CORPORATION, P.O. Box 50, Boise, ID 83728

CROWN-ZELLERBACH CORPORATION, One Bush Street, San Francisco, CA 94119

EDWARD HINES LUMBER COMPANY, P.O. Box 191, Laramie, WY 82070

GEORGIA-PACIFIC CORPORATION, 900 S.W. Fifth Avenue, Portland, OR 97204

INTERNATIONAL PAPER COMPANY, P.O. Box 579, Longview, WA 98632

POTLATCH CORPORATION, Box 3591, San Francisco, CA 94119

SCOTT PAPER COMPANY, P.O. Box 925, Everett, WA 98201

SIMPSON TIMBER COMPANY, 900 Fourth Avenue, Seattle, WA 98164

SOUTHWEST FOREST INDUSTRIES, 3443 N. Central Avenue, P.O. Box 7548, Phoenix, AZ 85011

ST. REGIS PAPER COMPANY, 150 East 42nd Street, New York, NY 10017

WEYERHAEUSER COMPANY, Tacoma, WA 98401

Professional Societies

SOCIETY OF AMERICA FORESTERS, Wild Acres, 5400 Grosvenor Lane, Bethesda, MD 20014, publishes the *Journal of Forestry*

THE WILDLIFE SOCIETY, Suite 611, 7101 Wisconsin Avenue, N.W., Washington, DC 20014, publishes the *Journal of Wildlife Management* and *Wildlife Society News*

METRIC CONVERSION CHART*

Symbol	When You Know	Multiply by	To Find	Symbol
LENGTH				
in	inches	2.5	centimeters	cm
ft	feet	30	centimeters	cm
yd	yards	0.9	meters	m
mi	miles	1.6	kilometers	km
AREA				
in^2	square inches	6.5	square centimeters	cm^2
ft^2	square feet	0.09	square meters	m^2
yd^2	square yards	0.08	square meters	m^2
mi^2	square miles	2.6	square kilometers	km^2
	acres	0.4	hectares	ha
MASS (weight)				
oz	ounces	28	grams	g
lb	pounds	0.45	kilograms	kg
	short tons (2,000 pounds)	0.9	tonnes	t
VOLUME				
tsp	teaspoons	5	milliliters	ml
Tbsp	tablespoons	15	milliliters	ml
fl oz	fluid ounces	30	milliliters	ml
c	cups	0.24	liters	l
pt	pints	0.47	liters	l
qt	quarts	0.95	liters	l
gal	gallons	3.8	liters	l
ft^3	cubic feet	0.03	cubic meters	m^3
yd^3	cubic yards	0.76	cubic meters	m^3
TEMPERATURE (exact)				
°F	Fahrenheit temperature	5/9 (after subtracting 32)	Celsius temperature	°C

*From National Bureau of Standards Special Publication 365.

METRIC CONVERSION CHART*

LENGTH

symbol	unit	number of meters
km	kilometer	1,000
hm	hectometer	100
dkm	decameter	10
m	meter	1
dm	decimeter	0.1
cm	centimeter	0.01
mm	millimeter	0.001

AREA

symbol	unit	number of square meters
km^2	square kilometer	1,000,000
ha	hectare	10,000
a	are	100
ca	centare	1
cm^2	square centimeter	0.0001

MASS
(weight)

symbol	unit	number of grams
t	metric ton or tonne	1,000,000
kg	kilogram	1,000
hg	hectogram	100
dkg	decagram	10
g	gram	1
dg	decigram	0.1
cg	centigram	0.01
mg	milligram	0.001

VOLUME

symbol	unit	number of cubic meters
cm^3 (or cc)	cubic centimeters	0.000001

CAPACITY

symbol	unit	number of liters
kl	kiloliters	1,000
hl	hectoliter	100
dkl	decaliter	10
l	liter	1
dl	deciliter	0.1
cl	centiliter	0.01
ml	milliliter	0.001

TEMPERATURE
Celsius scale

°C	degree Celsius
0°C	freezing point of water
100°C	boiling point of water

*Units given here are those most likely to be used in the PLT activities. See also *The International System of Units (SI)*. NBS Special Publication 330, U.S. Department of Commerce, National Bureau of Standards, Washington, D.C.

248

TOPIC INDEX

PLT Principles

ENVIRONMENTAL AWARENESS

(1) Sylvan Serenade; (2) Tree Verse; (3) Shades of Meaning; (4) Natural Materials Art; (5) A Cassette Tour of Neighborhood Trees; (6) Johnny Appleseed on Mars; (12) Local Recreation Preferences; (13) A Guide to Local Recreation

DIVERSITY OF FOREST ROLES

(4) Natural Materials Art; (5) A Cassette Tour of Neighborhood Trees; (6) Johnny Appleseed on Mars; (7) Nature's Air Conditioners; (8) Green Mufflers; (9) Forest Products All Around Us; (10) The Three Little Pigs — Revisited; (11) How Paper Is Made; (12) Local Recreation Preferences; (13) A Guide to Local Recreation; (14) Community Land Use; (22) A Day in the Life . . . ; (34) Urban Open Space; (35) Where to Plant; (37) We Can Work It Out?!; (38) What Is Wise Use?; (39) How Much Is Enough?; (41) pH and Plants; (42) Growin' Seeds and Savin' Soil; (50) How Clean is Clean?; (51) Mining and Renewable Resources; (53) The Value of 100 Acres of Forest Land; (70) Which Should I Buy?; (71) Biography of a "Favorite Thing"; (72) Christmas Trees and the Environment; (73) Paper Consumption; (74) Would You Like That Wrapped?; (75) . . . And a Side Order of Paper; (76) The Second Time Around; (80) Lovin' It to Death; (81) Plan a Trip; (85) A Comparison of Insulation Efficiencies; (87) Design with Nature

CULTURAL CONTEXTS

(1) Sylvan Serenade; (2) Tree Verse; (3) Shades of Meaning; (5) A Cassette Tour of Neighborhood Trees; (9) Forest Products All Around Us; (15) Where Are the Cedars of Lebanon?; (16) The Influence of Forests on Your State's History; (17) Artisans in Wood; (18) Native Americans and the Forest; (19) Native American Web of Life; (20) Indian Summer, Winter, Spring and Fall; (21) Pioneers in the Wilderness; (22) A Day in the Life . . .; (23) A Letter from Archy; (24) Economic Web of Life; (25) The Power of Literature; (26) Superstitions, Symbols, and Similes; (27) Ticky Tacky; (28) Cartoons and Headlines; (29) Wasted Words; (30) Environmental Editorials; (31) Environmental Advertisements; (38) What is Wise Use?; (45) Snow Use; (56) The Changing Forest; (78) The Continuing Adventures of the Truffle Tree Company

SOCIETAL PERSPECTIVES ON ISSUES

(3) Shades of Meaning; (14) Community Land Use; (21) Pioneers in the Wilderness; (27) Ticky Tacky; (28) Cartoons and Headlines; (29) Wasted Words; (30) Environmental Editorials; (31) Environmental Advertisements; (32) Participatory Democracy; (33) Who Runs This Place?; (34) Urban Open Space; (35) Where to Plant; (36) Ownership Objectives; (37) We Can Work It Out?!; (38) What Is Wise Use?; (39) How Much Is Enough?; (48) Land Allocation; (49) For Better or For Worse; (50) How Clean Is Clean?; (51) Mining and Renewable Resources; (53) The Value of 100 Acres of Forest Land; (59) Endangered Species; (66) A Treasure Hunt for Energy; (67) Impact Statements; (78) The Continuing Adventures of the Truffle Tree Company; (82) A Simpler Life; (84) Plan Your Community's Future; (87) Design with Nature

MANAGEMENT AND INTERDEPENDENCE OF NATURAL RESOURCES

(9) Forest Products All Around Us; (10) The Three Little Pigs, Revisited; (11) How Paper Is Made; (14) Community Land Use; (21) Pioneers in the Wilderness; (23) A Letter from Archy; (24) Economic Web of Life; (37) We Can Work It Out?!; (38) What Is Wise Use?; (40) Soil Compaction; (41) pH and Plants; (42) Growin' Seeds and Savin' Soil; (43) The Value of Wildlife; (44) Building for the Birds; (45) Snow Use; (46) Water We Doing?; (47) Loose Knots and Tight Knots; (48) Land Allocation; (49) For Better or For Worse; (50) How Clean Is Clean?; (51) Mining and Renewable Resources; (52) Hard Choices; (53) The Value of 100 Acres of Forest Land; (55) Wildlife Habitat; (58) Predator Prey; (59) Endangered Species; (60) Build an Ecosystem; (64) How Do You Bury a Pile of Dirt?; (65) Pollution Search: A "Sense" of Knowing; (66) A Treasure Hunt for Energy; (67) Impact Statements; (68) What Shall I Use to Build It?; (70) Which Should I Buy?; (71) Biography of a Favorite Thing; (74) Would You Like That Wrapped?; (75) . . . And a Side Order of Paper; (76) The Second Time Around; (78) The Continuing Adventures of the Truffle Tree Company; (80) Lovin' It to Death; (84) Plan Your Community's Future; (85) A Comparison of Insulation Efficiencies; (88) A Look at Lifestyles

249

LIFE SUPPORT SYSTEMS

(2) Tree Verse; (5) A Cassette Tour of Neighborhood Trees; (6) Johnny Appleseed on Mars; (11) How Paper Is Made; (14) Community Land Use; (20) Indian Summer, Winter, Spring, and Fall; (24) Economic Web of Life; (40) Soil Compaction; (41) pH and Plants; (42) Growin' Seeds and Savin' Soil; (43) The Value of Wildlife; (45) Snow Use; (46) Water We Doing?; (48) Land Allocation; (49) For Better or For Worse; (51) Mining and Renewable Resources; (52) Hard Choices; (53) The Value of 100 Acres of Forest Land; (54) Why Do Trees Grow There?; (55) Wildlife Habitat; (56) The Changing Forest; (57) Climax Forest; (58) Predator Prey; (59) Endangered Species; (60) Build an Ecosystem; (61) A Calorie's Cost; (62) Food Mobile; (63) Succession on the School Grounds; (64) How Do You Bury A Pile of Dirt?; (65) Pollution Search: A "Sense" of Knowing; (66) A Treasure Hunt for Energy; (67) Impact Statements; (71) Biography of a Favorite Thing; (79) ORV's and Us; (80) Lovin' It to Death

LIFESTYLES

(1) Sylvan Serenade; (2) Tree Verse; (4) Natural Materials Art; (6) Johnny Appleseed on Mars; (8) Green Mufflers; (9) Forest Products All Around Us; (10) The Three Little Pigs — Revisited; (12) Local Recreation Preferences; (14) Community Land Use; (18) Native Americans and the Forest; (19) Native American Web of Life; (23) A Letter from Archy; (24) Economic Web of Life; (25) The Power of Literature; (26) Superstitions, Symbols, and Similes; (37) We Can Work It Out?!; (44) Building for the Birds; (49) For Better or For Worse; (50) How Clean Is Clean?; (52) Hard Choices; (53) The Value of 100 Acres of Forest Land; (59) Endangered Species; (65) Pollution Search: A "Sense" of Knowing; (66) A Treasure Hunt for Energy; (67) Impact Statements; (68) What Shall I Use to Build It?; (69) What Wood Waste?; (70) Which Should I Buy?; (71) Biography of a Favorite Thing; (72) Christmas Trees and the Environment; (73) Paper Consumption; (74) Would You Like That Wrapped?; (75) . . . And a Side Order of Paper; (76) The Second Time Around; (77) You've Come a Long Way, Maybe?; (78) The Continuing Adventures of the Truffle Tree Company; (79) ORVs and Us; (80) Lovin' It to Death; (81) Plan a Trip; (82) A Simpler Life; (83) Careers in Forestry; (84) Plan Your Community's Future; (85) A Comparison of Insulation Efficiencies; (86) Dome Homes; (87) Design with Nature; (88) A Look at Lifestyles

The Senses

SIGHT

(74) Would You Like That Wrapped? (65) Pollution Search: A "Sense" of Knowing

SMELL

(65) Pollution Search: A "Sense" of Knowing

SOUND

(1) Sylvan Serenade; (74) Would You Like That Wrapped? (65) Pollution Search: A "Sense" of Knowing

TASTE

(7) Nature's Air Conditioners (65) Pollution Search: A "Sense" of Knowing

TOUCH

(65) Pollution Search: A "Sense" of Knowing

PSYCHOLOGICAL: EMOTIONAL EXPRESSION

(1) Sylvan Serenade; (2) Tree Verse; (3) Shades of Meaning; (71) Biography of a Favorite Thing

PSYCHOLOGICAL: IMAGINATION EXPRESSION

(66) A Treasure Hunt for Energy; (46) Water We Doing?

Subject Title

AESTHETICS

(9) Forest Products All Around Us; (35) Where to Plant; (13) A Guide to Local Recreation; (38) What is Wise Use?; (79) ORVs and Us; (80) Lovin' It to Death; (81) Plan a Trip; (43) The Value of Wildlife; (67) Impact Statements; (72) Christmas Trees and the Environment; (53) The Value of 100 Acres of Forest Land; (36) Ownership Objectives; (2) Tree Verse; (3) Shades of Meaning; (5) A Cassette Tour of Neighborhood Trees; (78) The Continuing Adventures of the Truffle Tree Company; (6) Johnny Appleseed on Mars; (25) The Power of Literature; (26) Superstitions, Symbols, and Similes; (29) Wasted Words; (30) Environmental Editorials; (82) A Simpler Life; (76) The Second Time Around; (74) Would You Like That Wrapped?; (4) Natural Materials Art; (1) Sylvan Serenade; (56) The Changing Forest; (60) Building an Ecosystem; (86) Dome Homes; (87) Design With Nature; (17) Artisans in Wood; (65) Pollution Search: A "Sense" of Knowing

AIR

(50) How Clean is Clean?; (9) Forest Products All Around Us; (22) A Day in the Life . . . ; (49) For Better or For Worse; (79) ORVs and Us; (80) Lovin' It to Death; (54) Why Do Trees Grow There?; (8) Green Mufflers; (67) Impact Statements; (53) The Value of 100 Acres of Forest Land; (6) Johnny Appleseed on Mars; (62) Food Mobile, (87) Design with Nature; (65) Pollution Search: A "Sense" of Knowing

CONSERVATION

(50) How Clean Is Clean?; (88) A Look at Lifestyles; (21) Pioneers in the Wilderness; (57) Mining and Renewable Resources; (48) Land Allocation; (9) Forest Products All Around Us; (38) What Is Wise Use?; (16) The Influence of the Forest on Your Region's History; (22) A Day-in-the-Life . . . ; (39) How Much is Enough?; (49) For Better or For Worse; (37) We Can Work It Out?!; (79) ORVs and Us; (80) Lovin' It to Death; (81) Plan a Trip; (8) Green Mufflers; (43) The Value of Wildlife; (67) Impact Statements; (72) Christmas Trees and the Environment; (53) The Value of 100 Acres of Forest Land; (36) Ownership Objectives; (3) Shades of Meaning; (5) A Cassette Tour of Neighborhood Trees; (77) The Continuing Adventures of the Truffle Tree Company; (6) Johnny Appleseed on Mars; (25) The Power of Literature; (29) Wasted Words; (30) Environmental Editorials; (31) Environmental Advertisements; (47) A Simpler Life; (77) You've Come a Long Way, Maybe; (70) Which Should I Buy?; (76) The Second Time Around; (4) Natural Materials Art; (56) The Changing Forest; (60) Build an Ecosystem; (63) Succession on the School Grounds; (59) Endangered Species; (64) How Do You Bury A Pile of Dirt?; (42) Growin' Seeds and Savin' Soil; (69) What Wood Waste?; (11) How Paper Is Made; (86) Dome Homes; (87) Design With Nature; (47) Loose Knots and Tight Knots; (73) Paper Consumption; (85) A Comparison of Insulation Efficiencies; (55) Wildlife Habitat; (66) A Treasure Hunt for Energy; (46) Water We Doing?

CONSUMER

(88) A Look at Lifestyles; (75) . . . And A Side Order of Paper; (48) Land Allocation; (9) Forest Products All Around Us; (10) The Three Little Pigs — Revisited; (16) The Influence of the Forest on Your Region's History; (49) For Better or For Worse; (79) ORVs and Us; (81) Plan a Trip; (8) Green Mufflers; (43) The Value of Wildlife; (67) Impact Statements; (72) Christmas Trees and the Environment; (61) A Calorie's Cost; (53) The Value of 100 Acres of Forest Land; (36) Ownership Objectives; (3) Shades of Meaning; (5) A Cassette Tour of Neighborhood Trees; (78) The Continuing Adventures of the Truffle Tree Company; (31) Environmental Advertisements; (82) A Simpler Life; (77) You've Come A Long Way, Maybe; (70) Which Should I Buy?; (74) Would You Like That Wrapped?; (62) Food Mobile; (86) Dome Homes; (87) Design with Nature; (17) Artisans in Wood; (73) Paper Consumption; (58) Predator Prey; (66) A Treasure Hunt for Energy; (24) Economic Web of Life; (71) Biography of a Favorite Thing; (46) Water We Doing?; (45) Snow Use

CYCLES

(16) The Influence of the Forest on Your Region's History; (80) Lovin' It to Death; (54) Why Do Trees Grow There?; (8) Green Mufflers; (67) Impact Statements; (72) Christmas Trees and the Environment; (61) A Calorie's Cost; (53) The Value of 100 Acres of Forest Land; (5) A Cassette Tour of Neighborhood Trees; (6) Johnny Appleseed on Mars; (25) The Power of Literature; (26) Superstitions, Symbols, and Similes; (82) A Simpler Life; (77) You've Come A Long Way, Maybe; (70) Which Should I Buy?; (74) Would You Like That Wrapped?; (62) Food Mobile; (63) Succession on the School Grounds; (41) pH and Plants; (7) Nature's Air Conditioners; (59) Endangered Species; (64) How Do You Bury a Pile of Dirt?; (42) Growin' Seeds 'n' Savin' Soil; (40) Soil Compaction; (11) How Paper is Made; (86) Dome Homes; (87) Design with Nature; (71) Biography of a Favorite Thing; (46) Water We Doing?; (57) Climax Forest

DESERT

(54) Why Do Trees Grow There?; (43) The Value of Wildlife; (57) Climax Forest

ECONOMICS

(50) How Clean is Clean; (88) A Look at Lifestyles; (33) Who Runs This Place?; (21) Pioneers in the Wilderness; (51) Mining and Renewable Resources; (18) Native Americans and the Forest; (84) Plan Your Community's Future; (9) Forest Products All Around Us; (10) The Three Little Pigs — Revisited; (13) A Guide to Local Recreation; (16) The Influence of the Forest on Your Region's History; (22) A Day-in-The-Life . . . ; (39) How Much is Enough?; (49) For Better or For Worse; (37) We Can Work It Out?!; (79) ORVs and Us; (80) Lovin' It to Death; (81) Plan a Trip; (43) The Value of Wildlife; (52) Hard Choices; (67) Impact Statements; (72) Christmas Trees and the Environment; (61) A Calorie's Cost; (53) The Value of 100 Acres of Forest Land; (36) Ownership Objectives; (3) Shades of Meaning; (78) The Continuing Adventures of the Truffle Tree Company; (82) A Simpler Life; (70) Which Should I Buy?; (76) The Second Time Around; (74) Would You Like That Wrapped?; (59) Endangered Species; (11) How Paper Is Made; (86) Dome Homes; (87) Design With Nature; (17) Artisans in Wood; (47) Loose Knots and Tight Knots; (83) Careers in Forestry; (73) Paper Consumption; (85) A Comparison of Insulation Efficiencies; (24 Economic Web of Life; (20) Indian Summer, Winter, Spring, and Fall

ECOSYSTEMS

(22) A Day-in-the-Life . . . ; (37) We Can Work

It Out?!; (79) ORVs and Us; (80) Lovin' It to Death; (81) Plan a Trip; (54) Why Do Trees Grow There?; (8) Green Mufflers; (43) The Value of Wildlife; (52) Hard Choices; (67) Impact Statements; (61) A Calorie's Cost; (5) A Cassette Tour of Neighborhood Trees; (78) The Continuing Adventures of the Truffle Tree Company; (6) Johnny Appleseed on Mars; (62) Food Mobile; (63) Succession on the School Grounds; (64) How Do You Bury A Pile of Dirt?; (55) Wildlife Habitat; (58) Predator Prey; (65) Pollution Search: A "Sense" of Knowing; (45) Snow Use

ENDANGERED SPECIES

(22) A Day-in-the-Life . . . ; (8) Green Mufflers; (43) The Value of Wildlife; (52) Hard Choices; (67) Impact Statements; (53) The Value of 100 Acres of Forest Land; (78) The Continuing Adventures of the Truffle Tree Company; (6) Johnny Appleseed on Mars; (59) Endangered Species

ENERGY

(88) A Look at Lifestyles; (75) . . . And A Side Order of Paper; (21) Pioneers in the Wilderness; (51) Mining and Renewable Resources; (48) Land Allocation; (9) Forest Products All Around Us; (10) The Three Little Pigs — Revisited; (16) The Influence of the Forest on Your Region's History; (49) For Better or For Worse; (79) ORVs and Us; (80) Lovin' It to Death; (81) Plan a Trip; (67) Impact Statements; (72) Christmas Trees and the Environment; (61) A Calorie's Choice; (53) The Value of 100 Acres of Forest Land; (30) Environmental Editorials; (31) Environmental Advertisements; (82) A Simpler Life; (77) You've Come a Long Way, Maybe?; (70) Which Should I Buy? (74) Would You Like That Wrapped?; (62) Food Mobile; (64) How Do You Bury a Pile of Dirt?; (11) How Paper is Made; (86) Dome Homes; (17) Artisans in Wood; (85) A Comparison of Insulation Efficiencies; (55) Wildlife Habitat; (66) A Treasure Hunt for Energy; (71) Biography of a Favorite Thing; (65) Pollution Search: A "Sense" of Knowing

ENTERTAINMENT

(79) ORVs and Us; (80) Lovin' It to Death; (81) Plan a Trip; (8) Green Mufflers; (5) A Cassette Tour of Neighborhood Trees; (78) The Continuing Adventures of the Truffle Tree Company; (23) A Letter from Archy; (1) Sylvan Serenade; (56) The Changing Forest

ENVIRONMENTAL IMPACT

(50) How Clean is Clean?; (14) Community Land Use; (51) Mining and Renewable Resources; (48) Land Allocation; (15) Where are the Cedars of Lebanon?; (10) The Three Little Pigs — Revisited; (12) Local Recreation Preferences; (38) What is Wise Use?; (16) The Influence of the

Forest on Your Region's History; (22) A Day-in-the-Life . . . ; (49) For Better or For Worse; (37) We Can Work It Out?!; (79) ORVs and Us; (80) Lovin' It it Death; (81) Plan a Trip; (8) Green Mufflers; (43) The Value of Wildlife; (52) Hard Choices; (67) Impact Statements; (72) Christmas Trees and the Environment; (53) The Value of 100 Acres of Forest Land; (36) Ownership Objectives; (3) Shades of Meaning; (5) A Cassette Tour of Neighborhood Trees; (78) The Continuing Adventures of the Truffle Tree Company; (6) Johnny Appleseed on Mars; (25) The Power of Literature; (26) Superstitions, Symbols, and Similes; (29) Wasted Words; (82) A Simpler Life; (23) A Letter from Archy; (77) You've Come a Long Way, Maybe?; (70) Which Should I Buy?; (74) Would You Like That Wrapped?; (4) Natural Materials Art; (60) Build an Ecosystem; (62) Food Mobile; (63) Succession on the School Grounds; (41) pH and Plants; (59) Endangered Species; (64) How Do You Bury A Pile of Dirt?; (42) Growin' Seeds 'n' Savin' Soil; (11) How Paper Is Made; (86) Dome Homes; (44) Building for the Birds; (73) Paper Consumption; (55) Wildlife Habitat; (58) Predator Prey; (66) A Treasure Hunt for Energy; (65) Pollution Search: A "Sense" of knowing; (45) Snow Use; (57) Climax Forest

EROSION

(54) Why Do Trees Grow There?; (63) Succession on the School Grounds; (42) Growin' Seeds 'n' Savin' Soil; (40) Soil Compaction; (65) Pollution Search: A "Sense" of Knowing

FIELD TRIPS

(34) Urban Open Space; (84) Plan Your Community's Future; (9) Forest Products All Around Us; (10) The Three Little Pigs — Revisited; (35) Where to Plant; (12) Local Recreation Preferences; (80) Lovin' It to Death; (81) Plan a Trip; (8) Green Mufflers; (43) The Value of Wildlife; (72) Christmas Trees and the Environment; (53) The Value of 100 Acres of Forest Land; (3) Shades of Meaning; (5) A Cassette Tour of Neighborhood Trees; (6) Johnny Appleseed on Mars; (76) The Second Time Around; (74) Would You Like That Wrapped?; (60) Build an Ecosystem; (41) pH and Plants; (59) Endangered Species; (40) Soil Compaction; (86) Dome Homes; (57) Climax Forest

FIRE

(79) ORVs and Us; (80) Lovin' It to Death; (81) Plan a Trip; (41) pH and Plants; (57) Climax Forest

FISH

(50) How Clean is Clean?; (37) We Can Work It Out?!; (80) Lovin' It to Death; (81) Plan a Trip; (43) The Value of Wildlife; (61) A Calorie's Cost; (62) Food Mobile; (41) pH and Plants; (59) Endangered Species

PLANT SUCCESSION

(63) Succession on the School Grounds; (57) Climax Forest

POETRY

(1) Sylvan Serenade; (2) Tree Verse; (3) Shades of Meaning

POLITICS

(88) A Look at Lifestyles; (33) Who Runs This Place?; (21) Pioneers in the Wilderness; (51) Mining and Renewable Resources; (32) Participatory Democracy; (34) Urban Open Space; (10) The Three Little Pigs — Revisited; (35) Where to Plant; (16) The Influence of the Forest on Your Region's History; (22) A Day-in-the-Life; (39) How Much Is Enough?; (49) For Better or For Worse; (79) ORVs and Us; (80) Lovin' It to Death; (52) Hard Choices; (67) Impact Statements; (53) The Value of 100 Acres of Forest Land; (36) Ownership Objectives; (30) Environmental Editorials; (82) A Simpler Life; (74) Would You Like That Wrapped?

POLLUTION

(50) How Clean Is Clean?; (14) Community Land Use; (9) Forest Products All Around Us; (22) A Day-in-the-Life . . .; (39) How Much Is Enough?; (49) For Better or For Worse; (79) ORVs and Us; (80) Lovin' It to Death; (81) Plan a Trip; (8) Green Mufflers; (52) Hard Choices; (67) Impact Statements; (3) Shades of Meaning; (78) The Continuing Adventures of the Truffle Tree Company; (6) Johnny Appleseed on Mars; (25) The Power of Literature; (74) Would You Like That Wrapped?; (59) Endangered Species; (64) How Do You Bury a Pile of Dirt?; (11) How Paper Is Made; (87) Design with Nature; (65) Pollution Search: A "Sense" of Knowing; (27) Ticky Tacky

POPULATION

(84) Plan Your Community's Future; (16) The Influence of the Forest on Your State's History; (22) A Day-in-the-Life . . .; (39) How Much is Enough?; (49) For Better or For Worse; (80) Lovin' It to Death; (81) Plan a Trip; (52) Hard Choices; (67) Impact Statements; (53) The Value of 100 Acres of Forest Land; (36) Ownership Objectives; (59) Endangered Species; (55) Wildlife Habitat; (57) Climax Forest; (27) Ticky Tacky; (19) Native American Web of Life

PREDATORS-PREY

(43) The Value of Wildlife; (78) The Continuing Adventures of the Truffle Tree Company; (59) Endangered Species

PRODUCTS, FOREST

(75) . . . And A Side Order of Paper; (18) Native Americans and the Forest; (9) Forest Products All Around Us; (79) ORVs and Us; (35) The Value of 100 Acres of Forest Lands; (78) The Continuing Adventures of the Truffle Tree Company; (4) Natural Materials Art; (60) Build an Ecosystem; (62) Food Mobile; (69) What Wood Waste?; (11) How Paper is Made; (86) Dome Homes; (17) Artisans in Wood; (47) Loose Knots and Tight Knots; (24) Economic Web of Life; (71) Biography of a Favorite Thing

RAINFALL

(80) Lovin' It to Death; (53) The Value of 100 Acres of Forest Land; (63) Succession on the School Grounds; (46) Water We Doing?

RECREATION

(84) Plan Your Community's Future; (12) Local Recreation Preferences; (13) A Guide to Local Recreation; (22) A Day-in-the-Life . . .; (39) How Much Is Enough?; (37) We Can Work It Out?!; (79) ORVs and Us; (80) Lovin' It to Death; (81) Plan a Trip; (43) The Value of Wildlife; (67) Impact Statements; (36) Ownership Objectives; (82) A Simpler Life; (71) Biography of a Favorite Thing; (45) Snow Use

RECYCLING

(72) Christmas Trees and the Environment; (78) The Continuing Adventures of the Truffle Tree Company; (82) A Simpler Life; (70) Which Should I Buy?; (60) Build an Ecosystem; (69) What Wood Waste?; (11) How Paper Is Made; (73) Paper Consumption; (65) Pollution Search: A "Sense" of Knowing

REFORESTATION

(72) Christmas Trees and the Environment; (57) Climax Forest

RENEWABLE RESOURCES

(88) A Look at Lifestyles; (75) . . . And A Side Order of Paper; (21) Pioneers in the Wilderness; (51) Mining and Renewable Resources; (9) Forest Products All Around Us; (38) What Is Wise Use?; (16) The Influence of the Forest on Your Region's History; (22) A Day-in-the-Life . . .; (49) For Better or For Worse; (37) We Can Work It Out?!; (79) ORVs and Us; (80) Lovin' It to Death; (81) Plan a Trip; (52) Hard Choices; (67) Impact Statements; (72) Christmas Trees and the Environment; (61) A Calorie's Cost; (53) The Value of 100 Acres of Forest Land; (3) Shades of Meaning; (78) The Continuing Adventures of the Truffle Tree Company; (29) Wasted Words; (82) A Simpler Life; (77) You've Come A Long Way, Maybe; (70) Which Should I Buy?; (74) Would You Like That Wrapped?; (60) Build an Ecosystem; (62) Food Mobile; (59) Endangered Species; (86) Dome Homes; (17) Artisans in Wood; (47) Loose Knots and Tight Knots; (73) Paper Consumption; (85) A Comparison of Insulation Efficiencies; (66) A Treasure Hunt for Energy; (71) Biography of a Favorite Thing; (57) Climax Forest; (20) Indian Summer, Winter, Spring, and Fall; (27) Ticky Tacky; (19) Native American Web of Life

SCHOOLYARDS

(54) Why Do Trees Grow There?; (2) Tree Verse; (3) Shades of Meaning; (4) Natural Materials Art; (60) Build an Ecosystem; (63) Succession on the School Grounds; (41) pH and Plants; (7) Nature's Air Conditioners; (59) Endangered Species; (40) Soil Compaction

SERE

(57) Climax Forest

SEWAGE

(33) Who Runs This Place?; (28) Cartoons and Headlines; (66) A Treasure Hunt for Energy

SHELTER

(21) Pioneers in the Wilderness; (18) Native Americans and the Forest; (9) Forest Products All Around Us; (13) A Guide to Local Recreation; (16) The Influence of the Forest on Your Region's History; (22) A Day-in-the-Life . . .; (19) Native American Web of Life; (67) Impact Statements; (3) Shades of Meaning; (86) Dome Homes; (44) Building for the Birds; (85) A Comparison of Insulation Efficiencies; (55) Wildlife Habitat; (27) Ticky Tacky

SNOW

(79) ORVs and Us; (45) Snow Use

SOIL

(15) Where Are the Cedars of Lebanon?; (79) ORVs and Us; (80) Lovin' It to Death; (81) Plan a Trip; (54) Why Do Trees Grow There?; (67) Impact Statements; (53) The Value of 100 Acres of Forest Land; (5) A Cassette Tour of Neighborhood Trees; (78) The Continuing Adventures of the Truffle Tree Company; (4) Natural Materials Art; (60) Build an Ecosystem; (62) Food Mobile; (63) Succession on the School Grounds; (41) pH and Plants; (64) How Do You Bury a Pile of Dirt?; (42) Growin' Seeds 'n' Savin' Soil; (40) Soil Compaction

SUN/SHADE

(60) Build an Ecosystem; (62) Food Mobile; (63) Succession on the School Grounds; (69) What Wood Waste?; (66) A Treasure Hunt for Energy

TERRITORY

(21) Pioneers in the Wilderness; (18) Native Americans and the Forest; (16) The Influence of the Forest on Your Region's History; (22) A Day-in-the-Life . . .; (80) Lovin' It to Death; (67) Impact Statements; (53) The Value of 100 Acres of Forest Land; (36) Ownership Objectives; (59) Endangered Species; (55) Wildlife Habitat; (19) Native American Web of Life

THIRD WORLD

(2) Tree Verse; (26) Superstitions, Symbols, and Similes; (56) The Changing Forest; (19) Native American Web of Life

TRADE

(9) Forest Products All Around Us; (16) The Influence of the Forest on Your Region's History; (49) For Better or For Worse; (37) We Can Work It Out?!; (80) Lovin' It to Death; (8) Green Mufflers; (67) Impact Statements; (72) Christmas Trees and the Environment; (61) A Calorie's Cost; (53) The Value of 100 Acres of Forest Land; (77) You've Come a Long Way, Maybe; (64) How Do You Bury a Pile of Dirt?; (24) Economic Web of Life

TRANSPIRATION

(80) Lovin' It to Death; (54) Why Do Trees Grow There?; (72) Christmas Trees and the Environment; (60) Build an Ecosystem; (63) Succession on the School Grounds; (7) Nature's Air Conditioners; (46) Water We Doing?

TRANSPORTATION

(71) Biography of a Favorite Thing; (66) A Treasure Hunt for Energy

TREES

(8) Green Mufflers; (5) A Cassette Tour of Neighborhood Trees; (78) The Continuing Adventures of the Truffle Tree Company; (41) pH and Plants; (7) Nature's Air Conditioners; (68) What Shall I Use to Build It?; (11) How Paper Is Made; (87) Design With Nature; (57) Climax Forest

TREES-CONIFER, See Conifer

TREES-DECIDUOUS

(8) Green Mufflers; (5) A Cassette Tour of Neighborhood Trees; (78) The Continuing Adventures of the Truffle Tree Company; (41) pH and Plants; (7) Nature's Air Conditioners; (68) What Shall I Use to Build It?; (11) How Paper Is Made; (87) Design with Nature

WATER

(50) How Clean Is Clean; (9) Forest Products All Around Us; (13) A Guide to Local Recreation; (22) A Day-in-the-Life . . .; (79) ORVs and US; (80) Lovin' It to Death; (81) Plan a Trip; (54) Why Do Trees Grow There?; (67) Impact Statements; (53) The Value of 100 Acres of Forest Land; (5) A Cassette Tour of Neighborhood Trees; (60) Build an Ecosystem; (62) Food Mobile; (7) Nature's Air Conditioners; (42) Growin' Seeds 'n' Savin' Soil; (40) Soil Compaction; (66) A Treasure Hunt for Energy; (46) Water We Doing? (45) Snow Use; (19) Native American Web of Life

WATERSHEDS

(37) We Can Work It Out?!; (79) ORVs and US; (54) Why Do Trees Grow There? (46) Water We Doing?; (45) Snow Use

WILDERNESS

(21) Pioneers in the Wilderness; (12) Local Recreation Preferences; (13) A Guide to Local Recreation; (38) What is Wise Use?; (16) The Influence of the Forest on Your State's History; (22) A Day-in-the-Life . . .; (39) How Much Is Enough?; (37) We Can Work It Out?!; (79) ORVs and Us; (80) Lovin' It to Death; (81) Plan a Trip; (43) The Value of Wildlife; (52) Hard Choices; (67) Impact Statements; (36) Ownership Objectives; (3) Shades of Meaning; (25) The Power of Literature; (59) Endangered Species; (58) Predator Prey

WILDLIFE

(21) Pioneers in the Wilderness; (13) A Guide to Local Recreation; (38) What is Wise Use?; (22) A Day-in-the-Life . . .; (37) We Can Work It Out?!; (79) ORVs and Us; (80) Lovin' It to Death; (81) Plan a Trip; (54) Why Do Trees Grow There?; (43) The Value of Wildlife; (52) Hard Choices; (67) Impact Statements; (53) The Value of 100 Acres of Forest Land; (5) A Cassette Tour of Neighborhood Trees; (78) The Continuing Adventures of the Truffle Tree Company; (63) Succession on the School Grounds; (59) Endangered Species; (44) Building for the Birds; (55) Wildlife Habitat; (58) Predator Prey; (46) Water We Doing?; (45) Snow Use; (57) Climax Forest

WIND

(66) A Treasure Hunt for Energy